Kat.. .lexander is a .... author
who uses three different pen na.......... previous
career included working for the World Health
Organisation in Geneva and a historical foundation in
Canada. She now lives in Surrey, in the town where
she was born. She is a Vice-President of the Romantic
Novelists' Association.

BY THE SAME AUTHOR

Great Possessions
The Shining Country

THE HOUSE OF HOPE

Kate Alexander

ARROW

First published 1992

1 3 5 7 9 10 8 6 4 2

Copyright © Kate Alexander 1992

Kate Alexander has asserted her
right under the Copyright, Designs and Patents Act, 1988
to be identified as the author of this work

First published in the United Kingdom in 1992 by Century

Arrow edition 1993
Random House, 20 Vauxhall Bridge Road, London SW1V 2SA

Random House Australia (Pty) Limited
20 Alfred Street, Milsons Point, Sydney,
New South Wales 2061, Australia

Random House New Zealand Limited
18 Poland Road, Glenfield
Auckland 10, New Zealand

Random House South Africa (Pty) Limited
PO Box 337, Bergvlei, South Africa

Random House UK Limited Reg. No. 954009

A CIP catalogue record for this book
is available from the British Library

ISBN 0 09 914511 1

Printed and bound in Germany by
Elsnerdruck, Berlin

Prologue

It was a mild September evening and the start of a new season of sales in the major fine-art auction houses of London after the slack summer months.

It had rained earlier, but now the clouds had parted and lay across the western sky in bands of grey and gold. The road still gleamed wetly as the taxis and sleek cars pulled up outside the Piccadilly showrooms of Hope & Company, paused briefly – it was a difficult place for parking and the bus drivers held up in the queue muttered under their breath – and spilled out the passengers who then blocked the pavement as they greeted one another under the blue and gold awning which stretched out from the open door.

Inside, Richard Hope surveyed the shifting crowd with a certain amount of cynicism. Amongst them all were perhaps a mere twelve or fourteen serious buyers: together with the four telephone lines specially set up, that made under twenty who would actually be bidding. The rest had come because an evening sale at Hope's was a social event. High prices had been forecast for the Impressionist and post-Impressionist pictures on sale, and they expected to get a thrill.

Richard had been given the assignment of handling a telephone connected to a buyer in Tokyo. He refused to admit that he was nervous – 'keyed-up' was a better expression. He only hoped that if Mr Yakamoto became excited, his own knowledge of Japanese would hold up.

He was twenty-five, sloe-eyed and slim, with an engaging grace about him and the quick mind with which all the Hopes seemed to be blessed. Already, as he moved about, greeting friends and clients and trying unobtrusively to urge the obstinate knots of people towards their champagne and canapés, murmurs followed his progress – '. . . a future Chairman . . . very much the favourite . . . so like his father . . .'

The present Chairman of Hope's, Richard's father, was also

1

doing his social duty, his elegant wife by his side. Lady Hope earned some envious glances in her draped silk jersey gown from Yuki and the fine diamond necklace which was said to have been a wedding present from her husband's parents some thirty years earlier. Like his son, the Chairman was drinking only mineral water; he had decided to conduct this sale himself and needed to keep his wits about him until it was over. He had recently turned sixty and his knighthood in the Birthday Honours had helped to publicise this 'the first great sale of the Eighties'.

Richard looked round the room and decided he could relax and enjoy the pretty women in their smart couture clothes. He was temporarily unattached, but this was probably not the best occasion to find a new partner. There were plenty of goodlookers, but they were all either firmly married or too old. Except for one girl . . . Richard moved towards her in a determined way.

She had red hair, that was what had caught his eye; a true auburn, a gorgeous colour. In fact, now that he could see her properly, the whole girl was gorgeous. Lovely figure. She wore black with a couple of ropes of pearls and her skin had the same nacreous lustre. She was studying, of all things, the old family portraits that hung on the walls.

'You're supposed to be looking at Impressionist art tonight, not these old things,' Richard said, by way of introducing himself.

She turned and he felt himself reeling. Wow! This one was the real goods. A true, authentic, knock-down beauty.

'I'm interested in the family,' she said.

'Good, because I'm one of them. Richard Hope, at your service.'

Very *much* at your service. Ask me something, anything, like lying down and dying. Or, better still, standing up and living. She was American. How long was she going to be in London?

'Two or three weeks,' the girl said in answer to his question. 'I'm touring Europe with Mom and Dad.'

And who were Mom and Dad? Richard opened his mouth to ask but the girl was already saying, 'This is Vittorio Speranza, isn't it? The founder of the firm?'

'He certainly built up the business, under the name of DuFrayne & Speranza, but I suppose the credit for being the real founder must go to Charles DuFrayne.'

2

'Really? How come I've never heard of him?'

'He got overshadowed. Look, here he is.'

They turned away from the large portrait of a dark handsome man wearing a flamboyant waistcoat to a smaller, less ostentatious study of a quiet-looking man with receding hair and an expression of patient good humour.

'Not such a character as Vittorio,' the girl commented.

'No . . . and yet, if it hadn't been for Charles DuFrayne – and his daughter – none of us Hopes would be here today. Look, I have to go and man my telephone, but afterwards I'd love to take you through the family history.'

He looked at her hopefully and she smiled, revealing dimples in both cheeks. She was altogether enchanting and he had to see her again. Once more he started to ask her name, but a party of people surged forward and a woman in grey satin swooped on the girl – *his* girl.

'Veronica, my dear! How lovely to see you in London! Where are you sitting?'

As she was borne away the girl turned her head and smiled at him. Veronica, her name was Veronica, and if Richard had to move heaven and earth he was going to corral Veronica and tell her, if that was what she wanted, the entire history of Hope & Company.

Chapter One

Vittorio Speranza came to England from Sicily in 1862 because his father was anxious to get rid of him. An encounter with an English aristocrat who, to Enrico Speranza, seemed gullible to the point of foolishness, offered an ideal opportunity to dispose of his clever, but tiresome, son.

'My lord, allow me to lend you my son, Vittorio. He will go with you and help you on your journey. He will be your adviser on antiquities and see you are not cheated – as you have been, I must tell you, over this Greek statue. It is not ancient at all, but a fake.'

When Lord Kenrick hesitated, Enrico added encouragingly, 'I do you a favour by this. It will not be easy for me to part with Vittorio because he has great, great knowledge and he is useful to me in my business, but for you, my lord, I will make this sacrifice.'

'Well . . . I don't know,' Lord Kenrick demurred. 'What does Vittorio himself have to say about it?'

Vittorio would obey his father or find himself in considerable trouble. Enrico had already forgiven his son much over his involvement with Garibaldi and the movement to unite Italy. True, that affair had turned out well in the end, but if the uprising had failed, Enrico would have been forced to disown his most difficult child.

It was perfectly true that he was an asset in Enrico's business as an art dealer, for Vittorio had a talent that no amount of training could instil – an almost uncanny ability to distinguish between the true and the false. When he handled an object, something said to him, 'This is quality' or 'This is not genuine', and he was rarely deceived. The picture which looked so good was revealed to have been restored and repainted; the battered, blackened item over which Vittorio passed an apparently casual hand would emerge, when it was cleaned and reshaped, as a fine piece of silver.

Unfortunately, Vittorio lacked tact. He gave his opinion unasked and he contradicted his brothers and even his father. He

4

was the fifth child and youngest son of Enrico Speranza, and he should have deferred to his father and his three older brothers. But Vittorio deferred to no one, not when it came to asserting the provenance of works of art. He had even been known to throw doubts on the authenticity of something his father was about to sell at a fine profit, and that was unforgivable. He was twenty-eight, with no ties to keep him in Sicily, since his political activities had made his life too unsettled for marriage, and Enrico had no qualms about pushing him out into the world to make his own way. Vittorio would never starve, that was certain.

Ludovic, Earl Kenrick, had been travelling on the Continent in order to escape from an imprudent love affair with a girl who deserved better treatment than he and his mother had given her. He had arrived in Sicily with no particular aim other than to possibly climb Mount Etna, but he had already purchased a few costly objets d'art, souvenirs with which to embellish the fine Palladian house his grandfather had built in the last century, and once he became acquainted with Enrico Speranza he rapidly acquired more.

Once he was persuaded to accept Vittorio Speranza as his travelling companion and adviser, Ludo found the young Sicilian so useful that when he returned to England he took Vittorio with him, to supervise the installation of his new treasures in Mercia House.

Vittorio slipped into England in the wake of his patron, unobtrusive as a minnow following a whale. His luggage, stowed amid Lord Kenrick's many packing cases, was scanty yet weighty, since amongst his shirts Vittorio was also carrying his inheritance: a marble statue of Hermes, small and lively, a fifteenth-century wooden panel painted with a Nativity by Masaccio, and a gold cup attributed to Benvenuto Cellini. In return for these treasures Vittorio had undertaken to make no demands when his father died, and on these terms his brothers had been well content to see the back of him.

His plans were indefinite, but he hoped to settle in England, possibly starting up a business to rival his father's in Syracuse, making use of his natural ability for fine-art dealing. He knew that he had more brains than all his brothers put together; he spoke Italian, English and French fluently, and could manage a few words of Spanish, German and Greek when necessary. He was attractive to women and took what he could from them, but for Vittorio it was a brisk and businesslike proceeding, his real passion being reserved for the swelling curves of a marble Aphrodite rather than the flesh of any living woman.

In Syracuse Vittorio had been accounted tall, but he could not rival Lord Kenrick's elegant height, nor his fresh colouring. Vittorio was swarthy, with thick black hair waving back from a high forehead; he had black eyes, a thin nose and a well-shaped mouth. He was always immaculately dressed; even on a sea voyage from Genoa to Portsmouth which had all the passengers prostrate on their bunks, Vittorio's linen remained mysteriously fresh. He habitually wore black, but since he did not wish to be taken for Lord Kenrick's valet, he let himself go in the matter of waistcoats, and their flamboyance was the only indication of his passion for colour and texture.

Lady Kenrick, when she met him, did not like Vittorio, but then neither did she like the independent spirit Ludo had brought back from his travels. He was no longer her little boy. What was more, he had become shockingly extravagant.

'Really, Ludo, you seem to have been draining the estate in order to turn the house into a museum,' she complained as the packing cases were carried into the house, supervised by Vittorio. 'And this Signor Speranza, how is he to be treated? I presume he will eat in the Servants' Hall?'

'Oh, I don't think so, Mama. Vittorio's a cut above that and he's been a real friend to me on our travels. He's . . .' Ludo paused to find the right formula '. . . he's an expert!' he concluded triumphantly.

At a stroke Vittorio was elevated to the plane of the scholar who had catalogued the library in Ludo's grandfather's day, or the architect who had spent hours poring over the plans of the house with him. Lady Kenrick was forced to regard him as a professional man and a minor gentleman, which put him on quite a different level from the butler, the housekeeper and even the girls' governess.

The charge of extravagance did eventually strike home to Ludo.

'I got carried away,' he said ruefully to Vittorio, looking round the room littered with woodshavings and open packing cases. 'I'm

6

pleased with the way that Mercia House looks now, but I seem to have so much left over.'

'You have a London house,' Vittorio reminded him.

'Yes . . . that's an idea. Some of the pictures would look good in Grosvenor Square, and that marble sarcophagus would be just the thing for the conservatory. We'll take a trip up to town, Vittorio!'

There was another orgy of packing and the convoy set off once more, but even the Grosvenor Square house could not accommodate all Lord Kenrick's acquisitions.

'Have to get rid of some of them,' his lordship decided.

'You could make a gift to a museum,' Vittorio suggested.

'Mm . . . could do that. The truth is, Vittorio, I'm a little short of cash. I'm a rich man, but I've been making demands on the estate which I'm told are a bit out of line. I have two sisters getting married next year and . . .'

That was something Vittorio understood, the dowries required in order to marry off the females of the family. His quick mind took in the implications of what Lord Kenrick was saying, and when he spoke he was already seeing the transaction as his way of getting a foothold in the antique trade in England.

'I could arrange a sale of anything you decided to part with,' he said.

'That was what I had in mind,' Lord Kenrick admitted.

He fidgeted round the room until at last he decided to confide in Vittorio. 'There's a man I used to know . . . runs an antiquarian business. Perhaps we could use him.'

Vittorio was interested, since this was just the sort of person with whom he hoped to make contact.

'He may not like dealing with me, though,' Lord Kenrick went on.

'But surely, if it is his business, he will be pleased to handle such fine objects?'

'Ah . . . well, there's a difficulty. Before I went abroad, I thought I wanted to marry his daughter.'

Vittorio's social instincts told him immediately that this would not have been considered a suitable match for an English lord; obviously there had been opposition from the family and Lord Kenrick had been despatched on a tour of Europe.

'And now?' he probed gently.

'I've changed, just as everyone said I would. I still think Grace is a fine girl, but I can see it was a mistake to get engaged to her.'

Behind his mask of polite attentiveness Vittorio was filled with amazement. His lordship had been affianced to a girl, admittedly not his equal, but of a respectable family. He had broken his word and gone away and now he had come back and was proposing to do business with her father, apparently without any expectation of revenge. If the father was too old to deal with the matter, had she no brothers, no other male relatives? In Sicily Lord Kenrick would have gone in fear of his life.

'I'd like to know if she's all right,' Lord Kenrick said abruptly. 'I can't very well . . . Do you think you could find out for me, Vittorio? Approach Charles DuFrayne, see if he's interested in handling the sale and discover what's happened to Grace.'

'Perhaps she's married someone else,' Vittorio remarked, with a touch of malice.

The idea plainly did not please Lord Kenrick, but he said with a fair assumption of indifference, 'She might have done, of course. Good thing if she has. Two years is a long time – as I've found out myself.'

He still seemed to have something on his mind and Vittorio made a fair guess at what it was.

'There is no need to mention your name,' he suggested.

'Just what I was thinking,' Lord Kenrick said with relief. 'For one thing, I don't particularly want it known that I'm selling off what I've brought into the country, like a ruddy merchant. And then, of course, there's Grace . . . awkward all round, to do business with her father.'

Charles DuFrayne's business premises were situated in Piccadilly, on the north side between Bond Street and the Burlington Arcade. An expensive location, as Vittorio was quick to realise, taking in the mixture of luxury shops and fine town-houses with which he was surrounded.

From the outside the premises were smaller than Vittorio had anticipated, but once inside he saw that there was ample space for viewing items for sale and a good big auction room with an impressive mahogany podium. He liked the atmosphere of solidity, an impression reinforced when he met Charles DuFrayne.

A thickset man in his late fifties with iron-grey hair, bushy eyebrows and a short neck, DuFrayne had a way of thrusting his head forward which made him look like a belligerent bull, something quite at variance with the mildness of his nature. He was enthusiastic about the list of items Vittorio reeled off.

'Half a dozen Etruscan vases, some small Roman marbles, an earthenware sheep's-head rhyton from the fourth century before Christ, a porphyry Roman copy of a fifth-century Greek bronze of Poseidon, and some later items – a German drinking horn with silver gilt mounts of the fifteenth century, a collection of swords and daggers, a wooden cross, carved and gilded, several French paintings . . .'

'The artists?'

'Le Nain, Chardin, Oudry . . . possibly a Millet, but I am not sure whether that will go for sale or not.'

'It's a mouthwatering list,' Charles DuFrayne said. 'The Greek and Roman items could form a sale on their own.'

'You'd sell by auction?'

'I couldn't undertake to purchase so many different objects and hold them until I found a buyer. Besides, I think a better price will be realised by offering them at auction.'

'That is my thought, too. I should tell you, signor, that my own father in Sicily is a fine-art dealer. I shall be interested to see how such sales are handled in England. I hope you will allow me to give such assistance as I can.'

Charles DuFrayne considered him shrewdly. Such a collection could only have been acquired by a man of considerable wealth, someone perhaps who had toured Europe picking up what took his fancy with a certain lack of discrimination.

'You're not selling on your own behalf, are you?' he asked.

Vittorio hesitated. 'My . . . the gentleman for whom I am acting does not wish his name to appear.'

'We can bill the items as "The property of a gentleman", although such things sell better if they come from a known collection. However, for my own protection I have to know the name of your principal.'

'I'm sorry, I'm forbidden to reveal it.'

'For all I know, you could be asking me to deal in stolen property.'

9

Vittorio sprang to his feet, his face suffused with colour and his eyes flashing. 'Signor, you insult me!'

'Not at all, I merely ask you to see my point of view. The name of the gentleman need never go outside this room, but I must insist on knowing it.'

Vittorio remained on his feet, thinking swiftly. Once this transaction was over he had every intention of leaving Lord Kenrick – and if Mr DuFrayne refused to handle the items when he knew their owner's name, then Vittorio could always take his goods elsewhere.

'I understand that in the past there has been some trouble between you,' he said.

'Really? I'm a peaceable man and a straight dealer. Offhand I can only think of one man who might be reluctant to give me his name.'

'The trouble was of a . . . a personal nature, concerning your family.'

'My daughter is all the family I have.' He fell into a heavy silence and Vittorio waited. 'Your principal is Lord Kenrick?' Mr DuFrayne asked at last.

'Yes.'

'I read in the newspaper that he was back in England, and loaded with spoils. It sounded as if he were turning Mercia House into a branch of the British Museum.'

'The house is much improved.'

'No doubt. So he told you about his dealings with me and my poor daughter, did he? Though why I should say poor, I don't know. Grace was well rid of him and she shows no signs of regretting it.'

Charles only wished that were true. Grace never spoke of the past but she was too quiet, she stayed too close to home, and she was too pious for her father's liking.

'Has she married another man?' Vittorio enquired.

'Did he ask you to find that out? Ah, I can see from your face that he did . . . Damn him, if he tries to pick up where he left off I'll slit his throat with one of his own daggers, and so you can tell him.'

That was an attitude Vittorio could understand and approve.

'I think his lordship merely wished to know that your daughter no longer suffers.'

'She's in excellent health and spirits, thank you. No, she hasn't married, but no doubt she will when the right man comes along. We Catholics don't find it easy to make suitable matches in England, you know – it was our religion that was particularly repugnant to Lady Kenrick. I presume you belong to the Church?'

'Of course.' Searching for a way to reinstate himself in Mr DuFrayne's estimation, Vittorio said with more tact than truth, 'Now that I am settled in London I must resume going to Mass. I shall be glad if you can advise me of a suitable church.'

'Grace and I sometimes go to one of the Embassy chapels, but more often we attend the Jesuits' church in Farm Street.'

A small resolution formed in Vittorio's mind. After all, he had been requested to see Grace for himself if he could. Next Sunday . . .

'Thank you. Do you wish to handle the sale, Mr DuFrayne?' he asked.

'I suppose so. Business is business and it'll be a prestige event. It would gall me to hear you'd taken it to Christie & Manson's. I'll do my best for the silly young man – I suppose he overspent himself?'

Vittorio did not commit himself to an answer, but his shrug was eloquent.

'Just one thing,' DuFrayne went on. 'I'd rather his lordship didn't know that I've been told for whom you're acting. Can I trust you to keep it to yourself?'

'Certainly, signor. I shall not be with his lordship for very much longer.'

'Are you going back to Italy?'

'No, my intention – my hope – is to remain in England and establish myself in the trade in which I have been brought up.'

'I understand you. You're saying we're likely to be colleagues in the future.'

'Perhaps rivals,' Vittorio said with a smile that lit up his face.

They met after Mass at the Church of the Jesuit Fathers the following Sunday, as Vittorio had planned. He was wearing his best black suit, well-pressed and brushed, and a subdued waist-coat of grey and silver brocade. He was by no means the only

11

worshipper of Italian extraction, but Vittorio was an obvious new arrival. The cut of his clothes, the wide brim of his hat, his pointed shoes and his yellow gloves all marked him out.

Charles DuFrayne saw him at once and paused, his daughter on his arm. He had not wanted to introduce Grace to this emissary from Lord Kenrick, but he could hardly pass him by when they had just come out of the same church.

'Grace, my dear, this is Signor Vittorio Speranza, from Italy,' he said. 'My daughter, Signor Speranza.'

Vittorio swept off his hat. His bow was perfect, courteous but not flamboyant.

'Signor Speranza and I are organising a sale of some very fine Greek and Roman antiquities,' Charles DuFrayne explained. 'At least, from his description I believe them to be fine. When am I to see what you have to sell, Signor Speranza?'

'I propose to arrange delivery to your premises before the end of the week. Do you take an interest in your father's business, signorina?'

'I like to see the beautiful things,' Grace said.

'My daughter is too modest,' Charles DuFrayne protested. 'She knows as much as I do about English and Continental porcelain, though I think I have the advantage over her when it comes to Chinese.'

'Ah, porcelain! There I am ignorant,' Vittorio admitted.

They stood for a minute or two more and then parted. Vittorio was satisfied. He had done what he had undertaken to do and now he could report that Miss Grace DuFrayne was not pining for her lost love, although he would not have gone so far as to say, like her father, that she was in the best of health and spirits. There was something subdued about her. Her smile had been perfunctory; it had apparently meant nothing to her that she had just met a young and personable man. That was something Vittorio could not understand. He had looked for the quick, speculative glance he received from most girls, however cleverly they might conceal it, and from Grace it had not been forthcoming. Vittorio was piqued.

It was not that she was a plain girl. On the contrary, he had been pleasantly impressed. She was a little too tall and she lacked colour, but her hair was thick and shining, her features were good and her complexion was pleasing. It was just that some essential spark was missing – or had been deliberately suppressed.

Chapter Two

'We should take Signor Speranza to the International Exhibition –
don't you agree, Grace?' Charles DuFrayne took a quick look at
his daughter as he spoke.

'Oh . . . rather dull, don't you think?' Grace objected. She
turned to Vittorio to explain. 'The Great Exhibition, which was
held ten years ago, was such a success that it has been repeated,
but there's not the same excitement this time. I remember going to
the first exhibition when I was a child.'

'Several times,' Mr DuFrayne reminded her. 'That was before
we moved to Kensington.' And when her mother had still been
alive, but neither of them intended to speak of that.

'The new Exhibition Hall is very close to this house, Signor
Speranza,' Grace said. 'In fact, the building of it has been
something of an inconvenience to us. Work has even continued at
night.'

She turned to her father and suggested, 'Don't you think our
guest might prefer to come with us to a concert in Cremorne
Gardens?'

'Ah, music!' Vittorio exclaimed. 'That is something I have
missed since I began travelling. Perhaps, if you, too, have an
enjoyment of music, signorina, you and Signor DuFrayne will
allow me to invite you to the Italian Opera one evening?'

'I've never been to Covent Garden,' Grace said, and her
eagerness filled her father with pleasure.

Their acquaintance with the young Sicilian had grown rapidly
since their meeting at the Church of the Jesuit Fathers. Vittorio, it
seemed, was a pious young man who never missed attendance at
Mass. On weekdays he had taken to dropping in to see Charles
DuFrayne to discuss the details of the forthcoming sale, and now,
for the first time, he had joined them after church for their Sunday
luncheon.

'No spaghetti, I'm afraid, Signor Speranza,' Mr DuFrayne
joked.

No wine either, and Vittorio regretted that far more than the lack of pasta. For a moment he was visited by a fierce nostalgia for his homeland. He remembered the hot sun and fierce blue sky, the dark peasant girls with their flashing eyes, the ruined cities scattered with white marble, the secret alleyways and old women on wooden chairs in the doorways, and the smell of the scented land, its dark cypresses and glowing oleanders. All this he had left behind and might never see again . . .

He shook off the mood and turned to something he was anxious to know.

'Have you decided whether my own treasures should be included in the . . . the sale we are arranging?' He managed, just in time, to stop himself from saying 'the Kenrick sale'.

'I think it will be best to have two sales,' Charles DuFrayne said. 'One devoted to antiquities of the Ancient World will attract a particular sort of dealer, and your statue should certainly go into that. The other items can be included in a second sale. Do you think that will be agreeable to . . . to your client?'

From the way he, too, skimmed over the Kenrick name Vittorio guessed that Grace was still in ignorance about his connection with her former lover.

'If you intend to set up in business as a dealer then you might do better to keep what you've got and use it as the beginnings of your stock-in-trade,' Mr DuFrayne added. 'Or you may be attracted to the auction trade.'

There was a thoughtful silence.

'Grace can't follow me into my business and there's no one else to take over after me,' Mr DuFrayne said at last.

'Perhaps you would consider taking a younger partner to assist you?' Vittorio suggested.

'He'd have to buy his way in.'

'Of course.'

They understood one another. At the back of Charles DuFrayne's mind was another idea, concerning Grace, and he wondered whether it had occurred to Vittorio Speranza as well.

It had, of course. Vittorio was well aware of the advantages of marrying Grace DuFrayne. The only difficulty was that she had already shown an independent spirit which would not have been tolerated in Vittorio's own family. His sister Carlotta had been informed of her impending marriage only after the man had been thoroughly vetted and she would not have dreamed of refusing to comply. Even from the little he had seen, Vittorio knew that Charles DuFrayne would never impose a suitor on his daughter, nor would Grace accept a man merely because he was her father's choice. This left Vittorio in a quandary since, if Grace rejected him, it would be awkward for him to join the DuFrayne business.

He was turning this over in his mind that evening as he put on one side the items which were not going for immediate sale: his own fine painted panel and gold cup, his lordship's paintings, the swords and daggers, the carved and gilded cross from fifteenth-century Venice.

The cross had its own box, covered in red leather and lined with red velvet. Vittorio did not particularly admire it, although he accepted its authenticity. The crucifix had been bought before he had started guiding Lord Kenrick in his purchases. Now Vittorio took the cross out to examine it more closely; it was very thick and heavy, and had probably been a travelling piece carried by some cleric to hang on the wall of his lodging when he went on a journey.

It might also have been a reliquary. Certainly it was large enough to contain a sliver of the True Cross, a hair of a saint or some other sacred memento. Yet Vittorio could see no hidden spring, no way of opening it – which was a pity because such a feature would have increased its value. There was a loop of gold at the top of the cross by which it could be hung up. Idly, Vittorio slipped the loop over his finger and held up the cross, a silly thing to do because it was far too heavy to be supported from one finger. He winced at the weight and then frowned in annoyance as he realised that his finger was trapped in the ring. He had to tug hard to get it free, and the delicate loop twisted in the socket. Vittorio only hoped, as he sucked his sore and swollen finger, that he had not done any permanent damage to the cross.

As he picked it up to examine it, he felt a superstitious thrill because it seemed as if the gilded Christ had moved. Then he looked closer. The Christ figure had indeed moved! Formerly flat against the wooden background, it now stood proud; the beautifully carved, agonised figure could be swivelled to one side, he discovered. Just as he had suspected, the cross had once been a reliquary, and the accidental twisting of the loop had released some catch to reveal the hiding place.

What was more, *there was something within the cavity*. Completely forgetting his sore finger, Vittorio probed inside, to encounter a small package of softest silk containing something hard.

What Vittorio expected as he opened the drawstrings of the little purse was some gruesome relic – a finger bone perhaps, or the teeth from the skull of a long-forgotten saint. What he found, however, was not at all holy – and of far more immediate interest.

Vittorio tipped the flashing contents out on to the table: five perfect diamonds. He picked one up and held it to the light. It looked flawless, with a blue-white clarity, and then as he moved it the stone quivered with all the colours of the rainbow.

Who had owned these splendid stones? Who had concealed them so cunningly? Some priest perhaps, not so committed to a life of poverty as he appeared; or a merchant, congratulating himself on his cunning hiding place for his wealth. Whoever it had been, he was long since dead. The silk was soft with the rottenness of decay and the mechanism of the cross had been stiff from disuse.

To whom did the stones belong now? Reluctantly, Vittorio conceded that Lord Kenrick was the rightful owner. On the other hand, his lordship knew nothing about them and would be unaware of any loss if he remained ignorant of Vittorio's discovery. The Sicilian considered his lordship – his wealth and his carelessness with it, his assured place in the world, his houses and possessions, his acquisition of works of art which he coveted more because he was told that they were valuable than because he had any true taste for them. Above all, Vittorio thought about Lord Kenrick's treatment of Grace. He had once done the girl Vittorio was considering marrying a great wrong, and he had never been punished for it – not as he would have been in Vittorio's native country. Why should Vittorio not treat the keeping of the diamonds as a matter of honour – restitution for Grace's dishonour?

Grace stood in front of the cheval glass in her bedroom, tying the ribbons of her bonnet. She was wearing a new gown of blue-grey silk, just the colour of her eyes, and a short jacket of velvet which matched the silk exactly.

She was fully aware of the significance of wearing a new gown for her visit to Cremorne Gardens with Signor Speranza. She only hoped that her father would have the tact to refrain from remarking on her finery. The day might be of some importance to her, but she did not wish Signor Speranza to know how carefully she had dressed for it.

He had already spoken to her father and, somewhat hesitantly, Charles DuFrayne had sounded out his daughter about her feelings.

'It's a pity he's a foreigner,' he had said. 'But, of course, your own great-grandparents were all French, and it was only in my grandfather's day that we began to marry into English families. Signor Speranza seems to have formed a real attachment to you, my dear.'

'Do you like him, Father?'

'I do. He has a quick intelligence and he's extremely knowledgeable about antiquities. He seems to be of a good character, his manners are charming and I've lately discovered that he's rather better off than I first thought.'

Charles DuFrayne hesitated, not wanting to involve his daughter in business matters, but then he decided that he owed it to her to explain how things stood.

'Signor Speranza would like to join me in my business. He's offered to put in a considerable sum in fresh capital, which would be of benefit to us all, and I must say the idea of having such a forceful and talented young partner appeals to me.'

'Is marrying me one of the conditions of the partnership?'

'Certainly not! That's why I'm sounding you out myself. If you can't like the idea then nothing more need be said. Signor Speranza will still be prepared to join up with me no matter what your decision may be.'

Grace considered the matter coolly and decided that she might as well marry Vittorio Speranza as anyone else. Perhaps she was not in love with him; indeed, she was sure she was not since she experienced none of the sensations that had racked her when she had believed herself to be engaged to Ludo Kenrick, but she did like him and it was impossible not to be aware that other women noticed him and envied her when he was her escort.

'Tell him . . . tell him that I would like to know him rather longer before committing myself,' Grace had said at that time. 'I believe you are better acquainted with him than I am, Father.'

'But he need not despair?' Charles DuFrayne asked with a smile.

'Say that I suggest he takes his own name as his motto,' Grace said with an answering smile.

'Vittorio. . . ?' her father said in bewilderment. 'You mean – victory?'

'No – Speranza. I think the Signor will understand me.'

Vittorio also smiled when Mr DuFrayne related this conversation to him.

'Speranza means "hope" in English,' he said. 'So, I may hope. I ask for nothing more at the present time.'

He had gained in confidence in the last few weeks. Vittorio had never lacked assurance, but the secret hoard of diamonds had given him an extra conviction of his destiny. He had taken the stones to a reputable jeweller who had sent his spirits soaring by valuing them at between three thousand and five thousand pounds each. After haggling for some time Vittorio had arranged not to sell the stones, but to borrow on their security with the option of redeeming them, one by one if necessary, as his fortune increased.

The sale of Lord Kenrick's collection of antiquities from the Ancient World was highly successful. Vittorio saw that Charles DuFrayne had been shrewd in his estimation of the worth of the items and his admiration for his possible future father-in-law increased. The auction had been well advertised, it was attended by a good selection of dealers and even by one or two gentlemen buying for themselves. The conduct of the sale itself could not have been better. Charles DuFrayne seemed to acquire new authority when he took the podium and his eyes missed none of the unobtrusive bids from around the room. He had a way of pausing in apparent surprise when the bidding slackened, looking round and seeming to gather an extra bid out of the air.

Lord Kenrick was more than pleased by the profit he gained from the sale. Vittorio was equally satisfied since he had negotiated with his lordship for a five per cent commission, in addition to Charles DuFrayne's own fees. This, combined with his profit from the statue of Hermes and the fifteen thousand pounds he had wrested from the jeweller on the security of the diamonds, made him a wealthy man, and he still had the Masaccio panel and the Cellini goblet of which to dispose. Grace, he felt, would be doing well if she married him. He might even, if she continued to please him, give her the Masaccio painting as a wedding present. Lord Kenrick's wooden cross, in which the diamonds had been concealed, Vittorio intended buying for himself. He had a superstitious feeling that the source of his good fortune should remain in his hands.

Just as Grace suspected, Vittorio had decided on the visit to Cremorne Gardens as a suitable opportunity to propose. He hardly knew how to go about it, since he had never anticipated having to ask a girl to her face to marry him, but he had rehearsed a few suitable phrases so that he would not be at a total loss for words.

Cremorne Gardens covered an area of twelve acres by the side of the Thames, just to the west of Battersea Bridge. It was pleasantly rural, with shady walks under large trees, interspersed with Swiss chalets, kiosks and temples, a marionette theatre and the hall in which Grace and her father and Vittorio heard a concert which, to Vittorio's critical ears, was no more than second-rate.

'May we stay and see the fireworks?' Grace asked as they left after the concert. 'I take the most childish delight in fireworks, Signor Speranza.'

'I've no great love of them, as you know,' Mr DuFrayne said.

'I would be happy to escort Signorina DuFrayne home if you wish to escape from the noise, signor,' Vittorio said. He was stupefied by his daring, but it seemed that the Englishman saw nothing amiss in trusting his daughter to a young, unmarried man alone after dark.

'An excellent solution,' Mr DuFrayne said. 'But you must leave immediately after the display.'

'That's when the dancing starts,' Grace said, with a certain wistfulness.

'Precisely, and with it a lack of decorum . . . I'm sure you understand me, Signor Speranza.'

Vittorio understood perfectly. Grace was to be allowed the small indulgence of watching the rockets and golden rain and he was to be given the opportunity of asking her to marry him, but she was not to be exposed to the more raucous element which was already beginning to filter into the Gardens.

The firework display was excellent, but Vittorio found more enjoyment in watching Grace's upturned face and hearing her gasps of delight at the cascading stars. She caught hold of his arm and shuddered at the louder bangs and that did not displease him either. She was charming, especially when she was displaying a little more animation than she usually did.

When they turned towards the exit he had her hand firmly tucked under his arm, in order to keep her close to him in the crowd. A girl in a brilliant scarlet gown, displaying a striped petticoat and a pair of high-heeled boots, her hair dressed in elaborate ringlets and her face painted, brushed past them shrieking with laughter at the sallies of a group of young men. Vittorio saw what Mr DuFrayne had meant about the changing character of the crowd now that darkness had fallen.

In spite of that, he guided Grace away from the main thoroughfare and towards a quieter path where the lanterns in the trees gave no more than a gentle glow.

'Grace,' he said. '*Cara mia, carissima*, I have your father's permission to address you. I have for you the most ardent admiration and love. I wish for you to be my wife. Will you give me my wish?'

Grace's hand trembled on his arm and then she became very still.

'Yes,' she said. 'I will be happy to marry you, Vittorio.'

Vittorio's imagination had taken him no farther than that, but Grace seemed to expect something more, so he bent towards her and kissed her cheek and then, because he was suddenly on fire with pleasure at the thought of his success, he found her soft, unready lips and kissed her with gentle persistence until Grace drew back in confusion.

'Oh, dear . . . we mustn't . . . Dear Vittorio, we should go home and tell Father our news. He'll be pleased, I know he will.'

It was late before Vittorio left the DuFrayne house that night. Grace went off to bed, looking flushed and happy, and the two men stayed talking and drinking Charles DuFrayne's brandy until after midnight – and if their talk was mainly about their future plans for the business partnership of DuFrayne & Speranza, at least on Charles DuFrayne's part that was because he was quite satisfied in his own mind about the choice his daughter had made.

'Only one thing bothers me,' he said when Vittorio was finally making a move to go. 'Have you ever told Grace that we met because of your employment by Lord Kenrick?'

'No. And you, I take it, have not confided in her either?'

'It seemed better not to mention his name.'

'I think she has quite got over that past unhappiness. I am confident that she is genuinely attached to me.'

'All the same . . .'

'It might be better if she never knew about the connection?'

'I suppose so, although I don't like to be underhanded,' Charles DuFrayne said. 'Can we keep it quiet?'

'Why not? The main sale is over, I have already told him that I am leaving him and . . .'

'Did you tell him your plans?'

'I said I was setting up in the antiques trade. I did not mention your name nor, of course, have I spoken of my interest in Grace.'

'It should be all right,' Mr DuFrayne said, but he was uneasy.

'I would prefer not to speak of his lordship to Grace,' Vittorio said, and because he spoke firmly and because he was now Grace's affianced husband, Mr DuFrayne let the matter go.

Vittorio gave Grace an engagement ring set with three sapphires. Remembering the ring Ludo had set on her finger, the joy with which she had accepted it and the pain with which she had removed and returned it to his mother when he had deserted her, Grace had intimated that she did not like diamond rings. Their engagement lasted just three months and neither of them found anything to regret about their commitment during that time.

It was not until she was walking up the aisle of the church on her father's arm that Charles DuFrayne became alarmed at the way his daughter was trembling, and by that time it was too late to turn back.

Grace made her responses in a voice so faint that it was hardly audible. She felt dazed, as if this creature in a stiff, watered-silk gown and lace veil was someone quite alien to her. As for Vittorio, she knew nothing about him. He was a foreigner to whom she had given herself with a feeling of inevitability, but with none of the thrill she had once expected to feel on her wedding day.

22

Charles DuFrayne made one attempt to express his uneasiness to Vittorio.

'Be good to my girl,' he said.

'Of course.' Vittorio was all smiles. He, at any rate, seemed to have no doubts about his marriage.

'She's . . . I think she's feeling nervous.'

'That is natural.' Vittorio saw that his new father-in-law was seriously perturbed and set himself to reassure him. 'Signor, I am not without experience. I shall treat Grace as if she were one of those pieces of fine porcelain you handle with such care. Trust me.'

'I do,' Charles DuFrayne said.

For the honeymoon they were making a tour of the West Country, stopping for the first two nights in Cheltenham and then going on to Dorset, Devon and Cornwall. It would be new country for Grace and to Vittorio, of course, everything was new.

He thought Cheltenham an elegant town, though they saw little of it that first evening and a thin drizzle of rain obscured the terraces and squares of houses with their fine wrought-iron balconies for which the town was famous.

'You must eat, *cara*,' Vittorio said, noticing the way his wife was playing with her food as they sat over dinner in their hotel.

'We had such a rich meal earlier,' Grace excused herself.

'You ate little of that either.' Vittorio put his hand firmly over hers and stayed her restless fingers. '*Cara*, let us speak frankly to one another. You are about to walk through a door which before has been closed to you and you are a little afraid of what you will find inside it. But you must not be afraid. The step you are taking is the most natural one in the world and I will be there to guide you.'

Grace managed to smile and tried to be grateful for his understanding.

It was not, in the end, as bad as she had feared. Vittorio assured her that the day would come when she would find pleasure in the act which had joined them together as man and wife. Grace doubted it, but at least it was over and she had been able to go through with it and now she knew the great secret which was kept from girls like her – and was secretly astonished that such a fuss was made about it.

As for Vittorio, he was more disappointed than Grace. He had

23

thought he would be able to coax her round, but his wife had been stiff and cold in his arms, no matter how much he tried to please her.

They went out sightseeing the next day, a very proper young married couple. Cheltenham was no longer the important spa town it had once been, but there was still sufficient to see to keep them amused between meals.

Grace wore a particularly pretty gown that evening, a blue satin the colour of her sapphire ring with a deep flounce of Brussels lace round the boat-shaped neckline. She had relaxed a little, although it still seemed unimaginably strange to dress in a room where a man had the right to stroll in and compliment her before she was completely laced up.

She was pleased by Vittorio's admiration, and by the glances she collected as they made their way to their table in the dining room. She felt hungry after walking about all day and there was no need for Vittorio to chide her that evening for not eating.

They sat in the drawing room for a time after dinner, exchanged a few words with fellow guests, looked out of the door to see that the sky was clear and it promised to be fair the next day, and when they finally went upstairs Vittorio was hopeful of improving his relations with his young wife and Grace was feeling none of the nervous dread that had paralysed her the night before.

Vittorio retired decorously to his dressing room adjoining the bedroom while Grace's maid helped her mistress to undress, an operation he would have been pleased to perform himself. He would suggest it, he thought, one night soon when Grace was more used to him.

He strolled back into the room, pulling tight the tie of his dressing gown.

'That is quite the most beautiful dressing gown I have ever seen,' Grace remarked.

'Italian silk,' Vittorio said, stroking the garment admiringly. 'One day I must take you to my country, *cara*. It is very beautiful. An ancient land, full of great ruins.'

'We have old ruins, too,' Grace pointed out. 'I believe there are some strange standing stones in Cornwall and then there's Stonehenge . . .'

'Very impressive,' Vittorio admitted. 'Especially by moonlight.'

24

'But you haven't seen it!' Grace cried. She caught the look of dismay on Vittorio's face and added uncertainly, 'Have you?'

After months of watching his words he had been tripped up, distracted by the curve of her breasts beneath the delicate cambric of her wrapper, and made careless by his mounting desire for her.

'You've been to Wiltshire,' Grace said.

'Before I met you, when I first arrived in England, yes, I spent a few weeks in that part of the country.'

'You never told me. Even when we were discussing whether we should visit Aunt Cissie on our honeymoon you never said you had been in the county before.'

'It seemed of no importance,' Vittorio said, shrugging.

'Perhaps not, but it seems strange.' Grace looked away from him and asked in a strained voice, 'Was it because you knew that the last time I was in Wiltshire I became engaged to a man who jilted me?'

'Yes.'

'I see. Father told you.'

The quagmire into which he had strayed seemed to be getting deeper and deeper. Vittorio replied very carefully, 'We have talked about it.'

It might have passed off with no damage done, even though the pleasant mood which had been developing between them had been dispersed, if Grace had not asked, 'Where did you stay?'

Vittorio would have lied if he had been able to think of one single town in Wiltshire where he might reasonably have claimed to have passed some weeks on his arrival in England. As it was the silence stretched between them until at last he could do no more than tell the truth.

'This will not please you, *cara*, and I regret now that you were not told before. I entered England in the employ of Lord Kenrick and I spent two months at Mercia House helping him to install the works of art he had purchased on the Continent.' He glanced at Grace and her stillness intimidated him.

'Did Lord Kenrick speak of me?' she asked evenly.

'Yes.'

'It was his doing that you came to see Father and me?'

'He had things for sale and he asked me to approach your father to see if he would handle them.'

25

'The great sale of which Father was so proud. I thought he loved me, but it seems he puts his business above my feelings.'

Suddenly she was on her feet, flushed and shaking with anger.

'And so do you. You neither of you trusted me enough to tell me the truth. Why? I'll tell you. Because you were afraid that my distress would stop you making a profit!'

'That's not true,' Vittorio said, but he knew that it was.

'And our marriage – how nicely that has tidied everything up. Was that Lord Kenrick's idea, too?'

'No! He knew nothing . . . I had left his employ before I asked you to marry me.'

'Is that supposed to make me feel better? You discussed me with that . . . that feeble creature; you knew about my disappointment. You *pitied* me . . .'

'No, I didn't. I thought you got what you deserved. No Sicilian girl of good family would have behaved as you did.'

'Obviously you should have stayed in Sicily and married one of your own kind.'

Grace was pacing about the room, beside herself with fury, and as he watched her Vittorio began to feel not a matching anger, but admiration. Her agitation had carried Grace outside herself. She had forgotten her modesty and her shrinking from him. The cotton wrapper fell back from her shoulders unheeded and he feasted his eyes on her smooth curves. Here at last was the temperament he had always suspected lay behind Grace's careful control, and he was more in love with her than he had ever been during their months of decorous courtship.

When he laughed Grace turned on him, unable to believe her ears.

'Don't hit me,' Vittorio said. 'Yes, I can see you would like to and I sympathise with you. We did wrong, your father and I, to treat you like a child. We should have told you about the sale. Perhaps you, too, would have relished the profit we made out of your false lover. Come, Grace, forgive me. I am your husband and I love you. Your anger interests me more than your pretty manners.'

For a moment Grace did not know what she was doing. She swung back her arm, but Vittorio caught it by the wrist and twisted it behind her back, pulling her towards him.

'Oh, no!' he said. 'That is not the way it is going to be. If anyone gives blows then it will be me. Stop breathing fire and listen.'

'You're hurting me,' Grace gasped.

'I am not, though perhaps you are a little uncomfortable. I have made a discovery which I wish to share with you. I love you. Yes, it is very strange and not at all what I expected when I made my arrangement with your father to marry you. Now, at this moment, I have never wanted a woman in my life more than I want you.'

'That's a great pity,' Grace snapped. 'Because I hate you.'

'I think not. I think if you will forget this offence – yes, I have been wrong and I admit it, but if we are to live together it must be forgotten – above all, if you will allow yourself to release the passion that is in you and which I so ardently desire to share with you, then we can be very happy together, my Grace.'

'I hate you,' Grace repeated.

Vittorio let go of her arm and she stood rubbing her wrist and refusing to look at him. He ran his hand down the length of her arm and took her hand in his and kissed the wrist he had been holding and Grace did not move away. When he pulled her closer she went, with an appearance of reluctance, but not resisting him.

Vittorio moved his face against hers, seeking her mouth. As he kissed her he did what he had never done before and sought to put his tongue between her lips. Grace gasped and shuddered and then suddenly clung to him as she felt the delicate exploration inside her mouth.

She was still pressing herself against him when Vittorio asked in a low voice, 'Are you ready to be my wife?'

Unable to speak, Grace moved her head in assent and, still entwined, they moved towards the bed.

Chapter Three

In the first year of his marriage two things gave Vittorio supreme happiness. The first was seeing his name over the door of the Piccadilly premises. 'DuFrayne & Speranza' was a little clumsy, perhaps, and rather too foreign-sounding by the side of the other great auction houses – Christie & Manson, Sotheby's, Phillips, Bonham's – but that mattered little compared with the growing reputation of the firm.

Its new standing owed a lot to Vittorio. As soon as he was in a position to examine the books, he realised that he had come along just in time to save Charles DuFrayne from a disastrous decline. Now Vittorio saw why his father-in-law had agreed to handle the Kenrick sale and why he had been so ready to take into partnership a young man about whom he knew remarkably little.

Charles DuFrayne was a gentleman, and in spite of his knowledge and taste and the impeccable way he administered the sales that came his way, he was not the man to go out and look for business. Vittorio had no such scruples. He kept his eyes on the obituaries and at the faintest whiff of an executors' sale, he sent off a letter setting out the terms on which DuFrayne & Speranza operated together with a list of the excellent prices recently obtained in their auction rooms. This strategy was a form of advertisement which paid off – and business began to boom.

The second event which gave him satisfaction was the birth of his son.

Grace came back from her honeymoon pregnant, although it was a week or two before she realised it. She was proud of herself and gratified by Vittorio's delight, but there were times when she felt a little resentful that her newly discovered pleasure in her body had to be curtailed. Not that Vittorio was any less ardent, not at first, but Grace felt queasy most of the time and far less responsive than she had been during their weeks in the West Country.

Her confinement was difficult enough to frighten both Vittorio and her father. Vittorio, in particular, was bewildered since he had no knowledge of childbirth and had thought it a simple process, painful perhaps – or so the women always insisted – but not a matter that threatened the life of a young and healthy woman like Grace.

When he saw his wife drained of colour and looking curiously diminished, shortly after the baby's birth, he was too shocked to speak coherently.

'We have a beautiful son,' Grace said in a tiny whisper.

'He gave you a bad time, *cara*,' Vittorio said.

'He's so big – nearly nine pounds. Look at him. He's just like you.'

She moved aside the fold of shawl in which the baby lay wrapped in the crook of her arm, to reveal a creased red face and a round head with a shock of black hair. Vittorio could see no resemblance to anyone, but then the baby blinked, opened his eyes and looked straight up at his father, and as he gazed down at those dark, unfocused eyes, Vittorio felt a thrill of pride.

'He will be called Giorgio,' he stated.

'If you wish,' Grace said, too tired to take up an argument that had been going on between them for the last six months. She had wanted her baby to be called Charles, after her father, if it was a boy, and Margaret, after her dead mother, if it was a girl. Vittorio had insisted on his choice.

'Giorgio Giulini has been my friend in Syracuse since the day we were born,' he said. 'We were taught in the same school – and very naughty boys we were – and he was my comrade-in-arms when we fought with Garibaldi. Now perhaps we will never meet again, but I will do this one small thing in his memory: I will call my son by his name.'

When Vittorio became emotional about his ties with his homeland Grace knew better than to argue. She relented, telling herself that at least the name was one that could be easily Anglicised if little Giorgio wished it when he grew up.

Vittorio wrote that evening to give the news to his father in Syracuse. He had been sparing in his letters home, especially since his marriage, for the simple reason that he did not want his family to know how well he had done for himself. Enrico's own letters to his son, equally infrequent, had had a complaining note in them.

Union with the Italian mainland had not been a success so far as Sicily was concerned. There were new taxes which bore hard on the town-dwelling Sicilians while the rich farmers across the water got off lightly. Business was poor, he wrote, and the profits had to be divided between himself and his three sons remaining in Syracuse. There had been a strong hint in his last letter that Vittorio ought to do something for his family, perhaps even send for one of his brothers and give him a share in Vittorio's good fortune.

Vittorio shied away from that. In his announcement of the birth of his son he emphasised that his main concern now must be for his own family.

Grace was curious about his family in Sicily, but Vittorio was adamant that there should be no visiting.

'My brothers are very set in their ways,' he said. 'I have adapted; I have become almost an Englishman, but they would not be happy here, no, not even for a short holiday. It was their choice to stay in Syracuse while I set out on my own; let them stay there.'

Grace, who thought her husband was very far from being a typical Englishman, was amused.

'When we were on our honeymoon you promised to take me to visit Sicily,' she reminded him.

'Circumstances have changed. The country is very unsettled.' Vittorio sighed. 'It is not what I expected when I joined Garibaldi.'

The political situation in Sicily continued to worry him, but it diminished in importance beside his own domestic concerns. Bearing in mind the doctor's concern over Giorgio's difficult birth, Vittorio tried to behave with consideration towards his wife; it was Grace who was eager for their relations to be resumed. The result was that she bore him a second son just a year after Giorgio's birth, again after a protracted and difficult labour.

'*Cara*, we must be more careful,' Vittorio said, as soon as she was well enough to listen to him. 'I have seen too many women in my own country worn out by incessant childbearing to wish for the same fate for my own wife.'

'It's as God chooses,' Grace said.

'We are allowed to exercise a little discretion,' Vittorio reminded her.

30

He knew – and Grace, if she were honest, knew too – that her fecundity might be God-given, but it was Grace's own sexuality that drove her to entice her husband back into her bed as soon as she was sufficiently recovered. She was a constant surprise to Vittorio. Beneath her cool exterior his wife was as warm and sensual as any woman of the South. No doubt it was this secret inner need which had pushed her into engaging herself to the first personable young man who had shown an interest in her, and Vittorio thought he saw now how it was that Lord Kenrick had been persuaded into a commitment he must have known was a mistake. Grace, when her ardour was aroused, was difficult to resist.

The second boy was called Niccolò, and this time Grace did not protest about the name. Try as she would she could not feel the same rush of joy at his birth as she had known when Giorgio had been born. It was too soon, she had scarcely come to terms with having her first baby and again she had been deprived for months on end of her joy in her husband's love. She was very affectionate towards Niccolò, but at the back of her mind she slightly resented his rapid appearance.

The two boys grew up devoted to one another, so close that they might almost have been twins. Niccolò was quick for his age and Giorgio a little slow, so that there was never a gap in understanding between them. Giorgio resembled Grace's family. Indeed, she could see that he was the very image of her father. A handsome boy, big and strong, and with a sweetness of temper that endeared him to everyone. Niccolò, as Grace also recognised, and it ought to have made her love him all the more only somehow it didn't, was far more like Vittorio. He had a quickness of mind that Giorgio lacked. He was darker, thinner, lighter in build. He was also by far the more difficult child. There was a contentiousness in him which his placid brother had difficulty in understanding.

There were no more children, but Grace had a series of miscarriages which pulled her down and made her depressed. Three times in three consecutive years she lost the child she was expecting early in her pregnancy. Vittorio was concerned for her, but not altogether sorry that it seemed that his family was to be limited.

It was shortly after Grace's second disappointment that Vittorio came to her one day with a letter in his hand and tears running down his cheeks.

Grace struggled to sit up in bed and held out her arms to him. 'My dear, is it bad news from Sicily?'

They had read with concern an item in the papers about an uprising in Palermo which had been put down with great severity by the Italian authorities. It was said that forty thousand troops had been sent over from the mainland and Grace knew that Vittorio was worried for his family, even though the action seemed to have taken place away from Syracuse.

'Giorgio . . .' he groaned, forgetting in his anguish that this was also the name of their own son.

'Our Giorgio?' In her alarm Grace pushed back the covers and swung her legs down over the side of the bed. 'What has happened? Tell me, Vittorio, quickly.'

'No, no! Giorgio . . . *mio compagno, amico mio . . .*'

'Dead?'

'*Si, si . . . morto.*'

It was impossible for Grace not to feel relieved. She lay back on her pillows, still trembling. If anything had happened to her own Giorgio she thought that she would have died, too.

She tried to be kind about this friend who had meant so much to Vittorio.

'Poor man,' she said. 'Vittorio, dear, I'm so sorry. Was it in the fighting?'

'Of course. Fool, fool . . . to have allowed himself to become caught up in it. We are not children any more. He has a wife, a family.'

'How sad. Is there anything we can do to help them?'

'Ah, you are good, my Grace. Yes, I must give some help to Giorgio's family. There are three children, two boys and a little tiny girl.'

It was rarely spoken of between them, but Grace knew that in the following years, Vittorio from time to time made presents of money to the Giulini family. It did not worry her, since they could well afford it. Business was flourishing and much of the success was due to Vittorio's acumen.

After the third mishap, Grace showed no more signs of becoming pregnant and Vittorio began to forget his fears that they were destined to become the parents of a large, demanding family. His generosity towards his dead friend's family was too trifling to interfere with his plan to redeem the diamonds. One by one he bought them back and one by one he stowed them away inside the carved wooden cross which hung on their bedroom wall. He never told Grace about this secret cache, although he took care she should know that he set great store by the cross. It pleased her, because Vittorio's religious devotion was sometimes a little suspect to Grace. She herself was intensely pious and she brought up her boys to be good sons of the Church, at least as far as she could when one of them was an undoubted imp of Satan and would draw his older brother into trouble whenever possible.

It came as a considerable shock to Grace when, with her best-loved son within sight of his twenty-first birthday, she discovered that she was pregnant again. At first she hardly believed it, indeed she tried to insist that she was suffering from early symptoms of 'the change', but her doctor was adamant that his diagnosis was correct.

'You are forty-three, Mrs Speranza, enjoying good health and having marital relations with your husband. In a little over six months' time you will be a mother again.'

'If I keep it,' Grace said. 'You know about my miscarriages. Oh dear, what will the boys think? I shall hardly know how to look them in the face.'

She asked Vittorio to break the news to Giorgio and Niccolò, and because he warned them that their mother was embarrassed about her situation they became awkward and tongue-tied with her. Giorgio showed his concern with a silent solicitude which touched her, but Niccolò could find no way of expressing his own affection, so that both Vittorio and Grace thought him cold by the side of his warm-hearted brother.

Contrary to her fears, Grace carried the child full-term, but after all the agony of another difficult birth there was nothing to show for her pain: the infant, another boy, never breathed. And it killed her.

Chapter Four

Julia Turle lifted the skirt of her neat walking suit, revealing the toe of a well-polished black boot, and politely inclined her head towards the uniformed doorman who swung open the mahogany and brass door of the Piccadilly premises of DuFrayne & Speranza for her. Her air of composure was completely at variance with the nervous beating of her heart.

If it had not been a school holiday, if she had not arranged with Miss Williams to go with her to a matinée performance of *Dandy Dick* at the Court Theatre, if above all she had not seen the advertisement which the auction house had placed in the newspaper saying that its experts were available without appointment to give an opinion on articles of virtu, then she would probably not have nerved herself to take this step. As it was, everything seemed to have conspired to bring her to this awe-inspiring place.

It was not, when she got inside, as frightening as she had anticipated. The young man behind the reception desk seemed to see nothing out of the ordinary in her request to see the expert on what Julia could only describe as 'old china'. He asked her most politely if she would be good enough to take a chair while he sent a message to someone he described as Mr Niccolò.

She sat down, clutching on her lap a worn leather bag which contained not only her purse but also the china ornament which had been bothering her ever since it had come into her possession. She was not kept waiting long. There was a brisk step in the corridor, an inner door swung open and a man who looked far too young to be an expert on anything was introducing himself as, 'Niccolò Speranza at your service, Miss. . . ?'

'Turle,' Julia said, fumbling in her bag. 'Can you please tell me anything about this?'

Niccolò Speranza took the object from her with great care and then shot a look of increased interest at her.

'Come over here where I have a table and better light,' he said.

She followed him and watched as he turned the little figure

upside down. It was a charming piece, a Harlequin in a bright, diamond-patterned costume, masked and mischievous.

'Delightful,' Niccolò said. 'A Nymphenburg Commedia dell'Arte figure by Bustelli. You are a fortunate young lady, Miss Turle.'

'Is it . . . is it worth a lot of money?' Julia asked, sounding more worried than pleased.

'On its own, probably about two hundred pounds. If you have the Columbine then the combined value would be more than doubled. A complete set . . . well, I wouldn't like to hazard a guess.'

'Oh dear, I was afraid you would say something like that.'

Niccolò leaned back in his chair and looked at her in amusement. He still held the little Harlequin in his hands. Indeed, he was reluctant to put it down. On the other side of the table he saw a girl in her early twenties, probably about his own age, carefully dressed, but not fashionable. A girl who had to work for her living, he thought, noting the darned cotton gloves and retrimmed hat which completed her outfit. She was not exactly pretty, but she had an air about her that appealed to him, a shining quality made up of fastidious cleanliness and neatness, and a look of transparent honesty. She had very clear grey eyes, which at that moment were distinctly troubled.

'I think there are sixteen of these figures, but I never actually counted them,' she said.

Niccolò put the Harlequin down very carefully indeed. Sixteen Commedia dell'Arte figures modelled by Franz Anton Bustelli! It made his head reel.

'Are you thinking of selling the collection?' he asked. He tried to keep the excitement out of his voice, but he thought that his breathlessness was all too obvious.

'They're not mine to sell,' Julia replied. 'Only this one figure and from what you tell me I presume that to sell the Harlequin would lower the value of the other figures?'

'Very much so. I can't emphasise enough the importance of keeping such a collection together. I'd dearly like to see the other pieces.'

There was a hopeful question behind his words. Niccolò would give his eye teeth to look at the other fifteen figures, to handle them and examine them properly. Even better if he could be allowed to sell them, but it seemed that was unlikely.

'I think I'd better explain,' Julia said. 'I am, as you will probably have realised, not at all well off. I work as a school-teacher and I live as a boarder in a house owned by an elderly widow. She must be nearly ninety and almost her only income is the rent she receives from the rooms which are let to myself and another teacher. When I first went to live in the house a few years ago Mrs Cathcart was still quite active. I always liked her and she liked me and she often invited me downstairs to visit her. Now she is very infirm, although her mind is still alert, and I do what I can to help her. Nothing of any great importance, you know, just calling in for a talk in the evenings, fetching her medicines, paying the tradesmen's bills – that sort of thing. Quite suddenly one evening she asked me to take that Harlequin figure off the mantelpiece where it has always stood and pressed it on me. To repay my kindness, she said. At first I was pleased to have a memento of someone I always considered to be my friend, but then I began to be worried by the . . . the *quality* of the piece. It occurred to me that it might be worth money and I saw your advertisement and so . . .'

'And so you came along and gave me the great pleasure of seeing a remarkably fine piece of Nymphenburg porcelain,' Niccolò finished for her. 'If you want to sell it I shall, of course, be happy to handle the sale, but I must tell you that in my opinion it would be a crime to separate Harlequin from his friends.'

'It must be given back to Mrs Cathcart, of course,' Julia said. 'Two hundred pounds! It's a fortune.' She touched the Harlequin with regretful fingers. 'I shall miss him. I've grown accustomed to seeing him smiling at me on my bookcase.'

'If your friend is in such straitened circumstances, do you think she would consider selling the whole collection?' Niccolò asked.

'I doubt it. I think it would cause her too much worry.'

'We'd handle the sale with the greatest discretion, without bothering her in the least.'

'I'll talk to her about it,' Julia said. She began wrapping up the Harlequin in the tissue paper in which she had brought him. 'I'm rather sorry now that I'm going to the theatre,' she said. 'I shall keep a *very* tight hold of my handbag.'

'Won't you please give me your address?' Niccolò pleaded.

'And if you could possibly persuade your Mrs Cathcart to let me see the rest of the figures I'd be terribly grateful. I can't think how it happens that the collection isn't known, but one comes upon continual surprises in this business.'

'I'll ask her,' Julia promised. 'She never has any visitors. It might please her to see you, but she's very feeble.'

'Perhaps she has something else she might sell,' Niccolò suggested, desperate not to lose sight of this remarkable windfall.

'Yes, that's decidedly an idea,' Julia agreed. 'Thank you for your time and your kind attention, Mr Speranza.' She looked at him with a smile that took a couple of years off her age. 'You can't be *the* Mr Speranza?'

'His son – his second son,' Niccolò said. 'And the DuFrayne of our name was Charles DuFrayne, my grandfather. He died three years ago.'

'How pleasant to have a family business and to be as interested in it as you obviously are,' Julia commented. She was going and he still had not obtained her address.

'Your address,' he reminded her.

'I will get in touch again if Mrs Cathcart decides to see you.'

Julia waited until the following evening to talk to her elderly landlady.

'And so,' she concluded, 'I really think that Harlequin must rejoin his companions on your mantelshelf, dear Mrs Cathcart. The expert at DuFrayne & Speranza – a most delightful young man, I'm sure you would like him – said it would be a crime to split up the set. Those were his exact words.'

Julia was helping Mrs Cathcart to eat the egg custard she had made for her on the cook-housekeeper's day out; it had a dusting of nutmeg on the top, just as Mrs Cathcart liked it.

'I gave the figurine to you,' the old lady said.

'But now that I know it's worth two hundred pounds of course I can't accept it,' Julia said patiently.

'A present is a present. I want you to have it. You like it, don't you?'

'Indeed I do! It's quite the prettiest thing I've ever owned. But Mrs Cathcart, have you considered? If you were to sell these figures – the whole set, I mean – you would be a rich woman.'

'Riches! What time have I got left to enjoy them? And my stupid nephew, who never comes near me, is all the family I have to inherit. I suppose he'll sell everything after I've gone – *if* I give him the chance.'

'Then why not sell them yourself and benefit from the sale?'

'My husband was very attached to those figures. He's been dead so long I've almost forgotten him, but now it's been recalled to me I remember he set great store by them. It's a sad thing, Miss Turle, to outlive all your contemporaries.'

She lapsed into silence and Julia waited, uncertain whether to urge her further or not. Suddenly Mrs Cathcart asked, 'He was a nice young man, you say?'

'Oh, charming! And knowledgeable, too, it seemed. I suppose if one is bred up from childhood in such a business then assessing the value of pieces like your Harlequin becomes second nature.'

'It's *your* Harlequin,' Mrs Cathcart insisted. 'I refuse to take him back. Tell your young man I'll see him. And tell him to come soon – I don't have much time left.'

Julia put her hand over the old woman's and pressed the dry, thin fingers which lay trembling on Mrs Cathcart's lap.

'You're a good girl,' her landlady said. 'A very good girl. Anyone else would tell me I'd still got years to live, but you and I know it isn't so and we're not afraid to face facts. Do you like being a school-teacher?'

Her train of thought seemed to be getting more and more haphazard. Adjusting her own mind to the change of subject, Julia answered honestly, 'Sometimes, yes. Teaching the children can be rewarding. At other times, no, it's drudgery.'

'And little chance of marriage. I married late myself and my husband was even older. Take your opportunity when it comes, Miss Turle. Have children. Don't grow old alone.'

Chance would be a fine thing, Julia thought ruefully as she made her way upstairs to her own room. *Dark eyes and a curling twist of hair that strayed down over his forehead as he bent over the Harlequin* . . . She must stop feeling so ridiculously pleased that Niccolò Speranza was to have his wish to see the rest of the Commedia dell'Arte figures.

*

38

As Julia had anticipated, Mrs Cathcart was charmed by Niccolò Speranza.

'Tell me about yourself. What is your background?' she demanded.

It seemed that Mr Speranza was prepared to pay this price for his chance to see the Bustelli figures.

'My father came from Sicily twenty-five years ago in 1862,' he said. 'He had a small amount of money and a great flair for identifying antiques. He joined Charles DuFrayne and married his daughter.'

'DuFrayne isn't an English name either.'

'They were descended from French émigrés.' Niccolò hesitated for a moment and then said, 'Both my mother and my grandfather died a few years ago.'

He had thought he could speak of it quite dispassionately, but it still gave him a pang. His mother's death had hastened his grandfather's end, there was no doubt of that. Niccolò remembered, in the midst of his own grief, how stricken Charles DuFrayne had been, how he had dwindled from a vigorous middle-aged man to an old one, shrunken in size and bewildered by sorrow. Even now Niccolò could not believe the swiftness with which his mother had been taken, nor could he entirely forgive his father. To have embarked on a pregnancy at her age . . .

Giorgio had taken Grace's death even harder than Niccolò. Nothing could spoil the sweetness of his temper, but from being his brother's constant companion Giorgio had become solitary. Something was weighing on his mind, something more than the loss of his mother, a profound conflict which occupied all his waking thoughts. His attention was forever turned inwards and he walked like one in a daze.

More and more, Niccolò was having to cover his brother's absences from the business, while being himself entirely unable to account for them since Giorgio was certainly not indulging in drink or any other dissipation. It should have been Giorgio covering the front desk on the day when Julia Turle brought in her Harlequin, in which case the result would have been very different. It was not Vittorio's elder son who had inherited his passion for antiques. Giorgio was learning the business because his father wished it, but he did not have Niccolò's commitment,

39

nor his flair. Giorgio was reliable; Niccolò was brilliant.

Giorgio would not have been avid to see the rest of the collection, as Niccolò was. He drank the tea Mrs Cathcart had provided and made polite conversation, but all the time his eyes were straying towards the shelf over the fire where the line of figurines was ranged in artless poses. Mrs Cathcart saw the way his attention wandered and was amused.

'Miss Turle will take the tea tray out and you may bring the figures down and stand them on the table,' she instructed. 'It's a long time since I've seen them properly and I shall be pleased to look them over once more.'

One of the figures had a tiny chip on the base, but apart from that they were in perfect condition.

'I expect Miss Turle will have told you that they are worth a considerable sum of money,' Niccolò said, caressing the dainty Columbine.

'Don't bother to tell me how much. I have no intention of selling.'

'I don't want to dissuade you from your very generous present to Miss Turle, but you really should keep the set together.'

'That's my business, not yours, Mr Speranza. I don't believe in giving a present and then taking it back. However, you may have a look round to see if there's anything else worth selling to provide me with a bit of comfort in my old age.'

Niccolò looked around. The furniture was beautiful, but not currently in fashion. It would certainly sell, but for less than it would if it were kept for a few years until the wheel came round full circle again.

'My own speciality is porcelain, both European and Chinese,' he said.

'I've a couple of Chinese bowls, but they were packed away somewhere when I had to give up living in some of my rooms,' Mrs Cathcart said. 'There are one or two other things in that china cabinet over there.'

'I've already noticed,' Niccolò said. 'A pair of Meissen bocage candlesticks, I see. And is that a maiolica dish at the back? Yes . . . both of those would sell quite well. Perhaps I ought to tell you, Mrs Cathcart, that if you were to get in touch with a dealer he would buy these things immediately for cash in your hand, whereas if you entrust them to me I shall have to wait two or three weeks until we have a suitable sale.'

'I'm not having anything to do with dealers, poking and prying about. I've already seen the way your eyes glitter as you look around, but I'm prepared to trust you. Are you married?'

'Er . . . no,' Niccolò said, considerably startled.

'Engaged? Promised?'

'No, nothing of that sort.'

'How old are you?'

'Twenty-three.' His eyes were beginning to dance at her forthright questions.

'I can see you're a bit of a scamp, but I suppose that's only natural at your age,' Mrs Cathcart said tolerantly. 'Have you any brothers or sisters?'

'One brother.'

'Older or younger?'

'Older, but only by one year.'

'So which of you is going to inherit when your father passes on?'

Out of the corner of his eye Niccolò saw Julia make an embarrassed gesture as if to stop the flow of questions, but he was enjoying himself.

'That's an interesting question,' he said gravely. 'I presume we shall share equally.' As he spoke, the recollection of Giorgio's isolation came back into his mind. There was something wrong with Giorgio and the time was coming when Niccolò was going to have to probe into it.

'Something troubles you,' Mrs Cathcart said.

'My brother has never got over our mother's death. I wish I could help him,' Niccolò said simply.

'You have a good heart. That's the most important quality – kindness.'

She slumped in her chair, suddenly tired. Niccolò glanced at Julia and she nodded, so he stood up and began to make his farewells.

'Julia will pack up those pieces you're going to take,' Mrs Cathcart said, rousing herself. 'She's a good girl. Kindness . . . yes, that's the most important thing.'

Outside in the hall, Julia said, 'Will you come into the kitchen? I'll find a box to take those pieces of china. How much do you think they'll fetch? As much as the Harlequin?'

'At least that. Possibly more, but I think Mrs Cathcart can count on two hundred pounds.'

He watched as Julia made up a neat parcel. She looked up and caught his eye and said abruptly, 'If you're wondering about that Harlequin then I must tell you that I've decided to keep it, but only temporarily. When Mrs Cathcart is no longer with us then I shall return it to the collection.'

'That's very honourable of you. Do you anticipate that Mrs Cathcart . . .' He hesitated, at a loss to know how to put his question delicately.

'She's over ninety and she grows a little feebler every day. I think that the two hundred pounds you hope to raise for her will be needed very soon to pay for a nurse.'

'I see. You're fond of her?'

'Very. We both understand what it is to be alone in the world. Mrs Cathcart has no family except for a nephew who has only been to see her once in the last two years. I have nobody.'

Her head was bent over the string she was tying. The nape of her neck looked curiously vulnerable, as if she were a victim bowing her head for the axe. Niccolò felt a rush of compassion. It seemed to him a terrible thing, to be so young and so alone. Poor, too, and rigidly honest. What she proposed to do about the Nymphenburg Harlequin was quixotic, given her circumstances.

'Will you come to the sale?' he asked.

Julia shook her head with a smile. 'I shall be working,' she pointed out.

He might not see her again. Niccolò was surprised how regretful he felt about that, until it occurred to him that he could make one more opportunity to call at the house.

'I'll bring the money to Mrs Cathcart as soon as the sale is over,' he said.

'Do you usually do that for your clients?' Julia asked.

'No.'

He was watching her face as he said that one deliberate word. Julia gave him a startled glance and then looked away, a flush rising to her face and an involuntary smile curving her lips.

It was all she could think about after he had gone. He wanted to see her again. That must have been what he meant. A little fountain of joy seemed to be bubbling up inside of her and Julia tried to suppress it. Foolish, foolish, to read so much into a careless word. She must stop thinking about him. She paused on the way back to Mrs Cathcart's room to give herself one last luxurious moment to remember him – his ease and grace, his beautiful dextrous hands as they held the fine porcelain, the slight darkening along his cleanshaven chin, his mobile mouth and dancing, mischievous eyes. Julia closed her eyes and shuddered. No more; she must not dwell any more on Niccolò Speranza's physical presence. He was not for her. But at the back of her mind a rebellious voice repeated, 'Why not? Why not?'

When Niccolò arrived home he found his father already there, which was unusual since Vittorio had taken to staying late in his office since Grace's death.

'What have you got there?' he asked as Niccolò put his parcel down on the table.

'A couple of things I've been asked to put in a sale. I thought in a fortnight's time with the other European ceramics?'

He undid Julia's careful knots and showed his father the leafy candlesticks, one with a shepherd playing his pipe and the other with a coy shepherdess, and the large maiolica platter which had caught his eye.

'Nice pieces,' Vittorio said.

'But you should have seen the ones that got away! Sixteen Nymphenburg figures by Bustelli.'

'Are they likely to come on the market?' Vittorio asked, his interest quickened.

'They belong to a very old lady and as far as I can judge from the way she spoke about him, I doubt whether her heir has any great interest in such things. I have hopes . . .'

'You'll keep in touch?'

Niccolò thought of the sweet white nape of Julia Turle's neck, her upswept hair and the clear regard of her grey eyes.

'I'll certainly do that,' he promised. He hesitated, not wanting to provoke trouble, but sufficiently worried to risk asking, 'Is Giorgio in?'

'Up in his room. As usual.'

Vittorio sounded grim, but at least Giorgio was safely at home and Niccolò was sufficiently encouraged to say, 'I feel there's something wrong with my brother. More than losing Mama, I mean. We used to be so close and now he never talks to me. Papa, do you know. . . ?'

For once he had chosen his moment well. Vittorio was ready to unburden himself and he knew that Niccolò's concern for Giorgio was based on an affection as deep as his own.

'Yes, I know . . . at least I think I do. I told him something I see now I would have done better to keep to myself. Grace's death shook me . . . I mean, apart from my sorrow, it made me realise that I might go as suddenly myself and so I told Giorgio . . .'

He stopped and looked at Niccolò with sombre eyes. 'You wouldn't have taken it in the same way,' he said. 'No, you are too like me, you would have accepted that I had a right to do what I did.'

'I still don't know what you're talking about,' Niccolò pointed out.

Tersely, Vittorio told his son the story of the diamonds and Niccolò listened, not with the moral concern his brother had shown, but with sparkling eyes and a smile ready to break out.

'The man jilted your mother,' Vittorio concluded. 'He should have had his throat slit. Keeping some diamonds he didn't even know he had seemed like a small revenge to me. Besides, I needed them more than he did.'

'In your place I would have done the same,' Niccolò said. 'But Giorgio . . .'

'He says that even if I had found the diamonds after I bought the cross I would have been under an obligation to tell Lord Kenrick, but that finding them first and concealing my discovery amounted to stealing. Yes, he dared to say that to me – his father!'

'He's so unbending,' Niccolò said.

He was still not satisfied. Obviously there had been a deep disagreement between his father and brother, but that still did not explain Giorgio's avoidance of family life.

'Shall I talk to him?' he asked.

'I wish you would. He might listen to you. I want the boy to come round because there's something else, something very important I want to discuss with him, and I daren't bring it up while he's being so pigheaded.'

Niccolò went up to his brother's room, rehearsing in his mind

44

what he would say to Giorgio. He found his brother, just as he had known he would, quietly reading by the window.

'Don't you think we could have some light in here?' Niccolò demanded. 'I don't know how you can see to read.'

'As you wish,' Giorgio replied.

He got up to light the lamp and Niccolò watched him in exasperation and affection, his big, handsome brother who had always needed to be looked after.

'You are an idiot,' he said. 'Papa has just told me about the diamonds. Of course he won't give them back, not to the man who jilted Mama. I say, that was a revelation, wasn't it? Can't you see that it's all mixed up with his Sicilian sense of honour?'

'And the money,' Giorgio said equably.

'That, of course. It must have come in extremely useful. He used it to buy his way into partnership with Grandpapa – and to marry Mama. Just think, Giorgio, if it hadn't been for that fortunate find you and I might never have been born.'

He was not sure that he was making much headway. Giorgio just stood by the lighted lamp, saying nothing, but looking unconvinced. Not for the first time, Niccolò contrasted his brother's austere room with the happy muddle in his own. Giorgio's room contained a small bed, a wash basin, a bookcase and one good rug. On the wall there was a religious picture with a rosary hooked over it, and by the side of his bed was a small table which held a photograph of their mother. Like a monk's cell, Niccolò thought, and a faint, cold touch of apprehension made him shiver.

'Come down and talk to Papa,' he coaxed.

Giorgio suddenly straightened his shoulders. 'Yes, of course, I must do that,' he said. 'I've put it off for too long, but I wasn't sure in my own mind . . .'

'Then there *is* something wrong – more than Mama's death, more than this business about the diamonds?'

The look Giorgio turned on him was haunted by hours of inner conflict, but there was a new air of resolution about him.

'I've been making the most difficult decision of my life,' he said. 'Perhaps the most difficult commitment any man can make. I only hope I can reconcile Papa to what I know I must do.'

He would say nothing more, leaving Niccolò behind as he went down the stairs, almost rushing in his eagerness to reach his father. Niccolò followed, that odd shiver still running through him.

By the time Niccolò reached the drawing room his father and brother were embracing.

'Papa, forgive me for distressing you,' Giorgio said. 'I can't bring myself to say that you acted rightly over those diamonds, but it is not for me to judge and it grieves me to know that you have been thinking that I condemned you.'

'My son, *figlio mio* . . . now we can be happy again. See, you have made your silly old father weep. Niccolò, open a bottle of wine. Sit down, sit down, Giorgio; let us talk to one another. Let me tell you of the plans I have for your future.'

The red wine glowed in their glasses, the firelight glittered on the cut-steel fireplace. Vittorio was fully restored to his usual bounce, but Niccolò was still silent, full of dread. There was more to come. The trouble about the diamonds was nothing, that was not what had kept Giorgio pacing about his room into the small hours of the morning.

He knew they had reached the crisis point when Giorgio said, 'I have plans of my own for the future, Papa, and I have been very remiss in not telling you what was in my heart sooner than this.'

'You're going to leave the business?' Niccolò guessed.

'No!' Vittorio turned on him fiercely. 'Do not put words into your brother's mouth. Leave the business? Giorgio will never do that! He is my good, obedient son. He will not wound me in such a way.'

'Papa, I must.' Giorgio's voice was hoarse with strain. 'I've wrestled with myself for so long – *too* long. Now my mind is made up and you mustn't try to change it. I'm going to be a priest.'

Chapter Five

'The atmosphere at home is like a Jacobean tragedy,' Niccolò told Julia.

They were walking slowly underneath the trees of Greenwich Park, where Niccolò had invited her to meet him in order, as he said quite frankly, that he might escape for a short time from a situation that was becoming intolerable.

'Poor Papa, you see, is torn two ways: as a good son of the Church, he should rejoice at giving a child to the priesthood, but as a father he rages at the thought of losing his son. If only Giorgio had reached this decision a few years earlier! Mama would have rejoiced, without any thought about worldly considerations, and she would have reconciled Papa to it.'

They strolled along in silence for a minute or two and then Niccolò said softly, 'I'm so afraid he's done it in order to please her.'

'Even though she's dead?' Julia asked incredulously.

'He admits it was her death that gave his thoughts a new direction.'

'In the end, there's nothing either you or your father can do, is there? Your brother's decision is made and you'll have to accept it.'

'You're right, of course, but I still rage about it – to turn his back on so much! – and Papa is beside himself. As I said, it's like a Jacobean tragedy. Papa is almost frothing at the mouth and chewing the carpet.'

'How sad. Of course, I don't belong to your religion and so I'm less sympathetic to your brother. In the Church of England we take the view that a married clergyman has more to offer his parishioners by way of understanding their problems.'

'So do I,' Niccolò said.

Julia looked at him in surprise and he grinned. 'I know, rank heresy – don't tell the Pope or, even worse, Cardinal Manning. I'm a despicable backslider, Miss Turle. How good it is of you to let me unburden myself like this.'

They had reached the edge of the hill, where General Wolfe's statue stood looking towards the river. Julia stared a little blindly at the vista below them, the Queen's House, looking small and exquisitely ordered, the sweep of the river. If Niccolò wished to unburden himself then she was prepared to walk by his side for hours. Anything, just so long as she could be with him, but that was something she had to keep hidden.

'I hope we can meet again?' Niccolò said.

Unconsciously, Julia straightened her shoulders. The moment had come and she must be brave. 'I'm not sure,' she said carefully. 'My situation is difficult. I'm alone, as you know, and I have no home to which I can invite you. I can hardly entertain you in my room. If we meet, it has to be like this – by prior arrangement in a public place. Do you realise, Mr Speranza, how easy it is for a young woman like me to lose respect because she is seen to be a little . . . fast? Perhaps you didn't notice, but already this afternoon I've been greeted by two of my pupils, walking in the park with their parents, just like us.'

'A harmless occupation, surely?'

'Certainly, but they will be curious to know who you are and if I'm seen with you again then questions may be asked.'

'Tell them I'm your long-lost cousin from Sicily.'

'I wouldn't lie about it,' Julia said, and the gravity of her reply reproved the frivolity of his suggestion.

Niccolò struck at the grass with his walking stick, frowning as he destroyed a patch of green. 'I want to see you again,' he said.

A rueful smile twisted Julia's lips in a way that was not at all happy.

'It seems you have yet to learn, spoilt child, that you can't have everything you want.'

Niccolò took a step or two away from her, still intent on rooting up the grass. He was perturbed to realise how dismayed he felt at losing touch with this quiet girl.

'I'll be coming to visit Mrs Cathcart to hand over the proceeds of her sale next week,' he suddenly remembered. 'You'll see me then?'

'Yes, I will. I'm sure she'll want me to do that.'

'I want it. Does that mean nothing to you?'

'A great deal.' Julia took a deep breath. 'More than it should.

There, that's a reckless admission for you. Make of it what you will. I'll say no more and I think we should be making our way out of the park.'

It was more than enough to keep Niccolò's thoughts engaged as he made his way home. The implication was clear: he was on the verge of making a good, respectable girl fall in love with him. She was honest and clear-sighted enough to see that her feelings could lead her to disastrous unhappiness and so she had warned him off. In her way she was rather wonderful. The next time he saw her he would try to let her know what a high regard he had for her. It was a pity that they had to part . . . if they *did* have to part.

The atmosphere at his home in Rutland Gate had not improved and, when he came to think about it, Niccolò was slightly puzzled by the degree of his father's rage. Vittorio was beside himself, and although Niccolò understood that his father did not like his plans to be frustrated, he still thought that Vittorio's frantic pleas to Giorgio to change his mind were overdone.

The three of them had dinner together that evening in strained silence. Giorgio drank one sparing glass of wine and refused the port with which his father indulged himself when the meal was over.

Giorgio made an effort to make conversation with Niccolò, but his question was unfortunate.

'Where did you go this afternoon?'

'Greenwich Park,' Niccolò said.

His father looked at him over the rim of his glass and the deep colour of the port glowed in the lamplight.

'Oh? Who have you got down there?' he asked.

Niccolò flushed. Because of the way Julia had spoken he felt guilty, and that annoyed him. He had not agreed with her objections to their meetings, but if that was the sort of construction his father was going to put on a perfectly innocent excursion then perhaps she was right.

'I visited the . . . the people who sent in those Meissen candlesticks and the maiolica platter,' he said.

'The ones who own the Bustelli figures? Oh well, I suppose I did tell you to keep in touch with them.'

'Mrs Cathcart said she had some Chinese dishes put away. I might try to get a sight of them some time,' Niccolò said, seizing on this possibility, which had only just occurred to him.

49

'No harm in asking to see them,' Vittorio agreed.

So far Giorgio's attempt to involve them in a little conversation had been successful, but Vittorio could not long be diverted from the subject that occupied his every waking moment.

'No need to ask where *you* were,' he said bitterly to his other son. 'Cooped up inside a church all day, I suppose.'

'I visited the Oratorians,' Giorgio said.

'Just as I thought. My dear son, *figlio mio*, I do not condemn your piety, but think again, I beg you, before you give up the world and everything it contains.'

'My mind is fixed on the world to come,' Giorgio said. His smile was very sweet, but he spoke with a certain abstraction, as if he did not really expect to be understood.

'Before you commit yourself . . .'

'I have committed myself.'

'No, no! You have taken no vows. Listen, my son. For many years I have had a dream. You could say that I, too, have committed myself. I made a vow to the memory of my dead friend whose name you bear. You know perhaps that over the years I have aided his family, but that is not enough. I have so much and he had so little, my old comrade-in-arms. He has left two sons, who are making their way in the world now, and a little daughter. Her name is Serafina and she is seventeen years old. It is time for her to be married.'

Niccolò's quick mind leapt at his father's meaning. Dear God, he was going to ship the girl over from Sicily and marry her off to Giorgio. No wonder his eldest son's decision to take celibate vows had come as a shock to him.

'I mean her to be your wife,' Vittorio went on emotionally. 'Think, Giorgio, think what this means. Lifelong happiness with a good Catholic girl, convent-educated, brought up to be exactly the wife you need. It is the dearest wish of my heart. Consider what you are doing before you turn your back on such a match. Think of your children – the consolation of my old age, the joy of your life.'

It occurred to Niccolò that his own sons were not at that time giving Vittorio much joy, but he kept a prudent silence.

Giorgio shook his head, too baffled and shocked to think of a ready reply.

'Does the girl know about the proposal?' Niccolò could not resist asking.

His father turned towards him, frowning. 'I have written to her mother asking her permission for the match.'

'Before mentioning it to Giorgio?' Niccolò asked, much diverted.

'I wanted to know that it was acceptable to her family before I raised Giorgio's hopes.'

Looking at his brother's downcast face Niccolò had to suppress a touch of hysteria. Giorgio's hopes were so patently out of touch with their father's that it would have been ludicrous – if there had not been pain behind Giorgio's frown.

'I'm sorry, Papa, it's quite out of the question,' he said. 'You must write again, very quickly, and explain the situation to Signora Giulini.'

The following week Niccolò went back to Greenwich to report the result of the sale of Mrs Cathcart's candlesticks and maiolica dish.

Julia was there, looking a little strained, but delighted when Niccolò told her landlady, 'After deducting our commission, the proceeds of your sale came to two hundred and thirty-six pounds ten shillings. I've brought it to you in cash. I hope that was the right thing to do.'

'I wonder you weren't afraid of being robbed,' Mrs Cathcart chuckled, and thanked him.

Julia began gathering the tea cups together. As she moved towards the door Niccolò went to open it for her, but before he could follow her through to the kitchen Mrs Cathcart called him back.

'Mr Speranza . . .'

She had sunk a little lower in the armchair in which she spent her days, and the shawl round her shoulders had risen up to muffle her head, but her old eyes were still bright and shrewd. It occurred to Niccolò that she knew all about the ambivalence of his feelings towards Julia. The reluctant attraction, the fear of making a false step, the longing for the balm of her sympathy.

'I wanted to say a word about the Harlequin I have given Julia,' Mrs Cathcart said. 'I know you're worried about the set being split up and I just wanted to tell you not to be concerned because that won't happen.'

For a moment Niccolò thought that she must have guessed Julia's intention of returning the Harlequin after her death, but something about the old lady's fixed regard told him that she meant more than that.

'Julia has been good to me,' Mrs Cathcart said. 'Very good. She deserves some reward. You understand me?'

'I . . . I think so,' Niccolò said, but at that moment Julia returned with a tray to collect the rest of the tea things and there was no opportunity to say any more.

So, Mrs Cathcart meant to leave the Bustelli figures to Julia. She would have all sixteen of the charming little pieces and no doubt he would have the selling of them. It would be a real coup! And what an improvement it would make to Julia's circumstances, too. Niccolò felt more excited and pleased than he had been by anything that had happened since Giorgio had thrown his bombshell amongst them.

When Julia showed him to the front door half an hour later, she held out her hand.

'It was good of you to come all the way out here to bring Mrs Cathcart her money. I can hardly imagine that's your usual way of doing business. So now it is all over and we must say goodbye.'

Niccolò took her hand and held it. 'What do you mean – goodbye? Do you imagine I shall let go of you that easily?'

Julia gave a tug at her hand, but he refused to release it.

'Mr Speranza, I've already explained my position to you,' she said. 'It will be better if we don't meet again.'

'Better for whom? For me? No! When I don't see you, I miss you. Better for you?'

She turned her head away, unwilling to look him in the face, but Niccolò insisted, 'Would it be better for you not to see me again?'

Almost under her breath, Julia said, 'It must be.'

She would have done better to have looked him in the face and spoken boldly. Niccolò had to bend towards her to hear what she said. His lips brushed her cheek and then, in spite of her gasp of dismay, he put his hand under her chin and turned her face to kiss her.

For a moment she stood very still and then she broke away with an incoherent murmur. 'No . . . no . . . Indeed, we must not . . .'

'One small, sweet kiss. It's not a terrible sin, Julia. Are you angry with me?'

'Yes. No. With myself . . .'

'You mustn't blame yourself. The fault was all mine – if it was a fault. Will you meet me next Saturday afternoon . . . mm, at the British Museum? Is that respectable enough for you?'

'I don't know,' Julia said, totally distracted.

'You'll come,' Niccolò said with confidence.

They met and it was a delight, but frustrating. Julia would permit no demonstrations of affection in public, but she could not prevent Niccolò from drawing her arm through his and holding it pressed tightly against him. Enlaced like that they strolled through the galleries and Julia, if she had been capable of attending to anything he said, would have been impressed by the knowledge Niccolò displayed.

Was he in love with her? She did not know and would have been bewildered to learn that Niccolò was equally uncertain about his feelings. She delighted him, he liked to be with her, a day when he was going to see Julia had a different feel to it from any other day, but this was not a girl with whom he could enjoy a passing liaison. Julia had to be taken seriously and Niccolò was not at all sure that he was ready to commit himself to a lifetime with her.

With the affair still in this unsatisfactory state Niccolò wandered home and walked into exactly the crisis he had been expecting ever since he had heard of his father's plans for Giorgio's marriage.

Giorgio had gone into retreat and after that he expected to be sent to the English College in Rome. Niccolò missed him sorely and all the more so because of their father's unremitting bad temper.

It was no surprise to find Vittorio pacing the floor and in a rage.

'Where have you been?' he demanded as Niccolò walked into the drawing room.

'To the British Museum,' Niccolò said, glad both that he had such an innocuous reply ready and also that it would annoy his father.

'Studying?' Vittorio demanded disbelievingly. 'I thought you knew it all already.'

'Not everything,' Niccolò said equably.

Vittorio collapsed into an armchair. 'I've heard from Catalina Giulini,' he said. 'Stupid woman! She was a fool when my friend Giorgio married her and so I told him, but he wouldn't listen, and she's not improved with the years.'

'What's she done?' Niccolò asked, intrigued.

Vittorio glowered at him. 'She's in ecstasies at the idea of her girl marrying my son – as well she might be – but instead of waiting for me to make the proper arrangements she's seized on the chance of a family connection sailing his ship to Liverpool, and she's embarked the girl and sent her off to England!'

For a moment Niccolò was tempted to laugh, but that impulse died as his father went on, 'Of course, there's only one thing to be done now. You'll have to marry her.'

'No,' Niccolò said.

'Yes, I tell you. I meant you to marry money. Giorgio for sentiment, I thought, and you – with your expensive tastes and highflown ideas – you I meant to introduce into the City to find yourself some rich banker's daughter.'

'Thank you for your thought for me, but I have other ideas.'

'You'll marry Serafina Giulini.'

'I'll do nothing of the sort.'

In his agitation Vittorio bounded to his feet and stood over his son, his face working.

'You have no understanding, none at all. If you had been brought up in the old country you would know what has to be done. We're talking of a young girl of good family, the daughter of an old friend. She believes herself to be affianced to a man who is waiting to marry her. Through no fault of her own the wedding will not take place. What is to happen to her? Do you think she can be sent back like an unwanted parcel? I would be dishonoured, you would be dishonoured and, worst of all, Serafina would be dishonoured. Who will marry her after that?'

'But, Papa, you've said yourself that it's not her fault. Can't we just give her a little holiday in England and then . . .' He stopped, shocked into silence by his father's adamant face.

'You speak as if it were some little matter that could be shrugged off,' Vittorio said.

'To me, it is.'

54

'It's the rest of her life – the whole of the rest of her life. She will be a spinster to the end of her days, disgraced, ruined . . . sent away to marry a man in England and then returned. Who in Syracuse will believe that it was not because some fault was found in her? No one!'

'But, Papa, that's mediaeval!'

Once again Vittorio turned on him fiercely. 'Yes! Has anything I have ever told you about my country ever made you believe that it is modern – enlightened as this benighted country believes itself to be? In Sicily we still understand honour, and I tell you that honour demands that you marry the young girl your brother has spurned.'

'No.'

'You will do this thing, Niccolò, or you are no more my son.'

'I can't promise to marry a girl I've never seen.'

'Then we will wait until you have seen her. From the way her mother writes – though the woman is a fool, as I have said – it seems that Serafina is everything a reasonable man could want in his wife. You will meet her, we will explain about Giorgio, there will be a little shock and then when this poor young girl has recovered, you will pay her your addresses and ask for her hand in marriage in place of your brother.'

For a moment, his head reeling, Niccolò could almost believe that what his father was suggesting was reasonable. Then he remembered the light in Julia's grey eyes as she looked at him, the smile that came and went on her mouth, so sensitive, so vulnerable; the soft brown hair and skin like velvet; her honesty and her kindness, the way her thoughts seemed to chime with his, her cheerfulness in adversity; even her poverty looked like a virtue at that moment.

'I can't do it,' he said. 'I'm sorry, Papa, but I've met the girl I want to marry. You won't approve of anything about her. She's poor, she's Protestant and she has no family, but I love her and I mean to make her my wife.'

'We hardly know one another,' Julia said.

'I knew you'd say that,' Niccolò told her.

'You'll come to regret quarrelling with your father.'

'My dear girl, if the price of staying in Papa's favour is marrying Serafina Giulini then I'm afraid a quarrel is inevitable.'

'Are you sure you're not using your . . . your liking for me as a way out of marrying this unfortunate girl?'

'If you hadn't existed I might have had to invent you,' Niccolò agreed. 'But you do exist and I've decided that I love you. Marry me, Julia.'

Julia shook her head, not so much in indecision as because she could not quite bring herself to believe in the unimaginable happiness of hearing Niccolò say that he loved her, that he wanted her to be his wife.

'You have so much and I have so little,' she said.

'Don't you believe it! I doubt whether Papa will allow me to go on working for DuFrayne & Speranza if I disobey him. Of course, nothing can take away the one-quarter holding in the firm I inherited from Grandfather . . .' Niccolò's eyes suddenly narrowed. He was amazed he had not thought of this aspect of Giorgio's defection before. What was going to happen to Giorgio's share in the family firm?

'I suppose I shall still get some income from that,' he went on, resolutely putting the other matter out of his mind, 'but don't imagine you will be marrying a rich man. I'll have to find something to do and at the moment I can't think what it'll be.'

'You might do better if you were not hampered by a wife,' Julia said, but a little smile played about her mouth because she knew now that whatever objection she raised, Niccolò would counter it.

'I need you,' Niccolò assured her. 'I'm sure you'll know how to manage on a limited income . . .'

'Oh, yes, I know all about that,' Julia agreed drily.

'Whereas I've been spoilt all my life. Yes, I admit it. I've always had a sufficiency of money and I need a good little wife who'll scold me if I behave recklessly.'

'Why not employ an accountant?' Julia enquired demurely.

'This is why not,' Niccolò said, taking her firmly in his arms. 'I love you. It's quite, quite ridiculous and I know we're almost strangers, but that makes it all the more exciting. We can explore our new life and one another at the same time. Tell me you love me.'

'I do,' Julia said. 'Oh, Niccolò, I do! So much! Dearest, dearest Niccolò.'

She wound her arms round his neck and raised her head for his kiss, as eager as he was for this embrace that would commit her to him. Her body, pressed against his, trembled with the force of the emotion she had kept suppressed. She clasped her hands at the back of his head and when the pressure of Niccolò's mouth on hers slackened she tightened her hold, prolonging the kiss until they were both breathless.

As they separated Niccolò looked down into her flushed face and laughed softly.

'So, my cool little English girl has a volcano concealed inside her! I thought I was the one with the fiery Sicilian blood!'

Julia broke away from him, pressing her hands against her hot cheeks.

'Niccolò. . . ! I've never behaved like that before!'

'I should hope not! Darling Julia, don't look so bothered. I love your volcano. I love you. Now, let's be practical. How soon can we be married?'

'We really ought to put off our marriage until you have employment.'

'I might consider setting up in business on my own account.'

'As an auctioneer?'

'Yes, why not? Modest premises to begin with . . .'

'But – in competition with your father?'

'Hardly that,' Niccolò said ruefully. 'DuFrayne & Speranza are leaders in the field.'

'You're throwing that away to marry me.'

'No, I'm walking out rather than fall in with Papa's dictatorial ways. Don't worry, Julia, we'll manage to make a living. The first thing I must do, the very first thing, is to buy you a ring and put it on your finger, then I'll be sure of your promise.'

'You can be sure of that,' Julia said quietly.

'Are we going to tell Mrs Cathcart?'

'I'd like to.' Julia's face clouded. 'She's not at all well. In fact, she hasn't got out of bed for the last two days and that's a bad sign.'

'You've been looking after her?'

'As far as I could. I called in the doctor this morning and he said there was little the matter with her except extreme old age. He's recommended a nurse, a nice, sensible woman, who'll start work tomorrow.'

'I'd like to see her.'

'Yes, and Niccolò, it may be for the last time.'

Niccolò remembered that warning when Julia ushered him into Mrs Cathcart's bedroom. The old lady looked very small with her head sunk down in the pillows. Below her frilled nightcap two meagre plaits of white hair were arranged over her shoulders. Her thin hands, covered in brown spots, played with the folds of the sheets. All the same, she was able to rouse herself to give Niccolò a triumphant smile.

'I knew it!' she said. 'I was sure you and Julia were suited to one another. Mr Speranza, this news has made me very happy. I'm so glad you've reached a decision before my departure.' She raised one hand and Niccolò clasped it in his.

'I'll take good care of her,' he said.

'No doubt – and the other way round, too. Julia will be good for you. Never try to bully her, she won't stand for that. She's a strong woman, for all her quiet ways. I've been very fond of Julia.'

'The daughter you never had,' Niccolò suggested.

'Don't be so sentimental! Julia's no more my daughter than you are my son. But she's a good girl and I'm glad she's not going to dwindle into an old maid. She has a capacity for love that merits an outlet. Well, you have my blessing, for what it's worth.'

Serafina Giulini arrived at Rutland Gate the following week, in the care of a bustling matron, the wife of the captain of the ship which had brought Serafina from Sicily. The Signora spoke no word of English, but she made it clear that if Serafina was to be accommodated in a house full of men then she intended remaining with her until after the marriage had taken place. Niccolò was not present when his father broke the news that the marriage plans were in disarray, but he heard about it immediately afterwards.

'I've told the Signora that one of my sons has a vocation for the religious life and the other is already affianced,' Vittorio said.

He sounded weary and Niccolò had a twinge of compunction.

'I'm sorry because I know how difficult it must have been for you,' he said.

'She had hysterics.'

Niccolò had a vision of the large Signora billowing around his father's study in a tempest of temperament. It might have been funny if the whole thing had not been so dismaying.

'Change your mind,' Vittorio said, as he had been repeating with monotonous regularity ever since he had heard of Niccolò's engagement.

'I can't. I'm sorry, Papa, but I've given Julia my promise.'

'Would she accept money? A nice little pension for life?'

'Certainly not! Papa, I *want* to marry Julia. Please don't make me angry by suggesting that she is mercenary. She loves me and I love her.'

'Oh, love . . . marriage is about more than that! This match you propose for yourself is entirely unsuitable in every way. What have you against Serafina now that you have seen her?'

'Nothing – except that she isn't Julia.'

Niccolò had not been impressed by the girl his father had fetched from over the sea to marry his brother. She was only seventeen, of course, and not yet fully mature. An ignorant girl, fresh from her convent, who had been given a few hurried English lessons when her good fortune had become known. She was of medium height, with a figure that promised to be good. Her waist was small and her breasts high and firm. She had long, narrow hands and feet, and bony wrists that stuck out from the cuffs of her gown, as if she had gone on growing during her voyage to England. Niccolò did not think that she was shy, but her lack of English and the modest demeanour drilled into her had not been conducive to many exchanges of conversation between them. She had thick black hair, strained back from a high forehead, a brown complexion and fine dark eyes.

What worried Niccolò was that it was impossible to tell what Serafina was thinking. Whenever she saw him she cast down her big black eyes and looked at the ground, responding in monosyllables to his halting attempts to talk to her.

'Does she know the situation?' he asked his father.

'Signora Amalfi will break it to her. I only hope she takes it calmly.'

'I can't imagine Serafina having hysterics,' Niccolò said.

'She will be very distressed,' Vittorio insisted. 'I wonder you can bring yourself to wound so young a girl. Think of that tender young heart, blighted by disappointed hopes.'

'Papa, you should join the ranks of the lady novelists. Tender young hearts are more resilient than you think. I doubt whether

59

Serafina will shed many tears over a young man – two young men – she knows nothing about.'

He found out how wrong he had been at the dinner table that very evening. Serafina did join them, wearing one of the frilly white muslin gowns judged suitable for her age and status, high at the neck and with sleeves that covered her elbows, but Niccolò was shocked by the look of tragedy on her face. She ate hardly anything, drooping over her plate with her head bent, and it was impossible to get her to say a word.

'You see?' Vittorio demanded when the two women had left them, Serafina leaning on the arm Signora Amalfi put round her as if she could hardly walk without its support. 'You see what you have done to this poor young girl?'

'Serafina will get over it,' Niccolò said uncertainly.

'Never! Never, I tell you! And what about me? The shame is unbearable. Change your mind.'

'No.'

'Then there is only one thing to be done. I must marry her myself.'

Chapter Six

'He means to do it,' Niccolò told Julia.

'But the girl? Surely she won't accept?'

Now that Mrs Cathcart was confined to bed Julia had been given the use of the drawing room in which to receive her fiancé, an amenity which she very much appreciated, especially on an occasion like this when Niccolò was so deeply agitated.

'She has accepted,' Niccolò said grimly. 'I find the idea most distasteful. She is seventeen and he is fifty-two – more than old enough to be her father. He might almost be her grandfather.'

'What will her family say?'

'There's no time to find out and the woman who brought her over, Signora Amalfi, who looks upon herself as standing in the place of Serafina's mother, seems to think that since Papa is not utterly decrepit, and by her standards rich into the bargain, then Serafina should consider herself lucky.'

Niccolò considered for a moment and then conceded reluctantly, 'Papa was right about one thing: Serafina would be utterly disgraced if she returned to Sicily unmarried. Signora Amalfi has made that clear.'

'If you and I had not met . . .'

'I couldn't have brought myself to do it,' Niccolò said, but he was not totally sure that he spoke the whole truth. Given Giorgio's defection, would he really have been able to forgo the temptation of becoming the favoured son, the sole inheritor of the family business?

'He's even talking of having more children,' Niccolò added, which was a censored version of Vittorio's furious boasting about his sexual prowess and the number of sons he intended fathering to make up for the two unsatisfactory ones his English wife had given him.

'He probably will,' Julia said equably.

'I suppose it's inevitable. I wish I could get hold of Giorgio, but he's totally incommunicado.'

'Could he persuade your father to change his plans?'

'No, but that's not what I need to talk to him about. I must know how he means to dispose of his share in DuFrayne & Speranza.'

'How does it stand at the moment?'

'Papa bought a one-half share when he joined Grandfather DuFrayne. When Grandfather died he left his half equally between Giorgio and me. While we were a united family that was a splendid arrangement, but now . . . If Giorgio handed his portion over to me I could keep Papa in order.'

'Even to the extent of stopping his marriage?'

'I doubt it.' With a reluctant smile, Niccolò admitted, 'The old devil says it's a matter of his honour and nothing is going to stop him except a sudden palsy stroke.'

'Which God forbid!' Julia said quickly.

'Yes, yes. I wish him no harm. If only Giorgio . . . but there, it's no use saying "if only". I just wish I could understand what drives him. Would you give up everything in the world for the love of God, Julia?'

'I wouldn't give up you and the chance of marrying you.'

'Dearest – you're so patient with me and my tiresome family. Are you prepared to marry a poor man?'

'You won't be poor while you still have an income from the business,' Julia pointed out. 'Your father can't stop that, can he?'

'He might try a trick or two to cut it down and he may find trade drops off without me. He's going to notice the loss of both Giorgio and me – Giorgio for his expert knowledge of Italian paintings and me for the ceramics. Papa's field has always been the earlier Greek and Roman period although he has a smattering of learning about almost everything, I'll give him that.'

'You've quite decided to leave the firm?'

'I can see no other way open to me. I shall start up for myself in another part of London.'

'Won't that cause confusion?'

'Not many of Papa's high-class clients will come my way, not at first, but you're right and I've given some thought to it. I've never liked being Niccolò, but Papa insisted his sons must have Italian names.'

'You'd like to Anglicise it?'

'Exactly. Both my Christian name *and* my surname. How would you like to be Mrs Nicholas Hope?'

'I think I'd like it very much indeed.'

Julia lifted her face and Niccolò . . . or Nicholas, as she must start thinking of him now . . . moved closer to her and accepted that mute invitation to exchange a long kiss.

They were strained together in a close embrace when the door opened and Mrs Cathcart's nurse interrupted them with an artificial cough which made Julia break away from Nicholas's arms, her hands going to her disarranged hair, her cheeks reddening in embarrassment.

'It's my opinion we should call the doctor,' the nurse announced. 'Mrs Cathcart's sinking fast. Is there any family?'

'A nephew. I'll wait until the doctor has been and then send him a telegram. Niccolò . . .'

'Nicholas,' he insisted with a smile.

'Perhaps you should go. When shall I see you again?'

'Tomorrow?' He looked at the nurse. 'The day after?'

'I doubt whether Mrs Cathcart will last out the night.'

'Don't come tomorrow,' Julia said. 'Wait until I send you a note. You're still living at Rutland Gate, aren't you?'

'For the time being.'

There was little more they could say in front of the nurse. Nicholas took Julia's hand and pressed it, smiled at the other woman and left.

Mrs Cathcart's unsatisfactory nephew was a thickset man with a thrusting manner. After the funeral, when the mourners returned for a cup of tea, he made it clear that he wanted possession of Mrs Cathcart's house at an early date.

'And I'll be obliged if you'll clear out all her old traps as soon as possible,' he said to Julia. 'You did know she'd left the contents to you, didn't you?'

'Everything?' Julia asked faintly.

'All except her silver tea service, which she seems to have left to the people next door. Pity about that because it's one of the few things my wife might have liked. Oh, and fifty pounds each to her old servant and to that other woman who lived here with you, I can't think why.'

Nicholas, overhearing this conversation, tried to will Julia to say nothing more, but he was not surprised when she said resolutely, 'Mr Cathcart, some of your aunt's old china is valuable.'

'Really?' He picked up one of the Commedia dell'Arte figures, handling it in a way that made Nicholas freeze in horror. 'Can't say it's the sort of thing that appeals to me – and as for the furniture, I can afford to have everything slap up and brand new, I'm glad to say. New wallpaper, new curtains, a good carpet and a nice bit of mahogany and this room'll be transformed.'

Nicholas put his hand on the back of one of the Hepplewhite chairs, as if to console it for its disparagement by this ignorant fool.

'Miss Turle and I are engaged to be married and we will no doubt use some of the furniture for our own house,' he said.

'Oh, is that the way of it? Well, if you want to make use of Aunt Mabel's bits and pieces to furnish your first home then good luck to you. I'm not likely to contest the Will, not for the sake of this old stuff.'

Nicholas closed his hand very firmly on Julia's arm and led her away.

'He doesn't understand!' Julia said in agitation.

'We are not in the business of educating idiots. I knew Mrs Cathcart meant you to have the complete set of Bustelli figures, because she told me so, but this is far better. Who knows what may be hidden away in the cupboards? I'm longing to have a good look round.'

'Nicholas, don't be so heartless. She was my dear, good friend and I'm grieving for her.'

'Sorry, dearest. I didn't mean to upset you, but I can't help exulting over such a bit of good luck, just when we need it. I've heard from Giorgio, you see, and it's not good news.'

'About his share in the firm?'

'He's handing it over to Papa. If only I could have talked to him first! It weakens my position unbearably. Now I really have no choice but to leave the company.'

Nicholas looked round the room with a frown, noting the desirable contents and mentally discarding the rest.

'I wonder how long it will take to get Probate. Come to that, I wonder who will value the contents?'

He left Julia abruptly and advanced on Mr Cathcart. When he rejoined her, Nicholas was smiling.

'My first independent commission,' he said. 'I'm to prepare an inventory and valuation. I must start tomorrow. The sooner the Will is proved, the sooner we can raise some money. If I'm to start up on my own I'll have to find suitable premises. I did think of coming down here to Greenwich, but it's rather too far out of London. I think somewhere in the Kensington or Knightsbridge area might suit me better.'

He glanced at Julia, surprised by her lack of enthusiasm.

'Is something wrong, dearest?'

'Mr Cathcart wants Miss Wilson and me to leave here within the month. Where am I to go? Come to that, where will you live? You can hardly carry on sharing your father's house if you're abandoning his business.'

'And quarrelling with him every time we set eyes on one another,' Nicholas agreed. 'I've spent the last couple of nights at my club, and could go on staying there, or take lodgings somewhere, but that doesn't settle your diffculty.'

The group of people who had attended the funeral was beginning to disperse. Mr Cathcart came up to Nicholas and Julia to say goodbye.

'Must get home to the wife,' he said. 'She didn't want to come. Can't say I blame her – dismal occasions, funerals, even when the deceased is such an old lady as Aunt Mabel. When you've totted up the value of the bits and pieces, you can send the papers straight to the solicitors, Mr Hope. And you'll bear in mind what I've said about giving me early possession of the house, won't you, Miss Turle?'

'Certainly,' Julia said coldly.

As Mr Cathcart turned away she said under her breath, 'Nasty little man.'

'Not a very choice specimen,' Nicholas agreed. 'Listen, dearest, I've decided the best thing for me to do is get a special licence so that we can get married straight away. Then I'll come and live here while I'm doing the valuation. At the same time must I start a search for suitable premises for my new business, preferably with living accommodation included, and as soon as possible we'll go and live over the shop.'

His eyes were dancing, but Julia's head was whirling.

'Nicholas! We can't get married, just like that!'

'Why not? If the room wasn't full of people I could persuade you in a trice.'

'It's not that I don't want to marry you,' Julia said uncertainly.

'Oh, good!'

'I must have time to think.'

'Why? I'll be back tomorrow with a licence in my pocket and the date of the wedding fixed.'

It was like being swept along by a strong wind. Julia wanted to catch hold of something, to slow herself down, to have time to get used to the idea. I do love him, she thought distractedly, I really do love him and I want to marry him, but I didn't mean it to be like this, all done in a hurry, no one at the wedding, his own family estranged. Suppose he comes to regret it? But it's not me who's rushing us into matrimony. It's what Nicholas wants. I wish . . . I wish I'd met his father.

Because of this last thought, Julia took a step about which she did not consult Nicholas. She would not communicate with his father without Nicholas's knowledge, but she gave in to her desire to see him, just once. She went to a DuFrayne & Speranza auction.

The Sale Room was larger than she had thought it would be from the outside of the building, easily able to accommodate the sixty or so bentwood chairs arranged in rows facing the rostrum. The walls were painted an unusual shade of reddish-brown which, if Julia had but known it, had been the subject of one of her fiancé's arguments with his father, since Nicholas insisted that the colour looked like dried blood and had wanted to change it to a pleasanter sage green. Some thirty of the seats were occupied and as Julia waited, a few more people, all men, drifted in and sat down. There was a feeling of expectancy, even excitement, in the room.

A door to the right of the rostrum opened and Vittorio Speranza entered, followed by two young men as observant of his movements as a couple of acolytes. It seemed to Julia that all the tension in the room had suddenly been given a focus. Vittorio mounted the rostrum, looked round and a hush fell as he picked up the gavel.

It was quietly done, but the force of his personality drew everyone's attention, just as he intended that it should. He was not as tall as Nicholas, nor as slim, although his figure was good for a man in his fifties. His dark, waving hair had receded a little from his forehead and he had two wings of white on either side of his head, which made his complexion look darker than Julia had thought it would be. There was a subtle likeness to Nicholas both in his face and his manner, especially when he raised his chin and looked round the room with an air of command. And his hands were very much Nicholas's hands – long-fingered and strong.

That afternoon Vittorio had a collection of antique bronzes for sale – Egyptian, Etruscan, Greek and Roman. This was a field in which he felt himself to be at home and he conducted the auction with all the authority of an acknowledged expert. His black eyes glittered as his glances darted round the room. He took the sale fast, building up the momentum and the excitement. He almost seemed to dance on the rostrum, turning from side to side as he took bids from every corner. The porters knew that in this mood Mr Speranza would brook no delays. If they fumbled with a statue, if they picked up the wrong item, he would give them a look that made them feel they were about to be blasted where they stood.

Fortunately, on that afternoon all went well. Poseidon and his triton went to Agnews, Mercury and his winged staff went to Colnaghi's, some fine coins were purchased by Spinks, the British Museum acquired two Egyptian gods and an unknown American was extremely active in bidding for the Greek discus throwers and javelin hurlers which were a feature of the collection.

Julia felt battered when it was all over, but she understood now what it was that attracted Nicholas to the profession his father followed. The excitement, the thrill of a good sale, the perpetual handling of fine objects, the feeling that there was always something to learn, always something round the corner which might throw a new light on an artist's work or a corner of history. It would be impossible for him to give it up and turn to a different branch of the trade, she quite saw that. He and his father were two of a kind, there was no doubt about that either. No wonder they had quarrelled; they were too alike to run in harness, quite apart from Vittorio's dictatorial attitude about Nicholas's marriage.

Watching Vittorio as he chatted after the sale to one or two favoured clients, unable to leave her seat until her neighbours chose to move, Julia considered him as a man. He had married Serafina the previous week. It had been a quiet ceremony and no announcements had appeared in the newspapers, but Nicholas had heard through his contacts in the trade that it had taken place. To Julia, immersed in her own happiness, it seemed a sad, strange match, even though now that she had seen Vittorio she had to admit that he was still a fine-looking man and the force of his personality was enough to sweep any woman off her feet. If he could have found a suitable widow in her thirties it would have seemed natural for him to remarry. But a girl not yet out of her teens . . . no wonder Nicholas was so disgusted.

Julia had no intention of making herself known to her future father-in-law. If they ever met it would have to be because he sought her out, not the other way round. She slipped quietly out of the room, down the stairs and out into Piccadilly, blinking in the sunlight.

She told Nicholas what she had done and at first he was not pleased, not until she had talked to him for a little while and then her praise of his father set free his own admiration and he admitted that given the right sale there were few auctioneers in London to touch Vittorio when he was in full flight.

'I've learnt everything I know from him,' he told her. 'And now I mean to make use of that training. I think I've found suitable premises for our new business. Will you come with me tomorrow to see whether you approve?'

'Where are they?'

'In the High Street, Kensington – quite a bustling area and not too far out for dealers to come.'

'What about the living quarters?'

'They're a little cramped, but I'm sure you can make a cosy apartment for us. We'll have to manage without a retinue of servants to begin with, I'm afraid. Can you cook?'

'Only a few simple dishes.'

'Then you'll have to learn,' Nicholas said, kissing her. 'I've done something else, too, dearest.'

Looking up into his face, Julia said, 'You've got our marriage licence.'

'I told you I would. And I've informed the Vicar of St Alfege's that we'll be married on Wednesday. About three o'clock in the afternoon, I thought.'

'But, Nicholas, is it in order for you to be married in the Church of England?'

'Not in the eyes of the Catholic Church, but your man took it for granted I was one of his flock so if he has no qualms, why worry?'

'I think you should have told him.'

'I'm a Christian. I was baptised and all that. If we start an argument about whether I'm to undergo conversion before the ceremony we'll never get it done.' He moved closer. 'Marry me next Wednesday, woman, or I'll ask Miss Wilson instead.'

With a laugh that was half a sigh Julia collapsed against his chest.

'You gallop over me like a runaway horse,' she complained.

'Is it so painful to you, to give me what I want?'

'When you put it like that, what can I reply? You're unscrupulous and domineering and . . .'

'And completely at your feet. I know I'm rushing you, but I will be a good husband to you, Julia, I promise I will.'

The ceremony took place on Wednesday, just as Nicholas had planned. The only witnesses were Miss Wilson and the neighbours who had been left Mrs Cathcart's silver tea service. Julia wore a gown of pink glacé silk, hurriedly purchased in the Gown Department of Peter Robinson's and altered to fit her slender figure.

It was over unbelievably quickly. The ancient promises were exchanged, the ring was slipped on Julia's finger and before she knew what was happening, she was signing her name and Nicholas was signing his – his *new* name, Julia noticed, and once again she was distracted by the thought that there was something not quite legal about this marriage.

They all went back to the Cathcart house, where Nicholas had provided champagne, but half an hour after their return Julia and Nicholas were alone, the neighbours being adamant that they must go, and Miss Wilson having found herself other lodgings where she was expected for supper.

'A brand-new wife and a whole house to romp in,' Nicholas said. 'How delightful.'

'Are we really married?' Julia asked, pressing the backs of her hands against her hot cheeks.

'I hope so. If not, you're going to be a fallen woman by morning.'

He was irresistible when he laughed like that, his whole face lit up with joy. Julia went into his arms and let him kiss away her misgivings.

'I've ordered a hamper from Fortnum & Mason,' Nicholas said. 'The champagne arrived, so I presume that has, too. Will it be in the kitchen?'

'I expect so.'

Nicholas seized her hand and pulled her out of the drawing room. Sure enough, a large wicker box had been left on the kitchen table.

'Do you like caviar?' Nicholas enquired.

'How can I possibly know? I've never tried it.'

Caviar was not the only exotic delicacy Nicholas had ordered. Julia tasted and considered, finding some things delicious and others too strange for her ignorant palate.

'You've been dreadfully extravagant,' she said.

'Well, it's our honeymoon, isn't it?'

By the time they came to try the peaches preserved in brandy they had migrated to a pile of cushions on the floor of the drawing room, their backs propped against the sofa on which Mrs Cathcart had once lain. Julia dipped her spoon in the brandy and peach juice and offered it to Nicholas and they fed one another, laughing as the sticky juice ran down their chins. Julia felt replete and drowsy, her head ringing from the unaccustomed champagne, her body relaxed in the circle of Nicholas's arm.

'I feel happy right down to my toenails,' she said.

'That's good. Mm . . . what a sticky kiss!'

They stayed where they were for a while, half-sitting and half-reclining, with Nicholas's fingers idly caressing the soft skin on the inside of Julia's arm. She gave a sigh and nestled closer and Nicholas laughed softly.

'I want to make you my wife,' he said in her ear. 'You understand what I mean, don't you?'

'Yes. I . . . I've made a room ready for us.'

Nicholas rather fancied the idea of subsiding amongst the

cushions they had spread on the floor, but perhaps that would be a mistake, the first time. Julia seemed all complacence at that moment, but he sensed a core of timidity in her which would only be melted if he behaved with a degree of decorum.

He did not even protest when she insisted on clearing up the debris of their meal.

'I know it seems unromantic, to be doing the washing-up in the scullery on our wedding night, but it would make me uneasy to think of coming down in the morning to a sordid mess,' Julia said.

It was all a novelty and an amusement to Nicholas.

'There's a first time for everything,' he said solemnly. 'I've never wiped up a plate before and you, Mrs Hope, have never been treated like this!'

He swept her up in his arms and carried her out of the kitchen, laughing and protesting.

'You can't carry me all the way upstairs,' Julia said.

'Can't I? No, you're right, I can't. This is not the night on which I wish to cripple myself. You may walk up the stairs on your own.'

'Will you put out the lights and lock up?'

'I will. How delightfully domesticated. I suppose there isn't a cat to be put out?'

'I'm afraid not.'

The mood of light-hearted amusement carried them past the moment when Julia might have felt any awkwardness in her new status. Nicholas was alight with desire and she was as loving towards him as she knew how to be. Everything was new and strange and wonderful.

'I feel like the first woman who was ever made,' she whispered.

'My lovely Eve. Am I your Adam?'

'You are my lord. I love you more than life itself. I'll never stop loving you, not to the end of my days. Oh, Nicholas, Nicholas, how is it *possible* to be so happy?'

Julia was the first to wake in the morning. Nicholas was sprawled beside her, his face half-buried in the pillow, his right hand resting proprietorially on her hip. She lay still, not wanting to disturb him, but gradually she realised that it was full day. Nicholas had laid his watch down on the bedside table. Moving cautiously, Julia reached across him to pick it up. Nine o'clock! She had never slept so late into the day before in her life. She replaced the watch, noticing how fine it was in its slender case and beautifully chased cover. Nothing but the best for Nicholas.

She slid away from the hand with which even in his sleep he tried to detain her. She was naked and had no idea where her nightdress might be in the wake of their tumultuous lovemaking. Fortunately, she had a dressing gown. As she tied the belt round her waist Nicholas stirred. He stretched and yawned and opened his eyes. For a moment Julia could see that he did not recognise his surroundings. Then he looked at her and smiled.

'Ah, yes, I got married yesterday. How is my wife this morning?'

'Very well, thank you kindly.'

'Come and kiss me.'

'I'm going to get our breakfast. Do you know it's past nine o'clock?'

'How very shocking. Come and kiss me or I'll chase you down to the kitchen just as I am.'

Since Julia believed he was perfectly capable of doing just that, she went back to the bed and was pulled down for a long kiss.

'You're very scratchy,' she complained.

'That's the way of us men. We grow nasty beards and have all sorts of undesirable habits. Do you still love me?'

'Yes, but I'll love you even more after I've had my early – not so early – cup of tea.'

'Is that a promise?' Nicholas asked with a smile that made Julia break away from him in confusion.

'No! Nicholas, we can't! It's practically the middle of the day. And we have work to do.'

'Oh, yes, how boring!'

He might protest, but Nicholas worked hard all day, sorting and cataloguing and putting a price on the contents of the house.

'Those Chinese bowls Mrs Cathcart thought she had are, in fact, Japanese,' he reported. 'Very nice of their kind and there's quite a vogue for Japanese artefacts, but the value isn't as high as it would have been if they were old Chinese.'

'Nicholas, how soon will we be able to arrange a sale?'

'Strictly speaking, nothing belongs to you until after Probate has been granted, which may take some weeks.'

'Have we any money?'

'Not a lot. I must keep enough in hand to pay the first quarter's rent for our new premises.'

'I broke into my savings to buy my wedding gown which, I may say, is disgracefully crushed and will need sponging and pressing before I can wear it again.'

'I told you we men had nasty habits.'

'The thing is, I was wondering what to do about housekeeping money. If I use up what I've got, will you be able to . . . well, to . . .'

'Keep you in the manner to which you are accustomed? We're not quite as broke as all that, dearest. If you can provide a light luncheon and if your best dress can be rescued from ruin I propose to take my new wife to dine in the West End this evening.'

'But can we afford it?'

'Don't worry your sweet head. I have a hundred or two in hand.'

Since a hundred pounds represented riches to Julia she allowed herself to be persuaded that they could well afford dinner at a good hotel. After all, as Nicholas pointed out, this was their honeymoon and they were staying on in Mrs Cathcart's house for no more than the rent Julia had paid for one room.

He took her to the Holborn Restaurant, knowing that its elaborate ornamentation would seem the height of luxury to Julia. He was amused by the way she looked round, wide-eyed with astonishment, at the marble pillars and stairways, alabaster walls, carved woodwork, oak panelling and stained-glass windows hung with rich curtains.

'They say a couple of hundred thousand pounds were spent on rebuilding,' Nicholas told her.

'I can well believe it,' Julia said faintly. 'The mirrors! The gilding! Can we really afford to dine here, Nicholas?'

'I think we can manage the three-and-sixpenny dinner,' Nicholas said solemnly. 'The food is very good, in fact. That's why the place is so popular.'

'An orchestra, too. It's all quite wonderful.'

'You're a most rewarding young lady to take out.'

'Have you entertained other young ladies here?'

'No, dearest, never.'

As she sipped the clear consommé which was served to her, Julia said, 'Nicholas, talking of money, which I know you think I do too often – but it's because I've always had to watch my pennies – I'd like to know how you suggest selling the Nymphenburg figures.'

'I'll handle the sale myself in due course,' Nicholas said. 'I didn't think there was any doubt about that.'

'I just . . . I wondered whether we shouldn't send them to your father,' Julia said in a rush.

'To Papa? What on earth put that idea into your head?'

'You know how impressed I was when I went and saw him in action.'

'I've never disputed Papa's ability. He's probably the best auctioneer in London.'

'Exactly. It occurred to me that if we let him sell the figures he would probably get the very best price for them, which would give us a useful amount of capital with which to start up in business. And perhaps he would see it as a friendly gesture and you could be reconciled.'

She had made a mistake. With a sinking heart Julia saw Nicholas's frown and the impatient way his fingers drummed on the tablecloth.

'It's not a gesture I would care to make, nor am I sure Papa would see it in that light. Besides, you don't seem to understand, that collection is going to be my chance to make my mark. I shall start in a small way, selling off stuff we don't need from the house and looking for similar clearances to handle. Then, when my Auction Rooms become known, I'll move into higher quality goods. That's when I'll hit the market with the Bustelli figures. They'll be a sensation amongst collectors and my name will be made.'

'That's what you've decided, is it?' Julia asked.

'It's the only logical thing to do. What's the matter, dearest?'

'The Bustelli figures and, come to that, the entire contents of the house belong to me.'

Again she had angered Nicholas. His face was flushed, but he spoke with careful restraint.

'Are we having our first quarrel? If so, I wish you'd chosen a less public place.'

'I hope we're not quarrelling. All I want to point out is that you've been making decisions on your own without consulting me. It's my life, too, Nicholas, and this legacy from Mrs Cathcart is the first time I've ever had any money. You should have told me – no, more than that, you should have asked my opinion.'

'You're my wife, dear, not my business partner.'

'I'd like to be both.'

From Nicholas's baffled look she could see that he did not understand her. Julia stretched out her hand across the table to touch his own.

'I want to share everything with you, Nicholas. Don't shut me out when you make decisions.'

'Particularly decisions concerning your own property?'

'*Our* property. Everything that's mine is yours. Dear Nicholas, we mustn't disagree over the lovely figures that brought us together in the first place. Do you remember the day I came to consult you about my Harlequin? I thought you were the handsomest man I'd ever seen.'

She had won him over. The ugly frown was replaced by a reminiscent smile.

'And I thought you had the most honest eyes of any young lady I'd ever met. Very well, dearest, I can see I've been taking too much for granted. Perhaps I was relishing my independence too much after being under Papa's dominance for so many years. In future I'll take you into my confidence.'

Which was not quite the same thing as consulting her before decisions were taken, but for the time being Julia was content.

Chapter Seven

The accommodation above the premises in Kensington High Street was only just sufficient to house Nicholas and Julia, a small maidservant and, just before their first wedding anniversary, baby Simeon. There was a roomy cellar, every inch of which Nicholas required to house stock awaiting sale, and a good, solid wooden extension in the back yard, also packed to the ceiling, in which Julia was allowed to keep Simeon's perambulator, although she joked that she lived in dread of the day when she would find that it had been included in a sale.

Business was brisk, though Nicholas sighed over the mediocre quality of the goods on offer. Still, he was making a living, he was becoming known and with a wife and child to keep he could not afford to be choosy over what he would and would not handle.

He knew that Julia had hoped that baby Simeon's birth might lead to a reconciliation with Vittorio. On her insistence Nicholas had sent his father a notification of the baby's arrival, but as he had expected – as he had warned Julia – it drew no response.

On a hot day towards the end of August 1889 Julia was getting Simeon ready for his daily walk in Kensington Gardens when she heard their doorbell ring. Remembering that it was the little maid's afternoon off and that she would have to go down two steep flights of stairs to answer it, Julia hesitated. Then she laid baby Simeon back in his cot, told him to be a good boy and ran down to the private front door which led directly to the street outside. By the time she arrived in the minute hallway the visitor was already giving a second imperious peal to the bell.

The caller was a young woman – indeed, no more than a girl, but very fashionably dressed – of medium height and very upright carriage, as if she were forever straining to appear taller than she was.

'I wish to see Mrs Speranza – Mrs Niccolò Speranza,' she said as soon as the door was open.

'I am Mrs Speranza,' Julia said. 'That is, my husband is now called Hope – Nicholas Hope.'

'It is not his right name. I, too, am Mrs Speranza – Serafina Speranza. I have come to see your baby.'

'Oh . . . yes. Please come in,' Julia said in a distracted rush.

There was a smart carriage waiting in the roadway. Serafina turned her head and said, 'You may call for me in half an hour,' then she lifted the hem of her apricot silk gown and prepared to follow Julia.

'The stairs are narrow and rather dark,' Julia apologised.

'Also they are steep and I must be careful at this present time. I shall walk slowly behind you.'

By the time they reached the second floor Julia was rather more distressed than her visitor, but it was Serafina who took out a lace-edged handkerchief and wafted it slowly to and fro in front of her face.

'In Sicilia I would have a fan,' she complained. 'But I am told that in England it is not the custom for ladies to carry fans in the daytime. Where is your baby?'

'In the bedroom,' Julia said. 'I'll fetch him.'

It was only after she had hurried out of the room that Julia remembered that she had not invited her guest to sit down. She picked Simeon up, implored him in a whisper to be good and do her credit, and went back to the drawing room to find that Serafina had made herself at home in an armchair by the window and was gazing out at the scene below with lively interest.

'You are very busy here,' she said, turning away. 'In Rutland Gate we are quiet. So this is Simeon? He is a very fine baby.'

'Would you like to hold him?' Julia asked, looking doubtfully at the apricot silk gown trimmed with fine lace.

'It would be as well for me to accustom myself.'

Julia laid Simeon carefully into Serafina's arms and as she did so she realised with stark incredulity that this was his step-grandmother, this young, abrupt girl with her heavily accented English, her fashionable clothes and lavish jewellery and her obvious incompetence with a small baby.

'It is very difficult to hold him when he folds up in the middle like this,' she complained.

'He's still very tiny. He can't hold up his head yet or use his back

77

muscles. But he's a lovely little man, aren't you, my honey?' Julia bent over the baby adoringly.

'It does not worry you that he is a . . . hm, I do not know the English word . . . *uno bastardo*?'

Julia straightened up, her face reddening. 'He's not!' she protested. 'Nicholas and I are legally married . . .'

'Not in the eyes of the Catholic Church.'

'By the law of this land and in the eyes of my Church we are. Let me take him, please.'

She took Simeon in her arms, giving him a tiny squeeze to console him for having been so maligned. She turned away to hide her indignation and distress, and went to sit on the sofa with Simeon on her lap.

'I have made you angry,' Serafina remarked, but she did not apologise.

When Julia did not reply, she went on, 'I wish to tell you that I, too, have hopes.'

'I thought that was what you must mean,' Julia said, struggling to sound normal. 'When. . . ?'

'I am in my third month. It is most uncomfortable and I do not like it at all, but my mother has told me that it would happen and I am reconciled to the Will of God.'

'You're young and healthy. I'm sure you'll find everything will go well for you,' Julia said encouragingly.

'I am now eighteen,' Serafina said. 'You are right, it is time I am a mother. Mr Speranza is most pleased.' She touched the pearl drops decorating her ears with a look of satisfaction on her face. 'He is a generous man, and kind.'

'I'm glad,' Julia said, feeling once again that it was difficult to find an adequate response.

She heard a door bang down below and then the sound of impatient footsteps on the stairs. As if sensing his father's approach Simeon stirred and opened his eyes. The door opened and Nicholas was in the room – impetuous, excited, his dark eyes alight and the unruly curls disordered on his forehead in the way that always touched Julia's heart.

'Splendid news, dearest!' he announced, without waiting to see whether she was alone. 'I've got the Spurland Collection!'

The sight of the small, decorative figure at the window brought him up short.

'I'm sorry . . . I didn't realise we had a visitor,' he said.

For a moment Julia grappled with the incongruity of introducing so young a stepmother, but then Nicholas went on, 'Why, it's Serafina, isn't it? You've become so grand I almost didn't recognise you.'

Serafina held out an imperious hand and Nicholas bent over it with an amused quirk to his mouth which Julia recognised, if Serafina didn't.

'Since I am a married woman I am allowed to no longer wear white muslin, which I never liked and which was not becoming to me,' she said.

'You do your dressmaker credit,' Nicholas said gravely.

Julia stirred, willing him to stop amusing himself at his young stepmother's expense, and he turned towards her, trying to catch her eye.

'Serafina very kindly came to see Simeon,' she said.

'And do you admire our little man?' Nicholas asked, bending over the baby in Julia's arms.

'He is a nice baby. Mine, too, will be beautiful.'

Nicholas glanced enquiringly at Julia and she gave a nod. She thought her husband looked disconcerted, as if the news was not altogether welcome.

'Does my father know you've come to see us?' he asked.

'No. I saw the announcement of the baby's birth which you sent to him and it had your address on it and I made up my mind I would come when it was possible. Mr Speranza has gone away to some place I do not remember because there is a great lord who is dead, and he would not take me with him.'

'Has he gone to Lord Kenrick's place in Wiltshire?' Nicholas asked, suddenly alert.

'I think perhaps that is the name.'

'He's still as angry with Nicholas as ever?' Julia asked.

'Oh, yes! Although he does not dislike being married to me, you understand.'

She smoothed the apricot silk of her gown complacently and the sparkle of a fine diamond ring caught the light.

'Is there any news of my brother?' Nicholas enquired.

79

'He is still in Rome. He does not write letters.'

Nicholas glanced at Julia and she realised that she was being remiss in not offering their unexpected guest any refreshment, but Serafina refused her offer of tea.

'Tea I do not like and no, thank you, I will not take coffee because now, in my state of health, I find it disagrees with me. Niccolò will go and watch for my carriage and as soon as it returns he will tell me and I will go.'

Nicholas accepted these instructions with a little grimace for Julia's benefit which she did her best to ignore. Serafina watched him as he moved towards the door and Julia watched Serafina.

The expression on her face was exactly the same as Julia had seen many times on the face of a greedy child. Envy, jealousy and resentment were present in that unguarded look. As clearly as if Serafina had spoken out loud Julia knew that she was thinking that here was the man she should have married, young, handsome and vital, and no pearl earrings or diamond rings could quite make up for the substitution that had been forced on her.

She did not speak, nor did Julia betray what she had seen. She pitied the droop of Serafina's shoulders and forgave the sullenness of the face that Serafina turned towards her, but the thought that came into her own mind most strongly was that she did not want Nicholas's young stepmother to visit them again.

They made polite, stilted conversation for the next ten minutes. Simeon, fortunately, behaved like an angel. When Nicholas came bounding up the stairs once more to announce the arrival of their visitor's carriage, Julia parted with her without regret.

'Poor Nick, you'll be worn out with all this running up and downstairs,' she commented when Nicholas came back once more.

'Not me! Self-willed little monkey, isn't she? I'd say the old man's got his hands full there. Interesting that he's gone to Mercia House. I saw last week that Lord Kenrick had died and Papa, you know, helped him to get together a most amazing art collection. I wonder if it's to be sold.'

'Was he an old man?'

'No older than Papa and his heir must be about my own age. A bit of a wild 'un, by all accounts. I wouldn't be surprised if he needed money. Lucky Papa, if he's to have the handling of that collection. And that reminds me, dearest, before I was distracted by my stepmama's visit, I was bursting to tell you that I've been round the Spurland house with Captain Spurland and he's agreed to sell practically everything his old uncle has left him. There are some excellent pictures, eighteenth-century – including a - Fragonard, a Boucher and a delicious Poussin. At last I can make a proper entry into the fine-art market. This is the sale in which I'll include the Bustelli figures, with your permission; it's just the opportunity I've been waiting for.'

'Nicholas, how splendid! Let me put Simeon back in his cot and then I'll make you some tea and we'll talk about it properly.' She looked down ruefully at a damp patch on the skirt of her blue poplin dress. 'Just look what he's done. But he was as good as gold all the time Serafina was here. It would have been a disaster if he'd misbehaved himself while she was holding him.'

'She was very fine, wasn't she?' For a moment Nicholas looked dissatisfied. 'You ought to be dressed like that.'

'Oh, my dear, you know I've no taste for fripperies.'

Nicholas knew that was true and it was just as well that Julia did not hanker after silk gowns and jewellery since he was in no position as yet to give them to her. All the same, he would like to see his wife dressed up and doing him credit, and as soon as he had some money in hand he would urge Julia to smarten herself up. Serafina was nothing more than a hard-up little girl from a poverty-stricken island. Julia could easily outshine her if she had the benefit of a modish dressmaker and a maid to dress her hair. After all, as Nicholas remembered with a stir of his conscience, the proceeds of the sale of the Bustelli figures would really belong to her.

The sale of the late Septimus Spurland's collection of French pictures and furniture brought many dealers to Hope's, while the auction of the Commedia dell'Arte figures caused exactly the kind of interest he had anticipated.

Nicholas held up the figures one by one to emphasise the completeness of the set, handling them with love and regretting the emptiness of the cabinet in his drawing room where they had been kept since his marriage. It was goodbye to Pulchinello, Pierrot, Pantaloon, Beltrame, Isabella (oh, the deliciousness of her little pointed foot), Columbine, Harlequin, Narcissino,

Mezzetin, *il Capitano*, *il Dottore*, Scapin, Scaramouche . . . as he told them over, Nicholas remembered the excitement with which he had first inspected them in Mrs Cathcart's drawing room. If it had not been for the Harlequin he now set down with regret, his entire life might have been different.

He had wanted Julia to attend the sale, but she had excused herself and he was sorry about that. She had admired his father's flair – would she not have found her husband equally competent?

'Well, Mrs Hope, you're quite a rich woman,' Nicholas greeted her that evening. 'What do you propose to do with all your money?'

'I should think the first consideration would be to pay off your debts,' Julia said, then she was sorry she had spoken so tartly as she saw Nicholas's disappointment at her response.

'I can clear my debts out of the commission on the Spurland sale,' he said. 'The Commedia dell'Arte money is yours – as you've more than once reminded me.'

It went to her heart to see him looking so deflated and she cast around for a way to make amends.

'If I'm really that well off I'd like to invite my clever husband to a slap-up celebratory dinner in the West End,' she said.

She was rewarded by the way his face lit up and something stirred in her, a faint uneasiness, a suspicion that Nicholas sometimes found her too 'workaday', too apt to squash his enthusiasms.

The extremely advantageous sale of the Spurland Collection and the Commedia dell'Arte figurines brought publicity as well as profit to Nicholas. He never alluded to his connection with the house of DuFrayne & Speranza, but inevitably it leaked out and it was said that the young man who had chosen to branch out on his own had just the same flair as his better-known father. A steady supply of good-class antiques and pictures began to make its way to his Kensington sale rooms, and Nicholas started turning away the less important items that were brought to him with a courteous suggestion that they would be better suited to another auction house.

They heard nothing more of Serafina, except that Julia pointed out an announcement in *The Times* of the birth of a daughter,

Anna, to Vittorio and Serafina Speranza. She wrote a brief note of congratulation to Serafina, but there was no reply.

All the same, that polite note did bring one benefit. Just as Serafina had been drawn to visit them by the notification of Simeon's birth, so Julia's letter paved the way for Giorgio to call on them.

'I've come to London to baptise the little girl, Anna,' he explained.

'So you're a fully-fledged priest?' Nicholas asked.

'I am and no, my dear Niccolò, I do not have any regrets.'

'Not even when you see my fine son?'

'I have children, many children, in my care.'

'Hardly the same thing,' Nicholas retorted. 'And although I don't mind you calling me Niccolò, you must know that I've changed my name.'

'Of course. "Niccolò" slips out too easily for me to suppress it. Papa doesn't like your new name.'

'I dare say not, but I couldn't set up in competition with him using the same name.'

'I found it a disadvantage in Rome,' Giorgio admitted. 'With a name like mine everyone expected me to speak fluent Italian, which was far from being the case.'

'Are you returning there?'

'No, I'm to join a parish in Liverpool.'

'So we may see you occasionally?'

'An impoverished parish priest has few opportunities to travel.'

'I would always be prepared to pay your fare and, if I expand as I hope, I shall be able to offer you a bed as well.' There was a short silence and then Nicholas said abruptly, 'But you won't come, will you?'

'I would find it difficult. I am pleased to have met . . . . Julia.'

'Call her my wife, damn you!'

'Don't curse me, Niccolò. Julia is charming and no doubt she's a good woman, but in my eyes she is not your wife. She has encouraged you to leave the faith . . .'

'I didn't need a lot of persuading. From being a sceptical Catholic I've become a luke-warm Protestant. I go to church because Julia likes it. I lead a decent, honest life and I spare what I can for charity. I'm liked and respected in my business and I'm loved in my home. I'm happy. I shan't change back just because my brother can't bring himself to sleep under my roof.'

'You reflect the spirit of the age.'

'Oh, don't be so pompous! You've lost your sense of humour since you took up religion.'

'I'd be sorry if I thought that was true,' Giorgio said, getting up to go. 'We look at life through completely different eyes, Niccolò. To you the world is important, but to me it is merely somewhere I have to pass through on my way to God.'

'But human relationships . . . no, I can see we'll never agree. To me my wife and family are all-important. And, in spite of everything, I still have a soft spot for Papa. You could try giving him my love if you don't think it'll make him spit fire.'

'I'll do it with pleasure. I wish I could persuade him to meet you. He tries to hide it, but he's proud of the way you've prospered. In fact, he sent you a message – though only in the way of business, I'm afraid.'

'It's something that he even admits I'm still alive. What did he have to say?'

'He said "Tell Niccolò to think again about the attribution of Lord Mettlesham's Bernini".'

'Did he indeed!' Nicholas was alarmed and worried. 'I've already had the catalogue printed. That's where Papa saw the information, of course. I didn't have any doubts, myself.'

'Papa saw it in an exhibition with Adelbert Kettle, and the old man apparently sniffed at it.'

'But he didn't speak up and say "That's not by Bernini".'

'Or only partly by Bernini,' Giorgio suggested.

'And as Mr Kettle has been dead these three years or more we can't appeal to him for a proper opinion.'

'What will you do?'

'If I could rely on Papa to keep his mouth shut I'd be tempted to let it go. It was bought by the Mettleshams as a Bernini and there's documentation to prove it. It's been exhibited as a Bernini and this is the first time I've heard of any doubt being thrown on the attribution.'

'Will you do yourself any harm by admitting to an honest doubt?'

'My reputation for shining integrity will glow brighter than ever.

And I doubt whether Lord Mettlesham will ever do business with me again!'

'Is that important?'

'I've been cultivating him with an eye to the future. His father-in-law is on his last legs and I doubt whether the family will be able to keep up the mansion he lives in or to hold on to his possessions, which are many and various and of considerable value.'

'So how will you handle this?'

'Ask Lord Mettlesham's permission to get an expert opinion, issue a correction to the catalogue if necessary and pray that he doesn't take umbrage and withdraw it altogether. I shall gnash my teeth in futile rage if it goes elsewhere and is successfully sold as a genuine Bernini.'

'I'll pray for you, too.'

Nicholas laughed, with affection and wry amusement. 'Well, I can't stop you and, who knows, it may do some good. I suppose you'd also better tell Papa that I'm obliged to him.'

'He may have stopped you from being involved in a damaging dispute.'

'He may have stopped me from making a great deal of money,' Nicholas retorted.

As Nicholas had feared, at the first hint of disagreement about his Bernini, Lord Mettlesham withdrew it from sale. A year later it was taken to America and sold at a very high price. When his father-in-law died Lord Mettlesham, as his executor, arranged the sale of his possessions through Sotheby's.

'If Papa does me any more favours, I may go out of business,' Nicholas remarked, but in spite of this setback he continued to flourish, as did the firm of DuFrayne & Speranza.

'Just as well Papa is making money,' was all Nicholas had to say when Julia reported that the names of Mr and Mrs Vittorio Speranza had begun to appear in the Society columns of the newspapers. Fêtes and galas and charity balls – Nicholas tried to picture his father at such affairs and found it difficult. It must be Serafina's influence and one of the penalties an aging man had to pay for marrying a young, ambitious wife. Nicholas wondered fleetingly why Julia read that section of the paper since she refused to go to any functions herself; she was not interested in social affairs outside her own home where, he had to admit, she had her hands full.

A second son was born to Nicholas and Julia, followed by a second daughter for Vittorio and Serafina. Still no son to supplant him, Nicholas noted. What would happen to the business when Vittorio retired – or died? Surely his father must be making some provision for the succession? He made some discreet enquiries, but from all he could learn it seemed as if Vittorio still kept the direction of the company very much in his own hands.

By the time his own little daughter was born Nicholas was able to expand by acquiring the shop next door to his premises, which was just as well since they were hopelessly overcrowded, both upstairs and down. A door was knocked through between the two sets of living quarters and suddenly Julia had two apartments and enough room for a larger kitchen and somewhere to house the cook and nursemaid she soon employed.

By the time the old century went out Simeon was eleven, Martin was nine and little Melisssa was two. Simeon was aware that somewhere in London he had two aunts who were mysteriously younger than him and that they were called Anna and Violetta, but he could not get his mother to tell him anything about them, so he tackled his father.

He was helping Nicholas to unpack a cardboard box full of pieces of old china, unconsciously learning something of his father's expertise.

'This is a nice piece,' Nicholas said, holding up a flower-strewn dish. 'Sixpence for you if you can tell me what it is.'

'Chelsea?' Simeon hazarded.

'I'd be more impressed if you'd examined it properly and looked at the mark on the back, instead of making a guess, but you happen to be right so you get your sixpence. So you've started to be curious about your family background, have you?'

'Someone at school asked if you were the Nicholas Hope who'd changed his name from Speranza and was my grandfather Vittorio Speranza, and I didn't know.'

'I see. Yes, I began life as Niccolò Speranza.'

'Why don't we ever see our grandfather? And is it true that he's got two daughters? And are they really my aunts?'

'It's all quite true, and we never see Papa because he quarrelled with me when I married your mother, mostly because I changed my religion. My own mother was dead and Papa married again and had a second family. You also have an Uncle Giorgio who is a Roman Catholic priest, and we haven't set eyes on him since you were a baby.'

'Cripes!'

'*What* did you say?'

'It's a thing some of the chaps at school say,' Simeon said defensively.

'Vulgar little guttersnipes. Don't use such an expression again, especially in front of your mother.'

'No, sir. Shan't we ever see Grandfather?'

Nicholas paused, his hands full of woodshavings and bits of old newspaper.

'I don't know,' he said. 'I've sometimes thought . . . perhaps I should make one more attempt.'

He wrote that evening, before the impulse born of his son's questions could dissipate. He thought it was probably useless and he regretted the letter as soon as it was posted, but to his surprise he received a reply before the end of the week.

'Papa wants to see me!' he exclaimed to Julia over the breakfast table. 'Here, read what he says.'

Julia read the brief, uncordial words: ' "*You can come and see me if you like. I have not been well and am kept at home at the moment. I suppose you heard that and wondered if I was going to die? I'm not, but it might be as well if we had a talk. Come to the house at three o'clock on Tuesday.*" He's signed it "Vittorio Speranza"' – that's not very friendly,' she remarked, returning the letter to Nicholas.

'At least he's prepared to talk to me.'

'After twelve years,' Julia said drily.

In view of the careless way his father had written about his health, Nicholas was unprepared for the obvious frailty of the man who was waiting to receive him in his old family home the following Tuesday. Vittorio was up and dressed, but wearing a padded maroon satin dressing gown instead of a jacket, and when Nicholas was shown in he did not rise from the armchair in which he half-sat, half-reclined with his feet propped up on a footstool.

He had aged, Nicholas saw that immediately. Twelve years . . . All the same, he was shocked by the change he saw in his father. His hair was white and he had lost the look of sleek well-being that Nicholas remembered. His face was deeply lined and the hands that rested slackly on his lap were thin, with thick veins standing out on the backs, the hands of an old man, a sick man.

'Sit down,' Vittorio said. 'Don't stand there towering over me. You're looking well.'

What was he to say? 'And so are you, Papa.'

'Don't be a fool. I know what I look like. I've had a heart attack and if I have another it'll kill me, but I don't mean to have another one. I'll do what the doctors say, live like a vegetable and survive another ten years or more. Serafina won't like it, but there'll be no more party-going for me.'

'I saw in the newspapers that you'd been living the high life.'

'Looked for news of me, did you? What about the business – have you been following our fortunes there as well?'

'Of course; your profits have been a welcome addition to my income. Besides, I keep an eye on all my rivals.'

He had surprised his father into a brief bark of laughter, but Vittorio quickly suppressed it.

'It took you long enough to get round to writing to me,' he said.

'Papa, is that fair? What response did you make when I let you know about the children's births? I even sent messages by Giorgio, but it did no good.'

'Father Speranza! He's still slaving away in Liverpool, you know. I think I took his desertion even harder than I took yours.'

'It wasn't a desertion in either case,' Nicholas said quietly.

'It felt like it. And you changed your name! Wasn't mine good enough for you?'

'That was a matter of business.'

'I daresay that wife of yours talked you into it.'

'If that's the line you're going to take I may as well go,' Nicholas said, standing up.

'Sit down, sit down. I'm not going to quarrel with you. We've got to get things sorted out and I'd sooner do it direct than leave it to the lawyers. I'm going to have to delegate more of the management of DuFrayne & Speranza to Howard Grimsby in future. He's a good man, but I don't want him to succeed me as Chairman.'

Nicholas's heart gave a leap and he sat down.

'I've no intention of dying just yet, but the finger of God has touched me and I'm having to admit that I'm no more than human. Everything I have goes to Serafina and the two girls.'

'It's no more than I expected.'

'She's no head for money, so I'm appointing a couple of trustees to manage it for her. I want one half of my interest in DuFrayne & Speranza to be kept for the girls and the other half – Serafina's half – is to be sold, with you being given first refusal. With the quarter you already hold it'd give you an unshakeable majority holding. In fact, apart from the two girls, who're unlikely to trouble you, you'd have everything your own way.'

'It would mean selling my own business,' Nicholas said.

'House clearance and old ladies' teapots. You can do better than that, Niccolò. I've got staff with knowledge – more than one man can accumulate in a lifetime – contacts, reputation and premises finer than any you can set up in Kensington. If the chance is offered to you, you won't turn it down?'

'Not if I can raise the price. I've got three children and I have to think about their future.'

'Ah yes, two sons isn't it, and a daughter?'

'And you have two daughters.'

'Yes, nice little things. I'd expect you to keep a brotherly eye on them. And on Serafina.'

He stirred restlessly in his chair and said, without looking at Nicholas, 'She's something of a handful. It worked quite well for the first few years. She was in awe of me and, of course, having the children kept her in line. Now, however, Serafina sees herself as a Society lady. She's expensive, which is why I'm not trusting her to look after the money herself.'

'She might marry again,' Nicholas said.

'If I die in the next ten years she probably will. Just as well if she does – she needs a man to keep an eye on her.'

'Does she know we're meeting today?'

'No, and I don't intend to tell her.'

A silence fell between them. Nicholas had a growing conviction, which he thought his father shared, that Vittorio was not likely to live even a short part of the ten years he had mentioned.

'Would you like to see the children?' Nicholas asked gently.

'Not at the present time. In the spring, when the weather improves, I may drive out one day and call on you.'

'You'd be very welcome. Young Simeon has been asking questions about you. He's only eleven, but he's developing quite an eye for porcelain.'

'Indeed? So the succession is assured. How gratifying.'

Vittorio sounded quietly sarcastic and Nicholas thought it better not to go on to speak about the other children. Indeed, there seemed to be little more for them to say.

'I'm glad to have seen you, Papa,' he said.

'Yes . . . it was time. Are you going?'

'Perhaps I could come again, now that . . .'

'The ice is broken? Yes, perhaps, but arrange it with me first.' He gave Nicholas a sudden, piercing look. 'There's one more thing. I've told you there's nothing for you in my Will except the chance to buy the business if you can afford it, but I'd like you to have something to remember me by.'

'I don't need . . .'

'I started by telling you not to be a fool and it looks as if I'm going to end the same way. Forget the polite protests. There's a box on the table. Take it and go.'

Nicholas took up the box, old, worn and rubbed. It was heavier than he had expected from its size.

'Open it when you get home,' Vittorio said. His hand shot out and grasped Nicholas's wrist. 'Look after my business,' he said. 'And my children.'

Vittorio closed his eyes, but not before Nicholas had seen the glitter of tears. He bent lower and kissed his father on the forehead and he thought, he always thought afterwards, that as he left Vittorio murmured, '*Figlio mio, figlio caro mio.*'

Nicholas scarcely knew how he got home. His head was spinning, partly from emotion and partly with thoughts of the future. The box he was carrying was heavy under his arm, and yet while he was talking to Julia, he forgot all about it, until she suggested that he open it.

Inside was the heavy wooden cross which had always hung on

his parents' bedroom wall. Julia was not particularly pleased by the sight of it.

'Is he still hinting that you should go back to the Catholic Church?' she asked.

Nicholas stared at the cross, and the memory of the old quarrel with Giorgio stirred in his mind. Almost holding his breath, he turned the golden hanging loop and the figure on the cross *moved*. Very gently and reverently he twisted it to one side. The cavity Giorgio had described was revealed. Nicholas could see nothing, but when he probed with his fingers they encountered an object that felt very like soft leather. He pulled out a small drawstring bag. His hands shook as he undid the string and opened it.

Out on to the table spilled five perfect diamonds.

Chapter Eight

Nicholas did not write and thank his father for his magnificent gift, nor did he attempt to get in touch with Vittorio again, even though Julia urged it on him.

'We understood one another when we met,' he said. 'Papa doesn't want me fussing over him. I'd like him to see the children, though. In the spring, he said, and I'll remind him of that at the right time.'

But Vittorio and Nicholas had both miscalculated. On a cold day just after the New Year, Nicholas received a distracted note from Serafina which made him drop all his engagements and hurry to his father's bedside.

Serafina met him in the hallway of the house where Nicholas had grown up, and even in that moment when she was over-wrought to the point of hysteria it passed through his mind that he would scarcely have known this sophisticated woman for the sulky young girl who had come out of Sicily looking for a husband.

'He had a fall, a slip on the ice, and broke his leg,' Serafina said, clutching at Nicholas's arm. 'The doctor says he is very, very ill.'

What the doctor told Nicholas was that his father was dying. He had dressed it up in vague phrases for the benefit of the young wife, but once he got this self-contained son on his own he did not hesitate to give his opinion bluntly.

'Pneumonia's set in, and with his heart condition that's serious,' he said. 'I've been sitting with him and expecting every breath to be his last.'

'Is he conscious?' Nicholas asked.

'Intermittently. He's been asking for someone called Giorgio.'

'My brother. He's in Liverpool.'

'Not much hope of him getting here in time, then.'

The thought of Giorgio put something else into Nicholas's mind. 'Has my father seen a priest?'

The doctor gave a little grimace. 'Mrs Speranza's had one

practically living in the house ever since her husband was taken ill.'

'You don't approve,' Nicholas said with a slight smile.

'Far be it from me to deny my patient the comfort of religion,' the doctor said unconvincingly. 'But it seems to me that Mr Speranza finds his presence more irksome than consoling.'

'My brother – the Giorgio for whom Papa has been asking – became a priest, very much against my father's wishes. I've sent him a telegram . . . I wish he could have been here. Now can I go and see Papa?'

'Certainly. When I left him to come and speak to you he was weak, but lucid. His breathing . . .' The doctor shook his head. 'It can't be long,' he said. Nicholas understood what the doctor had meant when he heard the breath rasping in Vittorio's chest. He was shocked by his father's appearance, his face sunken and unshaven, a white stubble of hair stiff on his chin. He was propped up high on his pillows; his eyes were closed, but his fingers moved restlessly on the fold of the sheets.

A young priest was sitting on a chair by the bedside. He stood up when Nicholas entered the room and came round to shake hands, a gesture that Nicholas found incongruous in the circumstances.

'I'm Father O'Leary,' he said, with a pronounced Irish brogue. 'You'll be Mr Speranza's son? I'll leave you with him for a few minutes. Not long because . . .'

'The end isn't far off?'

'I've administered the Last Rites.'

Nicholas bent over Vittorio and took one of the restless hands in both of his.

'Papa, it's Niccolò.'

Instinctively he had used his boyhood name and he was rewarded when Vittorio's heavy eyelids lifted. His eyes were dull, with none of the sparkle that had once given them life, but he managed to respond to Nicholas's presence with a slight pressure of his hand and a movement of his lips that might have been an attempt at a smile.

He was trying to say something. Bending close, Nicholas was not surprised to hear the name, no more than a breath, 'Giorgio . . .'

'He's on his way,' Nicholas said.

93

From the ironic lift of his father's eyebrows, so reminiscent of his old sceptical humour, it seemed that Vittorio guessed that Giorgio's arrival would be too late. His lips parted again, and once more Nicholas strove to make out what his father was saying.

'Good boys . . . both.'

Tears started into Nicholas's eyes. He found his handkerchief and wiped them away, still holding his father's weak fingers with his other hand, and then he felt Vittorio's hold slacken and there was a sudden frightening change in his breathing.

Nicholas went to the door and called urgently, 'Doctor!'

They all crowded into the bedroom, Serafina, the doctor, the priest and Nicholas. Vittorio drew half a dozen difficult breaths and then his eyes opened, as if with a last access of strength. He looked straight at Nicholas, standing at the foot of his bed.

'*Grace*,' he said, and was gone.

Serafina gave a cry and would have collapsed over the bed if the priest had not held her up.

'Now, now, dear child,' he said. 'Compose yourself, and pray for his soul. He made a good end, calling on the grace of God, praise be.'

Only Nicholas suspected that it was not God, but his first wife, of whom Vittorio had spoken at the moment of death, and he kept that conviction to himself.

Julia did not want to go to Vittorio's funeral, but Nicholas insisted. To her it seemed hypocritical to wear mourning and attend the long Roman Catholic service for a man who had never acknowledged her existence during his lifetime.

'He was coming round,' Nicholas said. 'He made me a significant gift and put me in the way of acquiring the family business.'

So Julia went to the funeral wearing a new black gown she resented having to buy, and tried not to look as impatient with the proceedings as she felt. She was left very much on her own because Nicholas had to support Serafina. Literally support her, since Serafina was so drowned in grief that she could hardly walk without aid. Heavily veiled, her head bowed, clutching Nicholas's arm, she accepted the condolences that were offered to her with no more than a mute movement of her head, and on their return to the house she retired to her room.

'Perhaps you could go to her, Giorgio,' Julia suggested. 'Try to console her. She can't go on like this, she'll make herself ill.'

For her part, Julia went to visit Serafina's little girls and was not surprised to find that they were as heavily draped in mourning as their mother.

'I'm your Auntie Julia,' she said. 'This is a very sad time for you, but when poor Mama is feeling stronger we must get to know one another better.'

She found them unresponsive and guessed that they were bewildered, as much by Serafina's excessive grief as by the death of their father. She talked to them quietly for a short time, looked at their dolls, asked about their lessons and had the satisfaction when she left of seeing them sitting up to the schoolroom table colouring pictures and looking forward to the particularly nice tea she had recklessly promised them, which was better than sitting unoccupied in front of the fire.

She found Giorgio and Nicholas talking together when she returned to the drawing room.

'Serafina is laid down on her bed. I think she's beginning to recover,' Giorgio said. 'Nicholas, she doesn't seem to know how things are left. Are you better informed?'

Quickly Nicholas told him of the plans their father had made.

'So you're to buy out Serafina's share of the company,' Giorgio said. 'Can you afford to do that?'

'Nothing will stop me,' Nicholas said. 'Beg, borrow or steal, I'll get the money somehow.'

Julia stirred restlessly. This was something they had already discussed and she was acutely disturbed by it.

'It'll be a terrible outlay,' she said. 'Nicholas . . .'

'This isn't the time to talk about it,' he interrupted her. There was a warning note in his voice and Julia subsided, but nothing could relieve her of the anxiety she had felt ever since her husband had told her his plans for the future.

Julia was afraid of poverty. She thought that Nicholas, brought up in comfortable circumstances, had never quite understood how difficult life had been for her, a single woman earning her own

95

living with no resources to fall back on if she became ill or lost her employment. Her father had never risen above being a clerk in a lawyer's office and her mother, the daughter of an impoverished curate who had died young, had had pretensions to gentility which her situation scarcely warranted.

All her life Julia had known the necessity of making every penny justify its expenditure. A visit to the theatre must be paid for by walking to work instead of taking the omnibus, and that decision had to be balanced against the cost of shoe repairs. A new skirt and jacket was a major investment, to be worn for five years or more. She trimmed her hats herself, darned her stockings, mended her underwear, turned the collars and cuffs of her blouses when they frayed, and kept a little box into which she tipped all her loose change at the end of every week as a fund against emergencies. At the time of her marriage this nest egg had amounted to nearly eight pounds, every penny of which she had spent on her trousseau. It was the most extravagant thing she had ever done in her life.

The habit of a lifetime was not easily discarded. Julia was appalled by the way Nicholas spent money. In his place she would have scraped and saved and paid for everything in cash, but Nicholas laughed at her fears, plunged into ventures she thought foolhardy and relied on his credit at the bank.

It was the one thing about which they quarrelled, quarrels which Julia resented since she was convinced she was in the right and it was only her careful management that kept Nicholas from bankruptcy and disgrace. A shilling saved without his knowledge was a small victory and she went back to the habit of saving her loose change in a small box, squirrelling it away against the bad days that might still come.

So when it came to selling up that successful enterprise in Kensington, she was appalled.

'We can't afford it,' was her automatic reaction.

'It was what Papa wanted,' Nicholas said. 'That was why he gave me those diamonds, the old devil. He knew they would tip the balance between being strapped for cash and having a comfortable capital sum in hand.'

'But to sell up here . . .'

'I can't manage it any other way and I certainly can't run two separate businesses, not at first anyhow. Darling, you like me to consult you, but what's the use if you always oppose me?'

Julia had no answer to that and Nicholas got his way, as he always did. He might talk about consultation, and he had been meticulously correct in dealing with the money she had received from the sale of the Commedia dell'Arte figures, but when he said that the best thing she could do was to allow him to plough the money back into their own business, Julia knew better than to demur. And, of course, he had been quite right; that injection of capital had brought them a greatly increased income, far better than Julia could have achieved from investing in stocks and shares.

In the space of a few hectic months, Nicholas acquired the family concern of DuFrayne & Speranza, disposed of his premises in Kensington, leased a house in Eaton Square which Julia thought was far too grand, and plunged into running his new company. His new toy, Julia thought, resigning herself to all these unwelcome changes.

She had one year's respite while Nicholas was too busy to think about anything but the ruthless reorganisation he had put in hand, and while they were in mourning for Vittorio, but once that year was up he began to talk of entertaining on a scale which frightened Julia all over again.

An examination of the accounts had shown Nicholas that although his father had been far from insolvent, he had not been trading well for the past three years. This was something Nicholas had already suspected because of the dwindling payments he himself had received out of the company's profits. He guessed that this had marked the beginning of Vittorio's illness, and he felt a pang of regret that he had not been available to help his father at a time when he must have been sick and anxious.

He decided to change the name of the firm to Nicholas Hope & Company, with the words 'Incorporating DuFrayne & Speranza' added beneath his letter-heading as an assurance of continuity. It was a massive undertaking – having everything reprinted, commissioning a new design for the sign over the front of the Piccadilly premises, sending out letters to dealers and old clients, changing bank accounts and even issuing a new uniform to the doorman.

'Now everything is ready for unveiling,' Nicholas announced

one day. 'I've a good sale coming up of splendid English silver, so we'll have a reception in the Sale Room and invite everyone who's likely to be interested to come along and view the silver as well as our refurbished premises.'

Julia was relieved to hear that he did not require her to cater for the dozens of people he insisted on inviting to this reception.

'No, these are professional contacts and we aren't well enough "in" with the Society crowd to invite them to our own house,' he explained. 'That's something we'll have to work on, dearest. All I want from you this time is for you to be there, supporting me, looking your most beautiful and being nice to everyone who tells you what a clever husband you've got.'

He could always coax a smile from his wife and he made it sound easy, but Julia knew that on the evening itself she would be rigid with nerves, unable to believe that Julia Turle, the impoverished schoolmistress, was really shaking hands with lords and ladies and men rich enough to buy up Nicholas Hope & Company three times over.

She went to the model gown department in Derry & Toms and chose a gown in grey silk. It was a perfectly suitable outfit for a woman of thirty-six, just coming out of mourning for her father-in-law. True, the effect was a little subdued, especially since she wore no jewellery except for a modest pearl necklace, but Julia told herself it was in good taste, which was more than could be said of the concoction in which Serafina chose to make her first social appearance since the death of her husband.

Serafina wore black taffeta and diamonds. She rustled, she shone, she glittered. It was difficult for Julia to recognise in this polished woman of the world either the gauche, abrupt girl who had once visited her in Kensington or the wildly distraught young widow. Her black hair, once a mass of unruly curls, had been subdued and elaborately dressed. Diamonds swung from her ears and encircled her neck, and far too much of that neck was exposed, in Julia's judgement. It was not exactly immodest, but Serafina's gown was cut wide enough to reveal the roundness of her shoulders and low enough to hint at the curve of her breasts. Julia had been pleased with the fit of her own gown, but Serafina's was tight to swooning point, without the trace of a wrinkle, and the skirt was pulled back in folds which emphasised her hips, bursting into a riot of pinked and gathered ruffles at the back. For the first time Julia saw the point of patronising a high-class dressmaker rather than a ready-to-wear shop. She herself looked nice, she still thought that, but Serafina had style.

She had another advantage over Julia, too; Serafina was already acquainted with the *haut monde* and could mix easily with the illustrious clients who had come along to satisfy their curiosity that evening. She moved amongst them, fluttering the black lace fan she carried, vivacious and at home, while Julia stood stiffly by the door and waited for Nicholas to introduce her to his important patrons.

When Nicholas decided to abandon her and to circulate amongst the crowd, Julia made a determined effort. She smiled at random at a man and woman admiring a heavy silver salver and murmured that it was a lovely piece. She had conscientiously read the catalogue and taken in enough to be able to converse. She was managing, it was not as bad as she had feared, but she was a long way from enjoying herself.

Nicholas came face to face with his young stepmother and asked, 'Do you approve of the changes I've made?'

Serafina shrugged, a movement which lifted her gleaming shoulders a little higher out of her gown. 'To me it seems strange that a man should wish to abandon the name of his father, of all his ancestors, and to give up the goodwill that has been created in the past.'

'I hope I'm not doing that. One reason for inviting everyone along this evening is to impress on them that the firm continues, just the same but better.'

Again Serafina shrugged. 'It is no longer my concern. You have bought me out of the company.'

'But surely you still take an interest? Do you like my new colour scheme?'

All the rooms had been freshly painted and Nicholas had at last got rid of the dried blood walls he had always disliked.

'It is pleasant, but I must tell you, Nicholas, that this silver would have shown to better advantage against the red which Vittorio favoured.'

Since Nicholas had already come to the same conclusion he was not pleased, but he laughed it off.

'What are your plans now, Serafina?' he asked.

'I shall remain in London and I shall enjoy myself very, very much.'

The relish with which she spoke made Nicholas laugh again, but he felt uneasy. He had paid a stiff price for Serafina's interest in DuFrayne & Speranza, and he hoped that she was not going to overspend her income and get into debt.

'May I fetch you a glass of wine?' he asked.

'Lord Kenrick is already getting me one,' Serafina said.

'You're acquainted with Lord Kenrick?' Nicholas was surprised.

'Of course. He is one of my flirts,' Serafina replied with perfect composure. 'Ah, there you are, my lord. I must tell you that you will never earn a living as a waiter. You are far too slow.'

She looked up at the young man who was trying to hand her a glass of champagne, mischievous and alluring, her black eyes reflecting the sparkle of her diamonds, and the thought passed through Nicholas's mind that when his father had described his young wife as a handful he might have been talking about more than her extravagance.

He put it to Julia as they clopped home in their carriage after the last guest had left.

'I was surprised by her appearance, and even more by her manner,' Julia said. 'Not at all like a widow, even though she was wearing black.'

'She's still young,' Nicholas said tolerantly.

'She must be approaching thirty, quite time for her to become a little more discreet.'

'I suppose so,' Nicholas said, taken aback by the tartness of his wife's reply. He took her hand in his. 'I must get you some better jewellery, dearest.'

'Don't try to match Serafina's diamonds, I beg of you. I'd never dare go out of the house in them. '

Nicholas took his hand away.

'I'll try to find something more to your taste,' he said.

Just as Julia had feared, that evening marked the beginning of the new, more sociable life Nicholas demanded of her. In the moneyed society of the new King the owner of a reputable auction house, it seemed, was perfectly acceptable at the tables of the affluent and well-connected. What galled Julia, and even grated a little on Nicholas, was that they owed something of the smoothness with which they progressed in Society to Serafina. The woman knew everyone and went everywhere. The rather odd fact that her stepson was older than she amused her circle of friends. They accepted Nicholas because of the novelty and then began to like him for himself. As for his wife, she was not as entertaining as Nicholas nor as alluring as Serafina, but she was a good-looking woman in her quiet way and a perfectly acceptable dinner-party guest. One could put Mrs Hope next to a difficult man and know she would do her best to engage him in conversation.

On those terms Julia found her niche in Society, but it did not make for sparkling evenings, and she was frequently as bored as Nicholas was stimulated by the company in which they found themselves.

What Julia failed to understand was that the excitement Nicholas found in conducting an important sale demanded to be worked off before he could relax.

'You never used to be like this,' she complained.

'I'm at the top of the mountain now and the air is headier,' Nicholas retorted. 'In Kensington I dealt in hundreds of pounds, but now it's thousands and tens of thousands. I had a Rembrandt in my hands today – a *Rembrandt*, Julia! But you're not interested.'

'I am,' Julia protested. 'Of course I'm delighted that you're enjoying your work and that it's profitable. I just wish you'd sit down quietly and tell me about it instead of always wanting to rush off to an evening in someone else's house where we never get a chance to talk to one another. Must we go to this tiresome party at Lord Kenrick's tonight?'

'Yes, we must. It's his wife's first reception since their marriage and it's an honour to be invited.'

'Poor girl, I wonder if she really understands what she's taken on?'

'Really, Julia, I know you don't like Lord Kenrick, but that's hardly the way to talk about him.'

'That wasn't what I meant, though it's true I don't like him and the way Serafina flirts with him is most unbecoming. I was thinking of the burden of entertaining that will fall on the new Countess.'

'I'm afraid you'll have to take up your own burden soon, my dear. We simply must give a proper dinner of our own.'

From her grimace Nicholas knew how unwelcome that idea was to Julia, but what was also occupying his thoughts was just how jarring her reference to Serafina's flirtatiousness had been. His young stepmother was a minx, there was no doubt about that, but she had at her fingertips the art of being amusing company, something which it seemed poor Julia would never learn, just as she obstinately refused to compete in the matter of fine clothes.

'Julia, you're not going to wear your grey silk gown again?' Nicholas demanded that evening.

'It's almost new and I feel comfortable in it,' Julia replied.

'You've worn it at least four times in the same company.'

'No doubt I have. That doesn't worry me.'

'Don't I give you a large enough allowance? I could increase it if you told me it was necessary, or if I could see some sign of you spending what you have on yourself.'

'Give me more money by all means. I shall do the same as I have with most of my present allowance: put it on one side for the benefit of the children.'

'Darling, that isn't necessary. I can provide for the children.'

'Can you?'

Julia turned to face him, her face flushed and her hands clasping and unclasping in agitation. 'You're so reckless! You never seem to think of the future. You're in debt to the bank. Yes, I know you were able to finance the purchase of the company, but how much more have you spent on this ridiculous reorganisation? Everything new! No thrift, no thought of what might have been reused. You never consulted me about any of your extravagant plans. Why not? Because you knew I'd disapprove – and rightly. Your profits for the last year were down, down, down. Can you deny it?'

'The past year has been difficult because of the loss of my father,' Nicholas said slowly. 'And because of the changes I've introduced. But what you haven't experienced, Julia, and I have because I'm there every day, is the entirely new spirit in Hope & Company. I've blown away the cobwebs . . .'

'And got rid of some old and trusted employees!'

'Decrepit hangers-on who croaked every time I wanted to make a change,' Nicholas retorted. 'I'm employing fewer people than Papa did, but every one of them is worth his weight in gold. We're an exciting new team and we're going to make Hope & Company the biggest and best auction house in London.'

'I hope Christie's and Sotheby's are properly alarmed.'

'Yes, I hope they are, too, because I'm going to make them compete with me for every item available for sale.'

At that point, if they had not been committed to attending the reception which the new Lady Kenrick was giving that evening, they might have sat down and had a proper discussion. They might even have had an out-and-out quarrel, which would at least have cleared the air. As it was, the disagreement petered out, leaving both Nicholas and Julia dissatisfied, each sure that they were in the right. Julia obstinately wore her grey silk gown with her single row of pearls. Nicholas had given her a very pretty necklace of sapphires set in gold, but she would not give him the satisfaction of seeing her wear it that evening.

They met Serafina at the Kenricks' house, of course; that could be taken for granted. She let her gaze flicker over Julia just once, in a way that filled Julia with impotent rage. Serafina had chosen to be very grand, in black lace over white satin, with a single red camellia tucked into the cleft between her breasts, and her diamonds glittering round her neck. By the side of her Julia felt like a grey London pigeon confronted by a bird of paradise, and it did nothing for her self-esteem to realise that Nicholas would have agreed with that comparison.

He was usually very good about remaining by her side, but that evening he wandered away almost as soon as they arrived. It was the type of entertainment Julia most disliked, without the focal point of a dinner, at which one could at least get to know the people on either side; just an aimless meandering round the enormous rooms, chatting and drinking champagne, until the musicians Lady Kenrick had engaged to amuse her guests began their programme.

Julia found a chair, but there were groups on either side of her who knew one another and she felt isolated. Glancing round she saw Nicholas leaning over the back of Serafina's chair. She was laughing up at him and making great play with that fan she used so effectively. Her lips were as red as the camellia at her breast. Julia was convinced that she painted them.

When the music began, Julia felt less conspicuous in her solitude. After a group of three songs the prima donna retired and there was a buzz of conversation until her place was taken by a renowned pianist. Julia glanced over her shoulder again. Serafina's chair was empty and Nicholas was nowhere to be seen. Julia sat staring straight ahead, her fan gripped so tightly that she was in danger of snapping the shafts; two spots of colour glowed in her cheeks, and she heard not one note of the sonata to which the maestro treated them.

It might have reassured Julia to know how mundane was the request Serafina had made to Nicholas.

'I wish to consult you on business,' she said, looking up at him with eyes that were suddenly wistful. 'It is so difficult for me without Vittorio. He managed everything. Will you take me out of this room for a moment, to somewhere quiet where we can talk?'

'If it's business, why not come to the office?' Nicholas asked.

Serafina pouted becomingly. 'Don't be so tiresome, Nicholas. I wish to talk to you *now*. At the office you are always busy. I know – I have been there in Vittorio's day. Always there are people wanting you. Come, I'm sure we can find a small corner in which to have a little talk.'

She stood up and moved away and Nicholas could think of no reasonable way to refuse her.

Since almost everybody had crowded into the great salon to hear the music, Serafina had no difficulty in leading him into a small unoccupied drawing room where she subsided on to a sofa and looked appealingly up at him.

'I suppose it's money?' he asked.

'Of course money,' she agreed. 'I am in a little difficulty and I do not know what to do.'

'That's easy – be less extravagant.'

'You are not at all a nice man, Nicholas. Not kind.' Serafina turned her head away, apparently fighting against tears, and Nicholas felt a pang of remorse. He sat down on the sofa with her and tried to get her to look at him.

'Come, don't be upset,' he said. 'I didn't mean to be unkind. I'm sure something can be arranged.'

Serafina wiped the corners of her eyes with a white-gloved finger, a childish gesture which touched Nicholas.

'I thought I would be very, very rich when I sold Vittorio's company to you,' she said. 'But there are people who wish to keep my money from me.'

'Your trustees.'

'That is what they call themselves,' Serafina agreed. 'Is it true, Nicholas, that they can refuse to give me the money I need to live on?'

'Absolutely true and there's nothing I can do about it. I presume they've settled a fixed income on you and you don't find it adequate?'

'It is not at all enough and now there are bills and they say I must pay them out of my next quarter's allowance and if I do I will have nothing on which to live, nothing at all!'

'You'll have to learn to live within your means, Serafina. You haven't been borrowing from money lenders, have you?'

'No! Can one do that?'

'It's a very, very bad idea,' Nicholas said hastily. 'The best thing you can do is to make a complete list of all your debts and then . . . well, I'd like to help you . . .'

'You will pay them for me?'

'No! I'll talk to the trustees and ask them to pay up this once. After that you'll have to manage, because I doubt if they'll do it a second time.'

'Why not? The money is mine.'

'Papa left very strict instructions about how his estate was to be administered. I'm sorry, Serafina, but I suspect you were an extravagant puss during his lifetime and he was worried in case you frittered away your capital and ended up with nothing to live on.'

'I think it is very disgusting to be a rich widow who has not, in fact, any control over her money,' Serafina said.

'Think how much worse it would be to be a poor widow,' Nicholas said. 'The truth is, you're not good at managing for yourself. Perhaps you need a husband to look after your affairs.'

'Oh, no! I have been married once and although Vittorio was

kind and it was not all disagreeable, I do not intend to have another husband. I want to be a rich widow with lovers.'

She spoke so blandly that for a moment Nicholas did not take in what she had said. Then, half appalled and half wildly amused, he countered, 'Serafina, you don't mean that!'

'But yes!' Serafina said in surprise. 'It is quite the thing to have lovers in high society. Already I have been approached, but I would not do anything indiscreet during the period of my strict mourning.'

'Or at any time, I should hope!'

'As to that, I shall please myself. I have decided to be a woman of advanced thinking and if I want to take a lover then I shall take a lover, and if I manage it well he will be rich and then he can pay my bills.'

'That's immoral.'

'Yes, it is very agreeable to be immoral.' She looked up at him through her ridiculously long lashes and this time her black eyes were wickedly inviting. 'Have you not discovered that, *Niccolò mio*?'

She was leaning towards him, displaying the delicious swell of her breasts. Her red lips were slightly parted. She was far too lavish with her scent; it rose about her like the perfumed air of a foreign land.

'I'm not easily tempted,' Nicholas said, his voice thick.

'Not easily,' Serafina agreed. 'But not at all? That I do not think.'

She touched his cheek with her folded fan and as the black lace rasped across his skin Nicholas lost his head. He was not conscious of moving, but somehow Serafina was in his arms, her open mouth crushed beneath his lips, her body pliant and willing against his.

'You see?' Serafina whispered, moving away from him. 'You, too, can be tempted and it will not be at all difficult for me to find a lover if I wish for one.'

She got up from the sofa, perfectly composed. 'I will send you a list of my tiresome debts and you will be very shocked, but because you're a little bit in love with me, you will be indulgent.'

She tapped him again with her fan, this time on the shoulder, like a queen conferring an accolade. 'And when you have settled matters with my robber trustees, you will come and see me.'

106

'No . . .'

'Oh, yes, Niccolò. Oh, yes, I think you will

Chapter Nine

Julia and Nicholas had had disagreements during their marriage, but Julia had never known anything like the coolness that had crept between them since she had spoken her mind about her husband's spending habits. Nicholas was a man whose temper flared up and subsided quickly, and he was never one to harbour resentment, not even when he had to give in and admit she had been in the right after one of their rare quarrels. She could not understand the change that had come over him.

'Nicholas, is there anything wrong?' she nerved herself to ask.

'No, of course not.'

The answer came so quickly that she felt suspicious. It was almost as if Nicholas had been expecting her question and had his answer ready.

'Are you worried about the company? Aren't things going well?'

To Julia it seemed that Nicholas's reply was deliberately cruel.

'Do you never think about anything but money?'

He walked out of the room, leaving Julia stunned and hurt. Her concern had been for his peace of mind, not for his profits. Just because she had once admitted to a worry about the future, he assumed that she was incapable of taking an interest in any other aspect of his business. The injustice of it made her angry.

The estrangement was still smouldering when Julia decided a day or two later to pay a duty call on Serafina. Try as she might she could not like the younger woman, and it was more because she felt obliged to keep up an appearance of friendship than because she really wanted to go that Julia pinned on her hat and ordered her carriage.

She took Melissa with her, feeling that the little girl would provide a subject for conversation. Melissa was nearly five years old, a sunny, pretty child, rather spoiled from being the youngest and the only girl, her father's pet and her mother's special delight. Serafina's own daughters were now twelve and nine years old.

Julia found them awesomely well-behaved and sometimes wondered how Serafina managed to keep them in such good order. Of course, they were left very much to the care of their governess, who seemed to have taught them miraculously good manners.

She was shown into Serafina's drawing room and looked round critically. Serafina's taste in dress might be impeccable, but Julia was by no means sure that she admired her touch with interior decoration. It was all a trifle overblown, just as Serafina might become herself in later life, Julia thought.

Certainly the woman who made her entrance – and Serafina was adept at doing that – was a dressmaker's delight, swathed in folds of black spotted organza, sashed in satin and frothing with lace. Julia, who had never adopted the tea-gown habit, thought the garment more suited to the boudoir than the drawing room, but part of that reaction was because Serafina made her feel stiff and formal as she sat bolt upright on her chair.

'Julia!' Serafina exclaimed, in apparent surprise. 'I thought . . . but it is no matter.'

'You were expecting someone else?'

'I looked carelessly at your card and thought Nicholas had called.'

'At three o'clock on a Tuesday afternoon, Nicholas is far too busy to be making social calls.'

Serafina did not reply, but she smiled, a slow, self-satisfied smile, and Julia felt a sick jolt in her stomach. It was not necessary for Serafina to say that if Nicholas called to see her that afternoon it would not be for the first time.

With an effort Julia concealed her understanding of that creamy smile.

'I've brought Melissa to see you,' she said. 'Say, "Good afternoon" to . . . Auntie Serafina, darling.'

It had been her own doing that Julia's children called Serafina "Aunt", and Serafina's daughters called her the same. What else were they to do, she had demanded of Nicholas. It had seemed a suitable solution at the time, but now Julia's tongue stumbled over the title.

Serafina held out a hand and Melissa went over obediently and kissed her on her scented cheek.

'Would you like to go and visit your cousins in the nursery?' Serafina asked.

Melissa gave her mother an alarmed look and Julia said, 'She's a little shy. Perhaps Anna and Violetta could come down here?'

The children were sent for and Julia searched for another subject of conversation to fill in the gap until they appeared.

'Have you been to the Royal Academy?' she asked.

'Oh, yes! Such a crush. Nicholas said he had never known such a crowd. You were wise to stay at home.'

She had not been asked to go. In silence Julia digested the realisation that her husband had visited the Summer Show without her and had met his young stepmother there. It was a public enough place, of course, and there was no reason why they should not meet, but what grated on Julia was the suspicion that Serafina had deliberately dragged in that reference to Nicholas. Pride made her grit her teeth and carry on the conversation.

'Was there any picture you particularly admired?'

'The Sargents, of course. The portrait of Lord Ribblesdale is particularly striking. Even Nicholas admired it although he laughs at me and says my taste is old-fashioned.'

'Nicholas's own taste is rather too *avant garde* for me, too, sometimes. He bought a French picture recently which bewilders me, something a child might have drawn.'

She was doing well, but it was a relief to Julia when Anna and Violetta joined them. They were quiet girls, dark-haired and dark-eyed and, to Julia's critical eyes, too thin and sallow. She suspected that they did not get enough of the fresh air she believed necessary for the well-being of children, especially London children. Melissa had roses in her cheeks and a sparkle in her eyes which, if Serafina had been a proper mother, she would have envied.

'I'm going to take Melissa to Kensington Gardens,' Julia said, making an impulsive decision. 'May Anna and Violetta come with us?'

'How kind. Yes, they may come. I shall stay in,' Serafina said, with a little shrug of her shoulders and a hint of the same secret smile that had already annoyed Julia. 'In case I have any more callers.'

In case my husband calls on you, Julia thought grimly. A vulgar expression she had once heard came into her mind – *I'll have his guts for garters*.

In the course of a slow walk round the Gardens while the children played on the grass, Julia came to a difficult and unwelcome understanding that it would be a mistake to tax Nicholas with making secret visits to Serafina. To do so might be to imbue the affair with an importance she hoped it still lacked. It was beyond Julia's belief that Nicholas could have allowed himself to be more than slightly indiscreet in his dealings with a woman he himself described as a minx. If they had been on better terms, Julia would have teased him about it and treated it as a joke, for Nicholas was not above being mildly flirtatious, as she had discovered in the past, and she found that laughing him out of it worked well. Not with Serafina, though. That young woman gave out an aura of sexual enticement which Julia deeply distrusted.

Painfully, Julia brought herself to acknowledge that she might in some small way be to blame if her husband had begun to look elsewhere for a companion. She had made a virtue of her naturally abstemious ways – and still thought she was right to be wary of unnecessary expenditure – and had deliberately exaggerated the need for thrift as a way of getting back at Nicholas when he disagreed with her.

From being merely dully dressed she had begun to cultivate shabbiness, as if that were a virtue in itself. It was not as if she had done anything useful with her savings, Julia admitted honestly. The money had piled up and she had taken pride in her nest egg. *Miserly*. The word came into her mind and made her ashamed. And not only with money. Because she had no natural talent for sparkling conversation, she had shunned making the effort; she and Nicholas did not entertain as much as they should have done. She had even refused to serve on charitable committees because she had felt herself inadequate. Of course she would be inadequate if she never made an effort to learn! She had a good brain, better than many of the other ladies, and she was beginning to let it addle through neglect. What had happened to the woman who had once claimed equality with her husband? She had let herself become swamped in domestic trivia that could perfectly well be left to someone else.

Julia dropped Anna and Violetta back at Rutland Gate an hour

111

later and then, before her resolve could weaken, she ordered the carriage to carry her to Bond Street and paid a call on that extremely expensive dressmaker, Nicole.

Julia studied her husband surreptitiously when he arrived home that evening, and understood for the first time the look of strain he always seemed to wear these days. If she had thought about it at all, Julia would have put it down to their own estrangement, but now she suspected another cause. Serafina had hooked her claws in him and was playing with him for her amusement. Julia doubted very much whether the affair had gone very far. What Nicholas wore was not the look of a man trying to hide from his wife the excitement of a consummated sexual passion, but rather the stress of an illicit appetite which was not being satisfied. In which case . . . unexpectedly, Julia had to hide a smile. Serafina might look like an Eastern houri and smell like the Garden of Eden, but she had not been married to the man for nearly thirteen years. Julia had cards to play that Serafina knew nothing about, and she doubted very much whether Nicholas would hold out against a return to the marriage bed if she showed him that he would be welcome once more.

'I went to see Serafina this afternoon,' she said, by way of an opening gambit.

'Yes, I know. She told me,' Nicholas said, surprising Julia by his openness.

'You had to call there, too?'

'She's got her money affairs into a ridiculous tangle. I've been trying to sort it out for her.'

With an heroic effort, Julia bit back a remark about the benefit of having a wife who could be trusted with money. Instead she went on with all the casualness in the world, 'I took the girls into Kensington Gardens. I worry about those children. They seem so pasty-faced compared with our scamps.'

'Serafina told me that, too. It was kind of you.'

'They were no trouble. Serafina herself I thought in radiant looks, but then she always is.'

Nicholas agreed, in a colourless way that did nothing to betray the turmoil raging inside him. Serafina had made a bad mistake that afternoon. He had gone to see her, appalled and disgusted by the craving that drove him to act in a way that made him a stranger to himself. Serafina was working towards a seduction scene, he knew, and he knew, too, that if she issued an open invitation, he would succumb.

When he had found her stretched out on the sofa in her loose gown of organza and lace and she had held out her hand to him, he had not been able to resist raising it to his lips.

'*Caro Niccolò*,' Serafina murmured, her eyes gleaming behind wickedly lowered eyelids. 'Have you come to tell me that all my tiresome debts have been paid?'

'I've managed to persuade the trustees, but don't do it again, Serafina, because they won't be so helpful a second time.'

Serafina pouted, fully aware that Nicholas was desperate to kiss her. He sensed that she knew what a struggle he had made against the lust she aroused in him, and that the knowledge was exciting to her. It did not make him like her any the better, but then liking had nothing to do with the way he felt about Serafina.

'Your wife has been here this afternoon,' Serafina said, giving the screw an extra turn.

'Julia?' Nicholas straightened up, as uncomfortable as if he expected her to walk in at any moment.

'She has taken the girls for a walk in Kensington Gardens. They will be gone for at least an hour so don't look so worried, *caro mio*.'

'I'm not worried.'

'No? Come, let me kiss you as a reward for your kind efforts with my tiresome trustees.'

Nicholas leaned forward and Serafina wound her arms round his neck. Under the luxuriant folds of her gown her body was soft and unconfined; no corsets and quite probably no underwear. Nicholas fumbled for an opening in all that froth of lace and Serafina laughed softly.

'I think you like me in my tea gown?'

I'd like you still better out of it, Nicholas thought savagely, but a remnant of pride kept him from pleading for unrestricted access to the warm flesh he could sense beneath that seductive garment.

That was when Serafina made her profound mistake.

'Julia did not like it,' she said lazily, pretending not to notice that Nicholas had found a satin bow and was untying it.

113

His hands were stilled, but Serafina did not understand his reaction.

'There she sat – so stiff, so disapproving – and so shabby! Poor Julia, she is hopelessly *démodée*! How I laughed to myself! It was such a joke I could hardly keep my face straight and I longed for you to come so that I could share it with you.'

Nicholas straightened up.

'It doesn't seem funny to me,' he said.

'No? But only consider, Nicholas – it was like a scene from a French play: the stupid, deceived wife, as old-fashioned as a schoolmistress – but she was a schoolmistress, wasn't she? – the beautiful woman her husband desires and, at any moment, the husband himself! If you had come in I would have had to burst out laughing.'

'At me, at Julia or at yourself?'

'At Julia!' Serafina said, opening her eyes very wide. 'It is the deceived one who is ridiculous. And perhaps a little at you, *caro*, because the man who chases what he knows he should not have is also . . .'

'A subject for farce. Thank you, Serafina. I know now how I appear to you.'

'Oh, *caro*, do not be angry! Can I be blamed if I feel a little triumphant? You, who refused to marry me, are now at my feet.'

She kicked with one foot and a black satin slipper flew through the air, revealing a plump bare foot.

'Do I not have pretty feet?'

'Charming. You are in every way a delectable piece of temptation. But, do you know, Serafina, at the moment you have disgusted me to the point where I think I can resist that temptation.'

Serafina sat up, her hair dishevelled and her black gown falling away from her shoulders. Her face was a study in disbelief.

'You are going? No, that is not possible! This afternoon I have made up my mind that I will yield. It is very wicked and exciting and I cannot wait to discover . . .'

'How I compare with my father? Oh, Serafina, you should have kept my mind away from that aspect of our affair. If I think of Papa when I look at you then I'm too ashamed to touch you. And you really mustn't laugh at my wife.'

114

The memory of Julia's honest eyes flashed into his mind and Nicholas closed his own eyes in sudden pain.

'Julia . . . is good,' he said with difficulty. 'She may not dress as well as you and, yes, we have had differences, but Julia is the very essence of honesty. How can I go home and face her, knowing that you and I . . .'

He began to pace the room in agitation, while Serafina watched him with sullen, uncomprehending eyes.

'After all, you are very dull,' she said. She swung her legs to the ground and stood up, tying the satin sash at her waist with vicious force. 'I tell you, Niccolò, that if you do not take me this afternoon then you will never have another chance.'

'So be it.'

'You don't care? You pretend now that you don't want me?'

'I daresay I'll hanker after you once in a while,' Nicholas said evenly. 'The thing is, Serafina, that if you don't want a man to wake up you shouldn't throw a bucket of dirty water in his face.'

With that scene at the back of his mind Nicholas would have preferred not to talk to Julia about Serafina. For one moment he considered telling her the whole thing, but what was there to tell? He had lusted after his father's widow, he had allowed himself to be enticed into caressing her, exchanging kisses, handling her body, but it had gone no farther than that. For one piercing moment he regretted all over again that he had not thrown himself on Serafina and rid himself of the desperate urge to slake his desire in her willing body.

He came back to the present to realise that Julia was saying something unexpected.

'I owe you an apology,' she said.

'Really?'

'You gave me a well-deserved lecture about unnecessary economy and I reacted by becoming even more thrifty. It was foolish of me and I know I owe it to your position to keep up a good appearance.'

'That doesn't sound like my independent Julia.'

'Give me credit for trying to see your point of view. Just wait till you hear what I've done. It was going to see Serafina that brought me to my senses.'

The reference to Serafina was like a jab on an aching tooth and Julia's remark about being brought to her senses was so ironical that Nicholas could have laughed out loud. You and me both, my dear wife!

'She's always so well turned out,' Julia went on, apparently oblivious to her husband's reaction. 'I suddenly saw myself through her eyes and the picture really wasn't attractive.'

'I wouldn't want you to look like Serafina,' Nicholas said, making an effort.

'No, indeed, that's not my style at all. I wonder if she ever means to come out of black? Of course, it's very becoming to her. What I did, my dear, was to go and visit a very expensive dressmaker in Bond Street and I've ordered an afternoon gown, a pelisse and two evening gowns. What do you say to that?'

'I'm . . . I'm too surprised to know what to say.'

'You must admit that when I make amends I do it handsomely,' Julia said.

She was laughing and Nicholas was too taken up with his own emotions to see that her eyes were still anxious.

They passed a difficult evening, not made any easier by the way Julia ignored her husband's sombre mood. She chatted about the children, and drew a smile from Nicholas with Melissa's latest delightful remark; she asked about the business and Nicholas roused himself to tell her about a completely unexpected Meissen dinner service which had come to light and was to be sold shortly; above all, she urged him to agree to spend a full month with her and the children in the cottage they were renting in Cornwall for the summer holidays.

'A month! I don't know about that.'

'You need the rest,' Julia said quietly. 'You've had a hard time since your father died.'

'It's been difficult,' Nicholas admitted. 'I've had to fight for the changes I thought necessary and with so many new people on the staff I haven't been able to delegate as much as I would have liked.'

'No man can know everything – the times I've heard you say that! You're employing experts, let them make their own mistakes.'

'It may be my clients who pay if mistakes are made. That's bad for the reputation of the company. All the same, you're right. I've been trying to spread my scanty knowledge over too many fields. In future I mean to concentrate on the porcelain I love, with a side glance at English silver.'

'And modern pictures,' Julia said with a smile.

'Can I still not reconcile you to the Bonnard I bought? Look again, Julia. I'm sure you'll come to appreciate it.'

So far, so good. At least she had coaxed him away from brooding over his sins and had kept his mind off Serafina for a while. When she got up to go to bed, Julia touched Nicholas on his cheek with the back of her hand as she passed his armchair.

'Don't stay down here too long,' she murmured. 'Come to bed.'

She had undressed by the time Nicholas came in to their bedroom and was sitting in front of her dressing-table wearing a white broderie anglaise wrapper, brushing her hair. As Nicholas moved about the room getting ready for bed he could hear the soft swishing noise as Julia drew the brush rhythmically through her long brown hair.

At last it seemed she was satisfied that she had removed every tangle and it never occurred to Nicholas that the moment when Julia put down her hairbrush was timed exactly to coincide with the untying of the cord of his dressing gown before he got into bed. She took off her wrapper and stood for a moment twisting her hair into a loose plait. Her lawn nightgown was soft from many washings and when Julia stood in front of the lamp on her dressing-table it was almost transparent.

She blew out the lamp and got into bed by her husband's side. She smelt of something fresh and sweet, like appleblossom. She smelt like sanity.

Julia could feel Nicholas beside her, tense as a newly coiled spring, needing her and refusing to acknowledge his need because he was ashamed of the way he had strayed from her. Julia abandoned subtlety, put her arms round him and whispered, 'Darling, I've missed you so much. We've been so silly, refusing love to one another. Make it up to me, darling. Love me . . .'

From the way Nicholas clutched her to him and the convulsive shudder that ran through his body Julia knew that she had got past the first barrier. For one moment she thought that he was going to tell her about his folly, but she stopped his mouth with a kiss. It was better not spoken about; it was better washed away into oblivion by the tide of their renewed passion.

In their early days they had been daring and inventive lovers. Then, Nicholas had led and Julia had followed, willing to do anything that would give him pleasure, feeding with exquisite sensuousness on their mutual joy. With the passing years they had fallen into less exciting habits, but now Julia set herself to revive something of the freshness of their honeymoon days. She refused to be satisfied and instead of turning away with a quiet kiss and a murmured, 'Good night, dear', after Nicholas had taken her she assaulted him with fresh kisses and caresses, her hands moving over his body, her own body writhing against him until Nicholas turned to her a second time, throbbing with an ardour he had only thought to experience with a different woman.

When he finally withdrew Nicholas was beyond thinking coherently. He was only aware of astonishment and physical ease, and a fatigue that felt like drowning. He moved his lips against the hollow at the base of Julia's throat with a sound that was half a laugh and half a groan and then he fell into a sleep so profound that Julia had difficulty in moving him so that she, too, could settle.

She smiled slightly as she drifted away to sleep, but somewhere deep inside her there was a strange sadness. She had got him back and he was still and for ever her dear husband, but Julia did not altogether admire the tactics she had used. Oh yes, dear Serafina, she thought to herself, listening to Nicholas's quiet breathing, we are sisters under the skin; I know my trade, too. But there is one difference between us: I love him, I really love him – faults and all.

Chapter Ten

'You won't be here for my birthday,' Anna said.

Her mother opened her eyes very wide. '*Cara*, you will be fifteen! Does it matter so very much that your mama will not be with you? You are no longer a child.'

It did matter to Anna, but she could see that there was nothing to be gained by arguing. Mama had made up her mind to go away and nothing would stop her.

She watched as her mother placed a hat on her piled-up mass of hair and skewered it into place with a pearl-headed hatpin. Just as Julia had anticipated four years earlier, Serafina had never given up wearing black, but with her travelling costume she wore a white silk blouse, lavishly trimmed with lace, and and her large hat was decorated with white roses and osprey feathers. It was all very dashing and smart, but Anna had a noticing eye and she did not think her mother looked well.

Something was wrong. Anna could not put her finger on it, but she was quite sure her mother was not only unwell but terribly upset about something and trying to hide it, which was so unlike her usual way of spilling out everything that concerned her that Anna was convinced it must be serious.

'Where can we write to you?' she persisted.

Again her mother's eyes flickered in the way that told Anna she was avoiding telling the truth.

'I shall be travelling about and can give you no address.'

'But, Mama, you're going to be gone three months!'

'Or possibly four. It depends on how amusing I find it.'

'But anything could happen.'

'Nothing will happen.' Sefafina gave a little shiver and added, 'I will be perfectly all right.'

'I wasn't thinking about you,' Anna retorted. 'What about us?'

'Don't be pert, Anna. You have Miss Henderson and, if there is an emergency . . .' She hesitated and then she said, 'You can ask Aunt Julia to help.'

'We hardly ever see Aunt Julia.'

'No, but Julia has a good heart. I see little of her because we move in different circles.'

Anna knew all about her mama's aristocratic friends. Indeed, one of the things that she did not understand was why Serafina had quarrelled with Lord Kenrick, who had been such a constant caller at the house. She had heard raised voices in the drawing room and had seen her mother in tears. And yet it was Lord Kenrick who was to call for her mother and take her away to a destination Mama was unable to name.

The carriage arrived and Serafina went down to the hall, where her trunk was waiting to be taken away. Only one trunk, Anna noted; Mama was travelling light.

Violetta was called and came running down from the school-room to kiss Mama goodbye. Violetta was twelve and young for her age; all she could think about was that Mama should bring them back presents from her holiday.

Serafina hugged and kissed her younger daughter and pre-tended not to notice when Anna proffered a cool cheek for her parting kiss. Another moment and she was gone and, as always, the house seemed empty without her.

Miss Henderson, their governess, came down to collect her charges and persuade them back to the schoolroom.

'You haven't finished your Italian translation, Anna,' she pointed out. 'Considering your ancestry I would expect you to make better progress with the language. You must learn to apply yourself, as I'm forever telling you.'

'Will Mama go to Italy?' Violetta enquired.

'I don't know where she's going,' Anna said.

Julia, happily restored to her place in Nicholas's life and work-ing, a little against the grain, to keep abreast of the round of entertaining he thought necessary, had found that once she was prepared to make the effort there were many outlets for any spare energy she might have. She discovered that Hope & Company were employing more female staff than they had in the past and Julia was quick to see office work as a useful alternative to teaching or shopwork for girls of reasonable education. She took an interest in their welfare and spoke her mind about such diverse shortcomings as poor light at desks, to inadequate lavatories.

She saw little of Serafina. They were not strangers and they exchanged formal greetings from time to time, even met at dinners or theatre parties, but Julia rarely did more than leave her card at Rutland Gate and Serafina was equally casual about calling on Julia.

The boys were growing up. At sixteen and fourteen both Simeon and Martin seemed to have no doubts that they wanted to join Nicholas in his business and, although he tried to keep it hidden, Nicholas was bursting with pride in them.

As for Melissa, she was the pet of all the family, and Julia insisted that she was getting spoilt, but she said it indulgently because Melissa had something of the same sweet nature of her older brother, Simeon, and it seemed that nothing could mar her.

'They're your children, Simeon and Melissa,' Nicholas told Julia. 'Martin is more like me, poor chap.'

'They're themselves and it's a constant mystery to me how different children of the same family can be,' Julia said.

She was so taken up with her own family that she rarely thought about Serafina's two daughters, but when she did spare them a thought Julia was troubled. They were neglected, she was sure of it; brought up by servants, spoiled when it suited Serafina and discarded when she was tired of them. Julia had it in her mind that she would ask them to Simeon's sixteenth birthday party. It was to be something rather more than a children's party and Julia thought that Anna, in particular, would appreciate the chance to meet other boys and girls of her own age.

She sent the invitation and was surprised to receive a reply from Anna.

'*Mama is away,*' Anna wrote in her careful, immature handwriting. '*But I am sure she would be pleased for us to come to Simeon's party. Thank you for asking us.*'

Julia was even more surprised when Anna and Violetta arrived at the party unescorted even by their governess.

'Miss Henderson has had an accident,' Anna explained.

'She's broken her leg and can't walk, and we aren't having any lessons,' Violetta added.

'Poor Miss Henderson! Have you let your mother know?'

'No. Mama is travelling . . . we don't have any address for her,' Anna stammered.

Trouble, Julia thought. Another moment and the child will be in tears. Oh, Serafina, what a nuisance you are!

'How very difficult for you,' she said. Her hand clasped Anna's in a warm and comforting hold. 'We can't talk now, but I'll come and see you tomorrow morning.'

She glanced over her shoulder and saw Simeon, and her heart melted with love for her tall and handsome son. He could be trusted to look after this unhappy girl.

'Simeon, dear, take your cousins into the drawing room,' she said.

'We've got a present for you,' Violetta said. 'It's a book. Anna said you'd like it, but I think it's dull – all about bits of old china.'

'Anna was right,' Simeon said, unwrapping what Julia was startled to see was an exceedingly expensive book.

'I charged it to Mama's account at Harrods,' Anna said, apparently guessing Julia's thoughts.

She was so mature in some ways and so unsure of herself in others. Fifteen . . . a difficult age for a girl, neither a child nor an adult. An age when a girl needed the guidance of her mother, which Anna palpably lacked.

Julia was relieved to see that the child obviously enjoyed herself that evening. She was not particularly pretty; her features were too marked, her black eyebrows were too heavy and, for all her fifteen years, her figure was not well developed. Indeed, she was too thin for Julia's liking, with bony wrists and angular elbows, and legs that would have been better served by rather longer skirts. Above all, Julia would have liked to have seen Anna without the air of anxiety and strain that showed on her young face.

The drawing room had been cleared of furniture and turned into a miniature ballroom for dancing and games. Violetta was romping away with the younger guests in no time. Anna hung back, but when Simeon led her into a country dance she performed well, even managing to look quite graceful. Serafina, of course, could be trusted to see that her daughters were well educated in all the social graces.

By the end of the evening Julia was pleased to see both girls

looking flushed, happy and excited. Violetta, indeed, was bois-
terous and Anna said apologetically to Julia, 'She's not used to
parties. I think perhaps we should go home now, Aunt Julia.'

'Uncle Nicholas will go with you. No, dear, I will *not* allow you
to go alone, even though you had the forethought to order Mama's
carriage to call for you.'

'We've had a lovely time.' For a moment the shadow was back
on Anna's face. 'You said you would come and see us . . .'

'Tomorrow morning at about eleven o'clock.' Julia leaned
forward and kissed Anna's cheek. 'Stop worrying, child. Everything is going to be all right.'

To Julia's expert eye it was obvious as soon as she stepped inside
the Rutland Gate house that the mistress was away. It was not that
there was anything wrong exactly, just a slight air of neglect, of
corners having been skimped and servants grown careless from
lack of supervision.

She was particularly surprised to see one of the maids about to
ascend the staircase carrying a tray set out with a glass, a soda
syphon and a decanter of what looked like whisky.

There was no need for Julia to do more than look at it with her
eyebrows raised for the maid to hurry into an explanation.

'It's for Miss Henderson, madam. She says it helps her leg, and
with her being in charge while Mrs Speranza's away of course I
couldn't refuse her.'

Julia nodded, not committing herself either to condoning or
condemning the governess's order. The maid scurried up the
stairs, while Julia was conducted to the schoolroom, where she
was touched to find Anna helping her young sister with her
arithmetic lesson.

'Tell me, Anna,' she said. 'Is Miss Henderson in the habit of
drinking whisky?'

'Well, she does always have some at night out of her own
bottle,' Anna said. 'But since Mama has been away she's been
asking for it from downstairs. Mama always keeps some spirits for
gentlemen.'

'I think that's why she fell downstairs and broke her leg,'
Violetta said. She giggled. 'I think old Hendy was tipsy.'

'Carry on with your lessons,' Julia said. 'You're doing very

123

well. What nice, neat figures. Anna, show me Miss Henderson's room.'

The governess was out of her bed and partly dressed, sitting in an armchair with her leg in a plaster cast propped up on a footstool. She was reading a novel and the tray of whisky was placed conveniently to hand on a small table by her side. From her look of shock when Julia entered the room after a firm tap on the door, it seemed that she had not been aware of her visit; Julia had a shrewd suspicion that the maid had deliberately not mentioned it because she wanted the governess to be caught out.

'I was sorry to hear of your accident,' Julia said punctiliously. 'I hope the fracture is mending?'

'It aches a great deal.' Miss Henderson made a vague gesture towards the decanter, as if excusing its presence.

'I would have thought that it was possible for you to sit in the schoolroom to supervise the girls. It would occupy your mind, if nothing else.'

'I shall resh . . . resume my duties as soon as I am well enough.'

'That may not be necessary. I'm thinking of suggesting a different plan. Tell me, Miss Henderson, do you know how long Mrs Speranza means to be away?'

'She said three, possibly four months.'

'And she's been gone. . . ?'

'Six weeks.'

'You have no address for her?'

'None at all. She said she would be touring around.'

'In this country?'

Miss Henderson shrugged. 'I can't say. Mrs Speranza didn't see fit to confide in me.'

'I'm reluctant to question the servants,' Julia said, hoping that the subtle hint that she did not consider Miss Henderson to be a servant might encourage the governess to be more forthcoming.

All she got was a sniff and the remark, 'You'll get nothing from them but gossip of a most unbecoming kind. I wouldn't demean myself by listening to them, particularly to Maude – she's Mrs Speranza's maid, you know. If you ask me she's peeved at being left behind.'

Serafina had gone away without her maid. Julia was so taken aback that she almost exclaimed out loud, 'How on earth will she manage?' She stopped herself, suddenly recalling that the Serafina who had become such a fine lady had once been a poverty-stricken girl who knew very well how to look after herself – and no doubt would be capable of it again if she were driven to it.

'I can see I shall have to talk to Maude,' Julia said, getting up to go. 'I've decided to take Anna and Violetta to stay with me until their mother returns. Maude can pack for them. And before I leave, Miss Henderson, I have to tell you that I do not at all approve of a governess who drinks whisky in the middle of the morning – or, indeed, at all – particularly her employer's whisky. In future, if you feel the need of spirits you will buy your own, but in my opinion you will do far better to take an aspirin if your leg aches.'

She shut the door behind her with a decided snap as she left the room. Julia could feel her temper rising and she had already begun to rehearse some of the things she would like to say to Serafina.

'Send Maude to me,' she asked the maid who came in response to her vigorous ring on the bell. 'And before I go, kindly remove the whisky decanter from Miss Henderson's room. Place it in the sideboard cupboard, lock the door and give me the key. I presume there is wine in the cellar?'

'Yes, madam.'

'None of it is to be consumed in Mrs Speranza's absence. Please inform Cook and anyone else who needs to know.'

Serafina's maid proved to be a sulky-looking young woman who accepted Julia's request for assistance in packing for Anna and Violetta with a martyred air that made Julia's fingers itch.

'You need pack very little for Miss Anna,' Julia said. 'She seems to have shot up suddenly and I've already noticed that her skirts are too short. I like young people to remain free as long as possible, but I think an inch or two more would be becoming for Anna. Since you have no other duties, you can occupy yourself in letting down the hems of the gowns I shall select. As soon as they're done you can send them round to my house.'

Maude accepted this order in silence, but she worked quickly and efficiently in the girls' bedroom, selecting and folding clothes under Julia's direction.

'Why didn't Mrs Speranza take you with her?' Julia asked.

'I'm sure I couldn't say, madam.'

Julia stifled a sigh. The answer had come so pat that it was obvious Maude had been expecting it.

'I think you must have some idea,' she said. 'You've been with Mrs Speranza for several years and I'm sure she relied on you a great deal. Is she visiting friends who can provide a maid?'

'If she is, I'm sure I don't know who they can be. Everyone who is anyone is in London.'

That was true, and one of the things Julia found most mysterious about Serafina's disappearance. The Season was in full swing and all the functions to which Serafina might have expected to be invited were taking place without her.

'What sort of clothes did you pack for her?' Julia asked.

'Well, of course, all madam's clothes are stylish, but she wanted to take only last season's things with her. She said she wasn't going to waste her new gowns and it would spoil them to wear them travelling.'

Julia tried to visualise Serafina economising by wearing out her old clothes on a journey, and failed.

'Was Mrs Speranza quite well?' she asked in desperation.

'No, madam, far from well.'

Again Julia tried to imagine Serafina going away quietly for medical treatment, but it would be wholly out of character. If she were suffering the whole of London would know it and be expected to rally round with flowers and sympathy.

'In what way unwell?' she probed.

She could see that they had arrived at the crux of the matter and that Maude was savouring the moment. She knew something, that was certain, and she was waiting for Julia to beg her to speak. Julia kept silent.

'A confidential lady's maid is in a very delicate position,' Maude said virtuously. 'If my lady thought I'd talked about her behind her back . . . well, madam, I'd not only lose my position with her, but there'd be no other opening for me either, not at the same level.'

'My only concern is for Mrs Speranza's well-being,' Julia said wearily. 'Whatever you tell me is entirely between the two of us, you have my word for that.'

'I'm not sure . . .' Maude said, dragging it out.

'Perhaps you'd rather talk to my husband?'

That did the trick.

'Oh, no, madam! I couldn't face a gentleman and talk about such things.'

'In what way was Mrs Speranza unwell?' Julia repeated.

'It was the morning sickness that troubled her most, madam.'

Maude observed with satisfaction that Mrs Hope not only changed colour, she had to sit down on Miss Violetta's bed to recover from the shock she had been given.

All the same, Julia spoke levelly. 'You're saying Mrs Speranza is pregnant.'

'I wouldn't dream of saying such a thing, madam. All I'm saying is that she couldn't fancy her breakfast and I had to let out all her gowns round the waist.'

'You are right to be cautious in speaking about this matter. I hope you've been equally discreet with other people.'

With a sinking heart Julia remembered Miss Henderson's remark about unbecoming gossip. Of course Maude had talked to the other servants and the whole household was agog with the scandal. There was nothing she could do except carry it off with a high hand.

'Mrs Speranza has always been subject to bilious attacks,' she improvised swiftly. 'I'm sure her illness was no more than a temporary inconvenience. She's very wise to take a rest from the fatigue of London. We'll say no more about it and you, if you please, will keep your quite unfounded suspicions to yourself. Finish packing that trunk while I go and collect Anna and Violetta.'

Serafina was pregnant. Not for one moment did Julia doubt her maid's diagnosis. In such an intimate relationship Maude would have been aware whether or not her employer was menstruating, but that was not something Julia wanted to hear about. She would have to tell Nicholas, but Serafina appeared to have covered her tracks so well that he would probably agree with Julia that there was nothing they could do until Serafina chose to reappear.

What was to happen to the child? Come to that, who was the father?

Nicholas was able to supply the answer to that question.

'It is almost certainly Lord Kenrick,' he said that evening. 'Serafina's been his mistress for years.'

'I'd heard hints,' Julia admitted. 'But Serafina has moved so far

127

away from our circle of friends that I wasn't sure whether I'd understood what was being suggested.'

'I could approach him – ask him whether he knows where Serafina is,' Nicholas said doubtfully.

'Better not. Presumably, if he is the father then he is helping Serafina. If it weren't for the girls I'd wash my hands of the whole affair. You do think I did the right thing in bringing them to us, don't you, Nicholas?'

'Absolutely. It makes my hair stand on end to think of Papa's daughters left alone in a house with just servants and a drunken governess to look after them.'

'They can join Melissa and I'll teach them, too.'

'Won't it be too much for you?'

'I'll enjoy it. You know I was a dedicated schoolmistress before you swept me off my feet.' She lifted a smiling face and Nicholas bent to kiss her.

'The best thing I ever did in my life,' he said, and the thought at the back of his mind was that if he had not torn himself away from Serafina's potent attraction in time, then he himself might have been in the middle of this sticky mess.

The girls settled in with surprisingly little difficulty. Melissa was enchanted to have her two 'cousins' in the nursery, and the two girls were so used to obeying orders that they were no trouble at all. In fact, to Julia's way of thinking they were far too docile, but then she was accustomed to her two harum-scarum boys, who thundered up the stairs and burst into the schoolroom, full of their day's doings at school, usually dirty, usually demanding help with their homework and always hungry. Simeon, however, had quietened down in recent months and showed signs of becoming more civilised, a state Julia was doing her best to foster.

'Simeon has started having dinner with us downstairs when we don't have company and I think it would be nice if you, Anna, joined us. Change into that pretty white dress with the broderie anglaise frills. I'll send Jane along to hook you up.'

The little innovation was a success. Anna was very much on her best behaviour, but she responded when Nicholas tried to draw her out and Julia could see that he was both touched and amused by her seriousness.

128

'I don't suppose you've ever been to an auction, have you, Anna?' Simeon asked. 'I say, Father, have you got anything good coming along? Anna and I could come and swell the crowd.'

'During school hours?'

'Well . . . if I happened to have a free period or if you wrote to the Head and asked for me to be let off,' Simeon suggested hopefully.

'I think not, though I give you full marks for a good try.'

'I am very interested, Uncle Nicholas,' Anna said. 'Simeon is wrong in thinking I've never attended an auction. Papa took me to watch several times, but not Violetta because she was still too small.'

Nicholas had a sudden, vivid picture in his mind of his father leading his daughter, dark-eyed and serious, into his auction rooms. Nicholas had no doubt that Vittorio had loved his little girls and had taken pleasure in interesting Anna in his work, but Nicholas had a conviction that it was because he missed his sons, and he was overwhelmed by regret for all the wasted years.

He roused himself to say to Simeon, 'I can't lay on an auction at a time to suit your timetable, my boy, but there'll be some fine Chinese porcelain set out for viewing next week and you and Anna are welcome to come along to see that.'

Simeon's eyes sparkled. 'May I handle it?'

'Under supervision. There's no other way to get the feel of what's right.'

Nicholas arranged for the elderly expert on Chinese ceramics to be on hand for the visit.

'Indulge the boy,' he said. 'He seems to be moving towards an interest in the Orient, which could be useful in a few years' time.'

Mr Goodwin understood perfectly: Simeon was to be encouraged to serve an apprenticeship under him in the hope that he would be ready to take over when Mr Goodwin retired.

All the staff knew Simeon and, to a lesser extent, Martin, and Mr Goodwin remembered Anna from one of her earlier visits, which made her feel happy and at ease.

She knew nothing about Chinese ceramics, but listened with awe as Mr Goodwin talked to Simeon about 'celadon' and 'crackle glaze' and the marks of the various dynasties.

'Just feel this, Anna,' Simeon said, handing her a deep red

bowl. 'Run your fingers over the inside. It's like orange peel, isn't it? When you turn it to the light you can see the slight irregularities on the surface.'

'Fifteenth century, Xuande period,' Mr Goodwin informed her. 'A copper glaze covered by a colourless glaze.'

'It's beautiful,' Anna said. 'And I like the blue bowl, too.'

'Cobalt glaze, of the Jiajin period, slightly later – sixteenth century.'

'If you had the money to buy one piece, which would it be?' Simeon asked Anna, making a conscious effort to keep her from feeling bored by Mr Goodwin's expert talk.

'Oh, there's so much . . . I think that grey-green long-necked vase or jar or whatever it is.'

'You have a discerning eye,' Mr Goodwin said, slightly surprised by her choice. 'A very precious item; tenth century, *yue* ware with incised petal decoration. What makes you like that vase, Miss Anna?'

'The shape and the way the decoration fits it; the colour – it's not strong, but it sort of glows. And I love the lid like a leaf with a bird sitting on it.'

'I thought you would choose something later and brighter. What do you think of this seventeenth-century vase?'

'The colour is wonderful, that deep, deep blue, and the way it contrasts with the leaping fish, but I still prefer my little green vase.'

She wandered away when Mr Goodwin and Simeon became technical once more, amazed by her freedom to walk through the rooms unattended. Simeon eventually discovered her standing enthralled in front of a group of drawings.

'Look, Simeon, just look. Aren't they splendid?'

'So they should be,' Simeon said. 'I didn't know Father had anything as good as this on offer. A Tiepolo, a Rubens, a Rembrandt . . .'

'If I were really rich I'd buy that drawing of the girl kneeling on the ground with her skirt all spread round her.'

'The Flemish saint? There's no attribution, so you might get it at a reasonable price. Do you want to bid for it?'

Anna grimaced. 'I have to ask Miss Henderson if I want any money and as we're no longer living with her I don't get any.

Anyway, the drawing may not be signed, but it's obviously good and far beyond my reach.'

'We have to go to Father's office now and he'll take us home in the carriage. It's been a good afternoon, hasn't it?'

'Splendid.'

Looking at their glowing faces, Nicholas felt well rewarded for the small effort of arranging their visit.

'You enjoyed it?' he asked.

'Very much,' Simeon told him. 'In fact, I feel quite inspired. You may be looking at your future Chinese expert.'

'That would be most satisfactory. There's plenty of time, but if you're serious we'll talk later about you doing Oriental Studies at University.'

'And Anna is going to be our expert on Old Master drawings.'

'Really? Do you prefer drawings to paintings, Anna?'

'I like the . . . the bare bones,' Anna said.

'That's why you picked out that *yue* vase,' Simeon smiled.

'I know the piece you mean,' Nicholas said. 'I must confess I prefer the later, more colourful work. I lack your refined taste, Anna.'

Without quite knowing how she had done it, Anna seemed to have earned the respect of the two men whose approval she most wanted. She was reduced to pink-faced confusion, but inside she was so pleased she felt she was one great smile all over.

'Could I really work for you one day, Uncle Nicholas?' she asked him on the way home.

'We don't usually employ ladies, except in the office, but as you're one of the family I might make an exception,' Nicholas said easily, not dreaming that to Anna that was a promise engraved on steel.

Simeon was full of a plan he had formed in his head that afternoon, but he managed to keep it to himself until he could speak to his mother alone.

'Mother, do you know that Anna isn't actually fifteen until next week?' he asked. 'I mean, she'll be having her birthday while she's staying with us. Don't you think we ought to do something about it?'

'Not another party, so soon after your own,' Julia said firmly. 'We'll have a small celebration just among ourselves.'

'But you'll get her a present?'

'Yes, of course.'

'If we made it from all of us could it be something rather expensive?'

'Darling Simeon, how I do distrust you when you look at me with that beguiling smile! How expensive?'

'I was thinking of the Flemish drawing Anna liked so much,' Simeon admitted. 'It'll be coming up for auction in a couple of days' time.'

'Oh, darling, that's a bit ambitious.'

'If it was her only present?' Simeon coaxed.

'I'll talk to Father.'

'Do you think she'll get anything from Aunt Serafina?'

Julia was at a loss. On the face of it, both her sons had accepted the visit from Anna and Violetta without question, but she realised now that Simeon, at least, was curious.

'I don't know,' she said at last. 'Aunt Serafina is travelling and might be in a place where there's no postal collection.'

'I wouldn't think Aunt Serafina would go anywhere so uncivilised,' Simeon commented.

'One never knows. Don't talk to Anna about it, please. I don't want her upset by the idea that her mother might forget her birthday.'

That was the thought that influenced Julia when she spoke to Nicholas about the Flemish drawing.

'If I can get it for under twenty pounds, the child shall have it,' Nicholas said. 'Perhaps I'll touch Serafina for a contribution when she returns.'

Two days later he came home with a small parcel and handed it to Julia.

'Sixteen guineas,' he said laconically. 'Underpriced, in my opinion, so we can look on it as an investment for Anna's future.'

To him the sum was trifling and he was more than repaid by the sight of Anna's face when she unwrapped her birthday present.

'I'll keep it all my life,' she said breathlessly. 'Always, always.'

'It was Simeon's idea,' Nicholas said carelessly, and for some reason this was something Julia would rather Anna had not known.

She realised why when she saw the look of blind adoration Anna turned on Simeon. Julia was startled by her radiance and by the intensity of her feeling.

Poor little girl, she thought. She's much too young for such emotions. Simeon has no such idea in his head, and it's just as well. Immature young love is far too unsettling. How am I going to handle it? No more outings on their own, even though Simeon can be trusted. If Anna betrays her feelings he'll be embarrassed and then she'll be hurt. That mustn't happen, not when the poor child is just beginning to find her balance. In a year or two's time Anna will laugh at her calf love for her cousin . . .

But they were *not* cousins. With a sick jolt Julia realised how dangerous any attachment between Anna and Simeon could be. It must be stamped on, far more vigorously than she had just been thinking. She must guard Anna and even more, since he was her son and the light of her life, she must keep Simeon from tumbling into an entanglement that might blight his life.

She took the first step the next day when she went into Anna's room to see where she had hung the precious picture.

'I'm so pleased Simeon put us in the way of giving you something you really wanted,' she said.

'It was wonderful of him,' Anna said, and once again her fervour disturbed Julia.

'He's a good boy,' she said indulgently. 'How absurd it is that he should be your nephew.'

She knew from the girl's frozen stillness that the realisation that had hit her the day before had just struck home to Anna, too.

'I'm glad you've become such good friends,' Julia went on, filling in the silence. 'We mustn't drift apart again when Mama comes home.'

'No, that would be a pity,' Anna said mechanically.

Something to be said for a rigorous schooling, Julia thought. Anna has learnt how to conceal her feelings. She slipped an arm round the girl's rigid shoulders and gave her a little hug. To say anything would be to bring out into the open something that was better buried and forgotten. Poor Anna. But she would get over it. She would have to.

It was another six weeks before Serafina reappeared. She swept

133

into Julia's drawing room and demanded, 'Why have you kidnapped my children?'

'Because they were living in most unsuitable circumstances. Please sit down, Serafina. Are you quite well?'

'Of course I am well. Why should I not be well?' She looked pale and thin and there were dark circles under her eyes, but Julia refrained from making any comment.

'We were extremely worried about you. Was it necessary to do such a complete disappearing act?'

'I was travelling.'

'Were you?' Julia touched the bell by the fireplace. 'We'll have some tea. The girls, you'll be pleased to hear, are well and happy.'

'Of course they are. Why should they not be? I left them in the care of their governess. How could I know she would tumble down the stairs and break her leg?'

'You might perhaps have known that she drank,' Julia said evenly. 'And if you had left any sort of address you could have been consulted before I brought Anna and Violetta here.'

Julia waited until the tea had been brought and she had poured out a cup for her visitor.

'Are you keeping Miss Henderson on?' she asked.

'If what you say is true I shall have to dismiss her.'

'The girls have been doing lessons with me.'

'So you are still a schoolmistress! How you must have enjoyed yourself. Have you turned them against me?'

'Of course not!' Julia was really shocked.

'Everyone else is against me,' Serafina complained. 'Even my maid has given notice.'

'Perhaps that's just as well,' Julia said.

Serafina's eyes narrowed. 'It is as I suspected. She has talked to you. She has said horrid things about me. *Mamma mia*, these servants! There is no loyalty, no respect. What did she say?'

'Nothing I would care to repeat.'

'She is trying to blackmail me, but I will give her nothing, nothing!'

'Has she grounds for blackmail?' Julia asked.

'You are pretending you know nothing, but you are being a hypocrite.'

Serafina burst into noisy tears, sinking down on the sofa and burying her head in a cushion. Julia went and rescued her fine china teacup and then she sat down on the sofa and took one of Serafina's hands in hers.

'If you want to tell me then you can,' she said. 'It will go no further.'

'You will tell Nicholas and he will despise me. Oh, Julia, Julia, I am so unhappy!'

With some disbelief Julia realised that there was real suffering behind Serafina's cry.

'My dear, I'm sorry, I really am,' she said. 'Was there . . . was there a baby?'

'Yes, yes! How could I know I would want him? My little boy, my little son. I have given him up and now he is with strangers and never, never will he know I am his mama.'

'He's been adopted?'

'Fostered only. It is not the same thing. Frederick said it was best. He arranged it. I hate him.'

'Lord Kenrick is the child's father?'

'Of course. Never have I had more than one lover – not together, you understand. Frederick and I, we were a couple. It was accepted; we were asked everywhere together.'

Julia tried to imagine a situation so far outside her own experience and failed.

'He was so beautiful,' Serafina mourned. 'A perfect little man. If only I could have given Vittorio such a son!'

She sat up and cast a spiteful glance at Julia. 'Nicholas would not then have had the chance to take away my company.'

'He paid you a fair price,' Julia pointed out.

'Perhaps. But he is making much, much profit and I have only what my stupid trustees choose to give me.'

'Nicholas works very hard. Without him I doubt whether the company would be in such good heart.'

'Perhaps. Vittorio always said that his son Nicholas was ambitious and I see now that it was true. He was in love with me once. Did you know that?'

'I know that you fascinated him for a time,' Julia said evenly. 'Don't try it again, Serafina. Nicholas has been inoculated and he's immune to you now.'

'That is what you think. But it is true that I am old and worn and

135

I think Frederick means to discard me. What am I to do? Oh, my baby, my baby!'

'Claim the child back, acknowledge him and bring him up as your son.'

'You are a fool!' Serafina stood up in a fierce swirl of silken draperies. 'How could I do such a thing? It would ruin me. It would spoil the girls' chances of a good marriage. No, he must stay where he is and I will never, never see him again.'

'Calm yourself. Sit down and let me give you some more tea. It seems that there is nothing to be done except to accept the situation.'

'You are so cool, so English. Would you not mourn if one of your sons was taken from you?'

'It would break my heart.'

'You see? Even you. My heart is broken, but I must pretend that it is not.'

Julia could think of nothing more to say. She felt inadequate and was cross with herself for not having anticipated this scene. Serafina needed comfort and it seemed that she had none to give her, even though her heart really did ache over the other woman's predicament.

'Have you seen your priest?' she asked hesitantly.

'Not yet. I must confess, of course, and do penance. Perhaps then I shall find some peace of mind. Julia, will you keep the girls with you until tomorrow? I am not equal to having them with me today.'

'Of course. Fortunately, Nicholas has taken all the children down the river to Greenwich for the day.'

'How brave of him. Nicholas the family man. One would hardly expect it of him.'

'Nicholas is devoted to his family – *all* his family,' Julia said. 'I shall tell Anna and Violetta that you are back and will be expecting them home tomorrow.'

'Do you think Anna suspects?'

'She knows there's something wrong, but I'm sure she has no idea what it may be.'

Julia thought that was true, though she also believed that Anna might put two and two together one day and come to a correct conclusion. For the time being she was reassured to see when the river party returned that the child was unreservedly relieved to hear that her mother had returned. Not that Anna wanted to leave the house where she had spent such happy weeks, but the news that Serafina was back visibly lifted a load from her shoulders.

Just as Serafina had anticipated, Julia poured the whole story out to Nicholas in bed that night.

'I do feel sorry for her,' she concluded. 'Just imagine it, Nicholas – to bring a baby into the world and not to know how he will be treated, how he will grow up, what sort of man he will become.' She shuddered and Nicholas gathered her close.

'Serafina will forget,' he predicted. 'I don't doubt that her suffering is real for the time being, but she'll put it out of her mind, perhaps begin to pretend it never happened. In a year or two it may give her a passing pang, but no more than that.'

'I hope you're right, for her sake, even though it seems heartless,' Julia said. 'It would haunt me to the end of my days.'

'Of course it would,' Nicholas said. 'But then, you're my lovely, caring Julia.'

The friendship between Simeon and Anna did not flourish once the girls had returned to their own house, mainly because Julia arranged that it should not. It saddened her to snub the child, but she let Anna see that Simeon's schoolwork must come first and that other calls on his time were not welcome.

The gulf between them became even wider when Serafina embarked on another adventure.

It was no more than six months after she had collapsed in tears on Julia's sofa that Serafina sailed into the drawing room one afternoon, looking fit and happy. Just as Nicholas had predicted, she had put the birth and loss of her child behind her.

I have news of the utmost importance,' she announced. 'You and Nicholas are the first to know. I am to be married again.'

For a moment Julia was too surprised to speak.

'But you said . . .' she began.

'That I would always be a widow. That was when I was still grieving for the loss of my dear Vittorio and also I thought it would be agreeable to be free, which it was, but now I feel the need of a man behind me. A permanent man. To no one else would I say this, Julia, but I am *thirty-four*! It is true that I am still beautiful and many men would be my lovers, but it is time I arranged my life. I am to marry Maurice Coppett.'

'I'm afraid I don't know him,' Julia said apologetically.

'Nicholas will know because Mr Coppett is a collector of pictures and many bids have been made for him at DuFrayne & Speranza.'

'Hope & Company,' Julia corrected her.

Serafina waved an impatient hand. 'You know what I mean. Congratulate me, Julia.'

'I do, of course. I'm delighted for you.'

Half a dozen questions chased through Julia's mind. What about Lord Kenrick? Presumably that affair was over. What did Mr Coppett do? What sort of man was he? Julia pulled herself together.

'We must have a little dinner party,' she said. 'Naturally we want to become acquainted with your fiancé. Do you have your diary with you, Serafina?'

They settled on a date ten days later. Serafina, it appeared, was too busy until then.

'Have you thought of a date for the wedding?' Julia asked.

'Quite soon. Certainly before Christmas because we must sail for New York before the New Year.'

'New York?'

'But yes! Did I not tell you? Mr Coppett is American. You would not think, would you, Julia, that there was a great deal of money to be made from flour? Mr Coppett is in flour and he is very, very rich.'

Serafina's tone was reverent and if she had not been so taken aback Julia would have had to suppress a smile.

'Do you mean you will be living in the United States?' she asked incredulously.

'Of course. Mr Coppett has a house in Minneapolis and an apartment in New York.' A faint shadow crossed Serafina's face as she added, 'I am not his first wife, as he is not my first husband. His wife died when their son was born.'

'How sad. Did the child die too?'

'Unfortunately not. He is crippled. It is very tragic. Mr Coppett comes to Europe seeking cures for him, but the doctors can do nothing. He is here in London now and I'm afraid, Julia, that it will be necessary for you to ask him to your dinner. You will have to leave a space at the table for his wheelchair.'

'Yes, of course,' Julia murmured.

She had a vivid recollection of Serafina, only six months before, and the way she had described her own son as 'a perfect little man'. It seemed that Serafina had the same thought because she said in a low voice, 'It is so unfair.'

'You're thinking of your baby?'

'Of course. So perfect . . . so sweet. But I must put him out of my mind.'

'You have no news of him?' Serafina did not answer until Julia pressed her further. 'You've found out where he is, haven't you?'

'It wasn't difficult. I knew the people who took him lived on Lord Kenrick's estate in Wiltshire. I was a guest at Mercia House this summer – he did not drop me immediately, that would not be the way of a gentleman, but I could see that my place had been taken by Lucia Courtney, silly woman – and I found out that a couple living in one of the lodges had taken a new baby into their family. I asked Frederick and he did not deny that was where he had placed the boy.'

'Rather close to home,' Julia remarked.

'To me also it seems strange – and risky. However, if Frederick does not mind if he is found out and as long as he never names me as the mother, then I do not care.'

'The baby is well and happy?'

'It seems so. The people are called Wood and they have given the baby the name of Hugo. That, to me, is a strange name and not what I would have chosen.'

'Does Mr Coppett know?'

'No! And he must never, never learn of my misfortune. It is not at all his idea of me.'

Julia invested in a new gown for the dinner party to welcome Serafina's future husband. She felt she needed the assurance it would give her on what was undoubtedly going to be a difficult evening, made none the easier by the wholly unexpected news that Nicholas's brother, Giorgio, was in London.

'Shall we ask him to come and meet Mr Coppett?' she asked Nicholas. 'Do priests go out to dinner?'

'Certainly they do. Giorgio is a bit of an ascetic, but he'll appreciate one of your good dinners nonetheless.'

In all the years of their married life Julia had met Giorgio just twice, once when he had come to London to christen Anna and a second strained meeting at the time of Vittorio's death. Perhaps she was over-sensitive, but she had thought that he sat in judgement on her and still did not regard her and Nicholas as properly married.

'At least it gives us an even table,' she said. 'But what a badly balanced party – four men and two women. Is there anyone else I should ask?'

'Let's keep it an intimate family occasion. What about Simeon and Anna? Are they too young to be included?'

'Goodness yes. I don't want the complication of steering them away from all the undercurrents that are going to be making themselves felt. A few civilised adults will be as much as I can cope with. You know this Mr Coppett, don't you?'

'I've met him more than once, but only in the way of business. He's wealthy, as Serafina told you. His family may have made their fortune in milling, but he's also got massive interests in iron ore and railways. He's something of a connoisseur of Italian *cinquecento* art.'

'How old is he?'

'Older than Papa was when he married Serafina. In his mid to late fifties, I suppose.'

'And the son?'

'Never set eyes on him. Didn't even know there was a son.'

Giorgio was the first to arrive for the dinner. Nicholas hurried out into the hall to greet him, and Julia had the impression that the brothers embraced. She tried to be glad about it, but was conscious that her own manner was stiff as she rustled forward to greet her brother-in-law. To her surprise Giorgio took her hand in both of his and looked at her kindly. He was very like Nicholas, much more so than she had thought the last time they had met, but painfully thin. Nicholas might call him an ascetic; Julia would have said he was half-starved.

'How fortunate it is that you should be here for this occasion,' she said.

'Yes, indeed! I haven't seen Serafina since Papa's funeral and

140

she was so heavily draped in crêpe that I could hardly make out how she had changed from the young girl I remembered.'

'She became a beautiful woman,' Julia said.

'I'm glad she is to be married again,' Giorgio said quietly, once more surprising Julia, who had expected him to disapprove. 'Tell me, Julia, may I call on you again tomorrow and meet the children?'

'Of course.'

A nightmare vision of Giorgio converting her children to Catholicism and Simeon disappearing in his turn into the priesthood flitted across Julia's mind, to be dismissed in a moment as she looked into Giorgio's face and saw nothing there but quiet friendliness.

As soon as Serafina appeared in the doorway of the drawing room Julia saw that she had at last shed her mourning and glowed like a full-blown rose in wine-red satin.

She was followed by a man who must be, as Nicholas had said, in at least his middle fifties; a heavy, pear-shaped man with a shining bald head. Serafina was certainly not marrying Maurice Coppett for his looks. On the other hand, as Julia swiftly recognised, he had enormous charm. In fact, he was not at all what she would have expected from the first American millionaire she had ever met. Maurice Coppett was quietly spoken, polished and very much at home in Europe.

As for his son, first impressions were quickly dispelled there, too. Bradley Coppett propelled himself forward in his wheelchair and after the first appalled realisation of the extent of his disability, Julia was overcome by the nobility of his head and the sweetness of his smile. It was heartbreaking that a man with his looks should be so pitiably crippled, but Brad ignored his twisted body and forced everyone else to do the same. By the time they arrived at the dinner table it seemed almost a matter of course that one of the guests should wheel himself up to an empty space and adjust the height of his chair so that he could eat in comfort.

How old was he? As she studied him surreptitiously across the table, Julia came to the conclusion that he was younger than he seemed at first. The lines etched round his eyes and mouth were misleading. Pain, she thought; poor, dear boy, how he must have suffered. He was probably no more than in his middle twenties, if that.

She had expected conversation to be difficult, but from the start the meal went with a swing, partly because of Serafina's vivaciousness, partly because Nicholas had discovered a kindred spirit in Maurice Coppett and partly because she found Brad easy to talk to. She was concerned that Giorgio did not play a great part in the conversation, but he seemed to be listening with enjoyment, although Julia would have been pleased to see him eating rather more of the meal she had provided.

The thing Julia and Nicholas were agreed upon when they talked it over afterwards was surprise that Maurice Coppett should have chosen Serafina to be his second wife.

'What does he see in her?' Julia wondered.

'A beautiful vehicle to show off his wealth?' Nicholas suggested.

'I would have thought better of him than that. No . . . I'm afraid he's fallen in love.'

'Is that so bad?'

'Not so long as he doesn't become disillusioned.'

'Serafina was a good wife to my father,' Nicholas said slowly. 'A little skittish perhaps, but there was no scandalous behaviour until after he died. Perhaps she needs the firm hand of an older man. She seems happy enough.'

'Oh, very set up with herself!'

'Don't look so worried, sweetheart,' Nicholas said, kissing her. 'It's not our problem and I must admit that it's something of a relief to think of dear Serafina safely settled on the other side of the Atlantic.'

'I was thinking of the girls,' Julia said. 'It's going to be a great uprooting for them.'

'Hm . . . Coppett will treat them well.' Nicholas yawned and stretched. 'What did you think of Giorgio?'

Something about the extreme casualness of that question made Julia look at her husband sharply.

'I'd be glad to know whether he looks ill because he doesn't eat or whether he doesn't eat because he's ill,' she said.

'Yes . . . I had something of the same thought,' Nicholas admitted. 'I didn't actually get out of him why he was visiting London. Perhaps we're wrong and he's just been fasting for some religious reason.'

He remembered that conversation when Giorgio called on him in his office late the following afternoon.

Giorgio looked round with an amused smile. 'You've made the old place very smart,' he said. 'How it all comes back to me. You've done well, Niccolò.'

'Niccolò . . . no one calls me that any more. Do you blame me for changing my name, Giorgio?'

'Of course not. Papa was an overwhelming personality. You had to strike out on your own – just as I did, in my way.'

'Do you have any regrets?'

'Very occasionally. I envy you your children. May I come home with you when you leave here and take the opportunity of seeing them?'

'Of course. Giorgio . . .'

'I think you've guessed that there's more to my visit to London than a few days off and a chance to see the family. I've just come from consulting a Harley Street doctor – a useless exercise paid for by one of my kind parishioners who wouldn't be denied.'

'Useless?' Nicholas repeated.

'I have cancer of the oesophagus. Swallowing is already difficult and will become more so. My fasting is no longer a matter of choice and my life is moving towards an early end.'

'Dear God!'

'Be careful how you use His name, *fratello mio*; I shall shortly be meeting Him face to face.'

'You can *laugh* about such things?'

'Why not? My Maker and I are on very good terms. I shan't be sorry to leave this weary body behind and go on to something new.'

Faced with his brother's serenity, Nicholas could not voice the horror he felt. He tried to be controlled, but he could feel the muscles of his face twitching and he had to find his handkerchief and wipe his eyes.

'At times like these my Italian side comes to the fore,' he said.

'Your human side. Why should you not weep for the death of your brother? Since we are being emotional then I'd like to seize this chance to tell you that I deeply regret the long years when I wouldn't accept your marriage. On *theological* grounds I suppose I still have to say that you and Julia ought to have been married in the one true Church, but I hope I am a little less dogmatic than I

143

was and I'm prepared to admit that you have a complete and happy marriage. Do you think Julia will forgive me?'

'I'm sure she will. She's realised you're ill. We spoke of it last night. Oh, Giorgio . . . damn it, there must be something we could do?'

'Nothing. I shall go back to my parish tomorrow and carry on with my duties for as long as I can. You'll be told when I give up and if you're able to visit me before the end I'll be glad to see you, but it's not important.'

'I'll come.'

Nicholas used their newly installed telephone to let Julia know Giorgio would be with them that evening, and he managed to get a few minutes alone with her after he had taken Giorgio back to the house. He put his arms round her and held her tight and she could feel his cheek damp against her forehead.

'My dear . . . my dear,' she whispered. 'Cancer?'

'Yes.' Nicholas released her and stepped back. 'You read my thoughts.'

Julia took his handkerchief out of his pocket and dried his wet cheeks.

'No tears,' she said. 'We must make this a happy evening. All the children will eat with us, which will be a treat for them, and they'll keep our spirits up.'

'Giorgio wants to know that you forgive him for saying we weren't properly married.'

'Oh, dear. I *was* hurt at first, but it's years since I gave it a thought. I suppose that amounts to forgiveness, but I'd better word it a little more tactfully.'

She cast a quick look at the clock. 'I've asked Serafina to let Anna and Violetta join us, so that Giorgio can feel he's seen all the younger generation.'

The result was an uproarious evening, since the children were excited by this impromptu party, especially Melissa, who had never been allowed to stay up for dinner in the evening before.

Only Anna was silent and Julia guessed why. As the girls were leaving Anna gave her a pitiful little smile.

'I don't want to go to America, Aunt Julia.'

'I know, dear.' For a moment Julia held the thin young body in her arms.

144

'I was going to work for Uncle Nicholas,' Anna said, with her face muffled against Julia's shoulder.

'Who knows what may happen in a few years' time? Mr Coppett has a wonderful collection of pictures. Study them, learn all you can and when you're old enough perhaps Mama will allow you to come back to Europe.'

'Yes.' Anna lifted her head and Julia was relieved to see that she looked more hopeful. 'I'll work terribly hard. Will you tell Uncle Nicholas? Then he won't be surprised when I write and ask him for a job.'

Julia suppressed her qualms and gave the promise in a firm voice. Time enough to face that one if it ever materialised.

Chapter Eleven

'Don't you recognise me, Aunt Julia?'

'I'm stunned,' Julia said, hurrying across the room with her arms outstretched. 'No, I *didn't* recognise you. If the maid hadn't given me your name I would have thought this smart young lady was a stranger. Dearest Anna, how lovely to see you.'

She put her arms round Anna, but this was not the thin young body she had embraced when Serafina had whisked her daughters away to America. Anna was taller than Julia now and she had developed into a fine young woman. Fashionable, too, in crimson velvet with a modishly narrow skirt and belted tunic jacket. She wore a hat to match, like a crushed velvet flowerpot with a long feather on one side, and she carried a large flat fur muff. But the fine clothes were nothing compared with the change in Anna's appearance. Gone was the colourless waif with anxious eyes. Anna glowed with colour, from the becoming flush along her high cheekbones to the full red mouth.

'Are the rest of the family with you?' Julia asked.

'No, Mama and Violetta have stayed behind. Father . . .'

'You call Mr Coppett Father?'

'Yes, it seemed simpler and he likes it. As I was saying, he's brought Brad over for some treatment and while he's in hospital Father is taking me to visit Italy. Just think, Aunt Julia, Florence and Siena and Rome!'

'Does that mean you'll only be in London for a short visit?'

'It rather depends on the verdict on Brad.'

'Goodness, I've so many questions I hardly know where to start! Your mama is quite well?'

'Very well. Rather cross because she's been putting on weight – I think she means to spend Father's absence being massaged back to shape.'

'And Violetta?'

'You wouldn't know her either. She's become amazingly pretty and she's very popular – with the young men, I mean. In fact, the real reason why Mama doesn't want to leave Minneapolis is that she thinks Violetta is about to become engaged to a most eligible boy.'

'She's very young.'

'Seventeen – not too young. In fact, Mama thinks I'm quite on the shelf. I'm nearly twenty, you know.'

From Anna's laughter it seemed that she did not agree with Serafina or regret her single state. She could hardly lack for suitors, not if the young men of Minneapolis had eyes in their heads.

'Tell me about the boys and Melissa,' she demanded.

'Simeon and Martin are both up at Cambridge. Simeon, of course, will be twenty-one soon and we're planning a big party for him. Perhaps you'll be able to come?'

'Oh, I must! Do you remember asking me to his sixteenth birthday party? What an age ago that seems.'

'And Melissa is attending a day school here in London. She'll be so pleased to see you. She's fascinated by the idea of having cousins in America.'

'Cousins?' Anna said with a smile.

'It's hard to slip out of that old habit. "Cousins" in the sense of "relations", shall we say?'

'I'm very happy to be Melissa's "cousin". Dear Aunt Julia, it is good to see you.'

'And to see you, dear. Tell me, have you been happy in America?'

'Happier than I expected to be,' Anna admitted. 'Girls have far more freedom over there and even Mama's old-fashioned ideas had to give way. I've been doing just what Uncle Nicholas suggested, taking history of art classes and studying Father's collection, and this trip to Italy will round off my studies. He's delighted that I take such an interest.'

In the few days before Anna and Maurice Coppett went off to Rome, they dined with Julia and Nicholas and invited them in their turn to join them for a meal at Brown's Hotel, at which Anna played the hostess with an aplomb far beyond her years. Brad was not present, having been taken into a clinic for observation. Between Anna and her stepfather there appeared to be a tie of genuine affection which Julia was pleased to see.

She was not quite so pleased when she learnt that the day after that dinner Anna had gone to Cambridge to visit Martin and Simeon. There was no reason why the girl should not go to see her 'cousins', especially since all trace of her earlier adoration of Simeon seemed to have disappeared, but there was something about the fact that Anna had sat through an entire evening, talking and laughing with Julia and Nicholas, and had never mentioned her plan – indeed, had not, as far as Julia could recall, spoken of either boy at all – that rankled with Julia. She told herself that the visit had probably been the impulse of the moment, but at the back of her mind she suspected that Anna had thought it all out carefully, demonstrating the same cool competence she displayed over organising the trip to Italy for herself and Mr Coppett.

Julia waited with some impatience to hear what the boys had thought of the unchaperoned visit. Neither of them was a good correspondent, but Simeon did say briefly in his next scrawled note, *'We had a visit from Anna, as she probably told you. What a surprise.'*

Martin, on the other hand, was more forthcoming:

Dear Ma,

Cousin Anna descended on us and created a stir. She flashed across the Cambridge sky like a meteor, undergraduates fainted in droves and you will shortly hear of despairing drownings in the Backs. One maniac was heard to remark that she was like the secret heart of a dark red rose – I've struck him off my visiting list.

Old Sim raises his eyebrows and looks superior, as befits a third-year man, but I think he was impressed. How did our family ever manage to produce anything so gorgeous and glamorous and altogether exotic?

Darling Ma, is Father feeling rich? Because I've committed a major extravagance at a country-house sale and bought a seventeenth-century chest. I have a sinking feeling that I'm going to be left without enough to pay my bills and, yes, I do know that I have a perfectly adequate allowance and buying oak chests is not a suitable occupation for undergraduates, but I think he'll forgive me when he sees it. In the meantime, however, what is to be done. . . ?

To which Julia replied sedately that he had better write to his father directly to confess his debts, and she was glad he had enjoyed seeing his Cousin Anna again. The letter made her smile. Nicholas had said himself that Martin was the son who was most like him in temperament. The impulsive purchase of a fine piece of furniture which he just had to have was typical of both of them, as was the conscience-stricken realisation that desire had outweighed prudence.

She made a visit to Brad in the clinic and was shocked to see how much older and more worn he looked.

'I've been in a lot of pain,' he said. 'And the examinations I've had in here haven't helped. However, the surgeon who has pioneered this new operation does hold out some hope of giving me more mobility, so I guess I'll go ahead and have it done.'

Three weeks later Anna and Maurice Coppett were back in London.

'Anna tells me we're invited to your son's twenty-first birthday celebrations,' Mr Coppett said to Julia. 'We found a little present for him in Florence. I hope he likes it because I covet it myself!'

'How very kind of you,' Julia said. 'Yes, we're having quite a big party for Simeon at Claridge's and we'll be delighted if you and Anna can come.'

Anna, it was obvious at Simeon's party, did not follow the convention of wearing the pastel shades most English mothers thought suitable for a young girl. She wore rich topaz-yellow silk and glowed like a jewel amongst the pinks and blues of her contemporaries.

Julia had thought Martin's letter no more than a typical Martin extravagance until she saw Anna that evening, surrounded by young men clamouring for her attention, coolly picking and choosing which of them should dance with her. She had what Serafina possessed, Julia realised – a sensuality all the more potent for being discreetly hidden. Those slumbrous eyes and full mouth promised secret delights, and the figure revealed by her ballgown would more than fulfil the most exacting man's requirements.

'I told you,' Martin said. 'Look at her, bowling them over. She'll probably marry a duke. Do you know any dukes, Ma?'

'No, dear, you know I don't,' Julia said absently.

Her eyes were fixed not on the group surrounding Anna, but on

Simeon, watching them from the other side of the room. Anna saw him, too. She did nothing, she did not even smile, but Simeon walked across the width of the dance floor with his gaze fixed unwaveringly on her face. He held out his hand, Anna put hers into it and she was whirled away as the band struck up the music of the next dance.

Simeon's party was held just in time. The following week the King died and the country was plunged into mourning.

'I suppose one might have held a private party, but it would have looked heartless,' Julia said. 'I'm glad we managed to celebrate Simeon's coming-of-age.'

'I've only just had a look at the present Maurice Coppett gave him,' Nicholas said. 'No wonder he coveted it for himself!'

'Simeon told me it was a painting of St Simeon.'

'Yes, *St Simeon Blessing the Infant Christ*. Umbrian School. Certainly from the workshop of Perugino, if not by the Master himself.'

'An expensive gift.'

'It must have set him back every penny of two hundred pounds and he hardly knows Simeon.'

'I expect Anna influenced him,' Julia said carefully.

'Probably. It's nice that those two – Sim and Anna, I mean – are such good friends.'

It was not, in Julia's opinion, nice at all and she had been feeling her way towards sharing her disquiet with Nicholas. Now she decided to let it go. Perhaps her husband was right and she was reading too much into a childish infatuation and the revival of an old friendship.

'What about Martin's oak chest?'

'It's a nice piece,' Nicholas admitted. 'There's no doubt it's authentic and he got it at a bargain price.'

'So he's forgiven for getting into debt?'

'He's promised to work for me during the long vacation.'

'That's not exactly a punishment, not for Martin,' Julia pointed out.

'I'm paying him nothing.' Nicholas laughed. 'All right, he's got off with no more than a mild wigging. The young brute was clever enough to photograph the chest as it was when he bought it and again after he'd had it restored. Some fool had fixed a pad to the top to convert it into a windowseat. It took a good eye to spot the real chest and I hadn't the heart to discourage him.'

'You spoil your sons, my love.'

'Is the pot calling the kettle black?'

'Perhaps.' Julia leaned against him, savouring the quiet happiness of their companionship. 'The poor King – such a short reign.'

'In some ways I feel it as much more the end of an era than when the old Queen died. As if the twentieth century has arrived, a bit belatedly, but very definitely. Edward had a style which was very much his own and the new King and Queen are quite different.'

'How will it affect the antiques trade?'

'The state funeral will bring foreigners into London. I've nothing really outstanding being catalogued at the moment, but we may see a few new faces in the Sale Room.'

On 21 May 1910 all the family, together with Anna and Mr Coppett, watched King Edward VII's funeral procession as it wound its way from the lying-in-state in Westminster Hall to Paddington Station for the interment in the family vault at Windsor. The new King, George V, rode on horseback beside his father's coffin accompanied by Kaiser Wilhelm of Germany and the Kings of Belgium, Bulgaria, Denmark, Greece, Norway, Spain and Portugal.

'That's an array of crowned heads I guess I'm not likely to see again,' Maurice Coppett commented at the luncheon Julia had laid on for them at Eaton Square. 'Mrs Hope, I'm glad to have been present at this historic occasion, even though it was a melancholy event. Now, if you'll forgive me I'll say goodbye and take Anna away to help me complete my packing.'

'I didn't realise you were leaving so soon,' Julia exclaimed. 'Anna has said nothing . . . Is Bradley well enough to travel?'

'By no means. I'm leaving him behind. He's had nothing yet but the preliminary examination and there'll be at least one, possibly two operations. Unfortunately, my business calls me back to the States and, of course, Serafina is anxious for me to return for Violetta's engagement party.'

'She's really engaged?'

'It'll be announced as soon as I get back. Peter's a fine young man. I daresay you're thinking she's young to be getting married, but Violetta isn't self-reliant like Anna. She's a lively little girl, pretty as a picture, but she'll always need someone to lean on.'

'I hope she'll be very happy,' Julia said automatically, while her mind grappled with a feeling of relief that Anna was leaving London. The sensation was short-lived.

'Of course I couldn't leave Brad here with no one of his own,' Mr Coppett was saying. 'Anna is a very adult, reliable young woman. I've taken a house for her and Brad, and she'll see he's looked after properly when he's not in hospital.'

'How long is the lease?' Julia asked faintly.

'Six months and renewable. I guess it'll be all of that before poor Brad is able to travel back to the States. Anna might even miss her sister's wedding, but she won't hear of leaving my son until we know the outcome of the operations – for good or ill.'

'For good, I hope,' Julia said, again making all the right noises while her mind examined all the nuances of Anna's willingness to remain in London.

'I'd appreciate it if you'd keep an eye on my two young people,' Maurice Coppett said.

'Of course.' Julia pulled herself together. 'Anna knows she can always come to me if she finds herself in difficulties, and I'll certainly visit Bradley. What does worry me, however, is that Anna really can't be allowed to live on her own in a London house. After all, she's only twenty.'

'That's been thought of – by Anna, not me. She's persuaded her old governess to come and stay, which I agree will be desirable, especially during the time Brad's in hospital.'

'Her governess? Not Miss Henderson, surely?'

'That's the name.'

'But she was most unsatisfactory. In fact, Serafina dismissed her.'

Maurice Coppett was visibly disconcerted. 'Anna said she'd be a most suitable person. It's not as if she's going to do any teaching. All that's asked of her is that she should be around as a chaperone. Brad's manservant will be in the house, too, and he's as good as a nanny.'

'I'm not happy about it.'

With an effort Julia forced herself to realise that this was not her problem. Mr Coppett had set up his household, she had given him a warning that one member of it might not be all she seemed, and it was up to him to sort it out.

As the summer progressed Julia increasingly regretted Anna's presence in London. The boys were free and heady with the sense of release from what they called their toils, especially Simeon, who had taken his finals and would not be returning to Cambridge. Martin, grumbling but really enjoying it, went to the Sale Rooms every day with his father, which left Simeon without his usual companion.

He seemed always to be busy and not very forthcoming about what kept him occupied, but it was not difficult for Julia to find out that he had taken Anna down the river to Greenwich – 'Do you remember we did that with Father when we were children, Mother, and Anna wanted to go again' – to Brighton to visit the Pavilion, and to Dulwich Art Gallery to see the pictures there.

'Did you take Miss Henderson with you?' Julia asked after the Brighton trip.

'Goodness no! Really, Mother, this is the twentieth century, not the Middle Ages. Surely a man can take his auntie to the seaside without dragging along a chaperone?'

Julia wanted to say that it depended on the 'auntie', but she managed to keep it back.

The results of Simeon's finals came through and were satisfactory.

'A decent Second,' he said with relief. 'You're not disappointed, are you, Father? Martin's your boy for a First. I never expected better than this.'

'You chose an exceptionally difficult field to study. You've mastered Mandarin Chinese . . .'

'Hardly that,' Simeon protested. 'To reach that level I'd need to spend time in China.'

'We might think about that. In the meantime, how about a celebration dinner at the Savoy?'

'Splendid! You'll ask Anna, won't you?'

'Why not? Is there any young lady you'd like to invite, Martin?'

'Martin won't want to favour one of his girls above any of the others,' Simeon said.

'That's right,' Martin agreed cheerfully. 'No point in raising false hopes.'

'Casanova.'

'Oedipus.'

'I love my old mummy, but not to that extent,' Simeon retorted.

'Aunts don't count?'

'Don't be silly.'

'No, please don't be silly, Martin,' Julia put in. 'I think this will be a delightful opportunity for Melissa to dine out with us. Dinner for six at the Savoy, please, Nicholas.'

Melissa, nearly thirteen and no longer the chubby little girl she had been, was in ecstasies at the idea of a real, grown-up dinner in a proper restaurant.

She had a bashful admiration for Anna, who took little notice of her, and that evening she was struck dumb by her aunt's appearance. Anna had discovered the fashion set by Poiret and was wearing a tunic of sea-green satin shimmering with gold thread over a plain green skirt; round her head was a twist of gold tissue like a turban. With her high cheekbones and dark, exotic colouring she looked like a young Tartar princess.

As they were shedding their cloaks Melissa said seriously, 'Mother, we do look beautiful, don't we – all of us?'

Julia gave a resigned glance at her own reflection, grey satin sewn with silver beads, and hair rapidly going equally grey, and agreed gravely that they were a sight to behold.

'And Father and Simeon and Martin, too,' Melissa persisted. 'They do look splendid in their evening clothes, don't they?'

Julia had no fault to find with that. After twenty-two years of marriage Nicholas could still make her heart turn over. As for her two sons, Melissa's word for them was exactly right: in their tailcoats and starched linen they were splendid. Simeon was slightly taller and fairer than Martin, who had inherited his father's dark curly hair and had an impudent grin that was all his own, but they were both beautiful young men.

Anna thought so, too. The little party fell naturally into three couples: Julia and Nicholas, Melissa and Martin, who was good-naturedly attentive to his little sister, Anna and Simeon. *Anna and Simeon*. I must stop thinking of them as a pair, Julia thought frantically. It can't *be*. Simeon knows that. Anna . . . for a fleeting second Julia saw a look on the girl's face that made her heart stand still. She had seen that look before – in Serafina's eyes when she had seen something she wanted, and meant to have. And what Anna was looking at was Simeon.

Apart from that one moment of terrible fear, which lurked at the back of Julia's mind and would not be driven away, the evening was an entire success, right until the end.

'Simeon will see me home,' Anna said. 'No, I insist, Uncle Nicholas. Regent's Park is quite out of your way. Come along, Simeon.'

'I don't think I can allow that,' Julia began.

Anna leaned forward and kissed her on the cheek. 'Now, don't be stuffy, Aunt Julia. I'm sure Mama would consider Simeon an entirely suitable escort.'

There were cabs waiting. Anna and Simeon were gone before Julia could think of any reasonable objection.

That was the start of what she came to think of as Simeon's haunted period. From being the quiet, but carefree young man who had come down from Cambridge, he turned into a creature of silences. His former easy smile became rarer, he began to smoke, which was not a habit Julia liked, and he looked heavy-eyed, as if he were sleeping badly.

Of Anna they saw little. Since Julia had no wish to ask Simeon whether he knew anything about her plans, she put on her best hat and went to visit the girl who called her 'aunt'.

She was received not by Anna, but by Miss Henderson. They greeted one another stiffly, Julia because she did not like the woman and Miss Henderson no doubt remembering that it was through Julia that she had lost her previous position in the Speranza household.

'Anna is walking in Regent's Park with Simeon,' Miss Henderson informed her.

'Is that quite right?' Julia asked. 'I don't want to sound critical, but doesn't Anna enjoy rather too much freedom for a single young woman?'

'She's been brought up as an American and that's the way they behave,' Miss Henderson said. 'Quite honestly, Mrs Hope, it's not in my power to stop her and surely there's no harm in a quiet stroll in a public park with a close relative?'

'I suppose not,' Julia said, far from satisfied.

'Of course, I defer to your judgement,' Miss Henderson went on, subtly spiteful. 'He's your son.'

The surge of anger in Julia made her curl her fingers into tight fists. It was only when she felt her nails digging into the palms of her hands even through her kid gloves that she realised what she was doing.

'Simeon would be a safe companion for any girl,' she said.

'Then there's no harm done, is there? Will you wait until they return?'

'I'll stay a short while. I'm a little uncertain of the situation here and I wanted to ask Anna about her plans. Mr Bradley Coppett has not come out of hospital since I visited him last week, has he?'

'He expects to be allowed home next Monday. Then he'll spend three or four weeks recuperating. All being well he should be free to sail for America in October.'

Julia relaxed. October. In October Simeon would be safe.

The door opened and Anna came in followed by Simeon. She had stopped to take off her hat in the hall and she entered the room patting her hair into place. She was flushed and smiling, with a look of blind happiness about her that struck Julia with terror. As for Simeon, he too came in smiling, but a wary look came over him when he saw his mother and Julia resented that change.

'Dear Anna,' she murmured as they kissed. 'Miss Henderson was just telling me that you will be leaving us in October.'

'Oh, no!' Anna said in surprise. 'You didn't say that, did you, Hendy?'

'I said Mr Bradley would be sailing. I hadn't begun to tell Mrs Hope of your plan.'

'I shall stay in London and study fine art,' Anna said. 'Hendy will live with me. It'll all be perfectly proper, so don't look disapproving, Aunt Julia. My *real* plan is to persuade Uncle Nicholas to employ me at Hope & Company.'

Over my dead body, Julia thought as she got up to go. The time had come to confide in Nicholas.

She tackled him that evening. 'Anna is going to ask you to take her on to the staff,' she said. 'I want you to refuse.'

'My dear, you're too late,' Nicholas said. 'She came to see me this afternoon and put the idea to me and I said yes.'

'Such ruthless efficiency,' Julia said bitterly. 'Oh, damn! I don't often swear, but Anna is enough to drive one to any excess. Nicholas, you must change your mind. Tell her she isn't old enough, that you haven't a suitable vacancy – tell her anything, just so long as she is discouraged and goes back to America.'

'But, dearest, why?'

'Simeon.'

'Having Anna on the staff is no threat to Simeon's position.'

'Nicholas, how can you be so blind? Simeon . . . Simeon and Anna . . . it's *dangerous*. They must be separated.'

She saw Nicholas's face darken with a look of horror and then distaste.

'You must be mistaken,' he said at last. 'They're much of an age, they have similar tastes, they share a family background . . . Simeon wouldn't step out of line, not in that way. It's unthinkable.'

'Really? What about you and Serafina?' She saw the shock that went through her husband.

'I didn't think you knew about that.'

'Of course I knew. Serafina took care that I should. Besides, I had eyes in my head. My dear, you had me to hold on to and the children to think about. Simeon is younger and unattached. I've seen him sinking deeper and deeper into this quagmire. As for Anna . . . poor child, I pity her; she seems to have had no moral teaching to guide her. I could never have believed that so young a girl could be so lacking in proper feeling. It's almost a sort of innocence, as if she can't – literally *can't* see she's doing anything wrong. She wants Simeon, therefore it must be right for her to have him. She makes my blood run cold.'

'You're suggesting there's a . . . a liaison?'

'Not yet. But that's what it will come to unless we keep them apart.'

'I can't believe Simeon would act so wrongly – or be such a fool!'

'Think back,' Julia said gently. 'Remember Serafina. She swayed in front of you like a cobra with its hood raised and you were hypnotised.'

The memory of that terrible fascination came back to Nicholas and he was silenced.

'You knew,' he said. 'All the time, you knew.'

'You might have suspected I did, considering the trouble I took to seduce you.'

There was a reminiscent gleam in Nicholas's eye as he held out his hand to her.

'I do seem to remember benefiting from my folly,' he said. 'What a horrid, conniving creature you are, my darling.'

'For your own good – and mine. Just as this is for Simeon's benefit.'

'I'll think of something,' Nicholas promised.

Because he had not quite made up his mind how to go about it, Nicholas delayed telling Anna of his change of heart. He left it until after Bradley came out of hospital, because Anna herself had said she would not be free until she had her stepbrother settled at home.

The operations had benefited Bradley to the extent that for the first time for many years he was able to stand upright; he needed callipers and sticks, it was true, but at least he was out of the wheelchair and able to take a step or two.

'He's immensely pleased,' Anna told Simeon. 'It makes me feel better about letting him sail for home on his own.'

They were alone in the drawing room of the small Regent's Park house. Anna had no scruples about sending Miss Henderson out of the house when she wanted privacy. Hendy was biddable, that was why Anna employed her.

Simeon got up from the sofa where he had been sitting and began wandering restlessly around the room.

'I think you should change your mind and go home with him,' he said.

'No.'

That simple denial was Anna's strength. She struck one clear note and held to it, ignoring reverberations.

Simeon was staring blindly out at the small, leafy garden.

'Anna, this can't go on. We've already done wrong in admitting . . .'

'That we love one another.'

'There's a sympathy between us that goes deeper than anything we're ever likely to find with anyone else. No matter how wrong the world may think it, we know that we belong together.'

'Call it love. Why can't you do that, Simeon?'

'Very well, call it love. It's a forbidden love, we both know that. We ought to strike it out of our lives before it destroys us.'

'It would destroy me to give you up.'

'But this . . . this torment . . . it can't go on.' Simeon leaned his hot, aching forehead against the cool glass of the window pane.

'Seeing you every day, having your dear company, always finding something new . . . yes, it's been a wonder and a revelation. You light up my life. If that were enough I'd plead with you to stay. But it's not. I can't keep it on this level much longer, Anna. I'll go out of my mind. I'm sorry. It's weak and despicable and everything you like to call it, but standing here now the ache to take you in my arms is almost unbearable. And once we start, where will it end? Your life will be ruined and I'll never stop reproaching myself.'

'You haven't understood me at all,' Anna said. She sounded disbelieving, as if she could hardly understand Simeon's scruples. 'What you're worrying about is what I intend. We will be lovers. There, that's plain speaking for you. Once Bradley has gone back to America I'll have this house to myself. Hendy will be here, of course, but I can handle her. You can come to me whenever you want. Of course, we can't marry, but apart from that there need be no restriction on the way we live.'

Simeon turned to look at her, horrified by the simplicity of her thinking. She was sitting bolt upright on the little sofa, shining with certainty. Anna had made her plans. That was the way it was going to be.

'There are other people to be considered,' he said.

'Fiddlesticks! The world isn't interested in us. Family . . . yes, Aunt Julia would be upset if she knew, but Mama is on the other side of the world and is in no position to throw stones. I've always known there was something odd about that time Violetta and I came and stayed with you. At the back of my mind I half-suspected . . . and now I've made Hendy talk. Mama went off to have an illegitimate baby.'

'No!'

'Oh, yes, I'm sure it's true. Don't ask me what happened to the poor little thing, because I've no idea.'

'Do you think Mr Coppett knows?'

'I'm sure he doesn't. He calls Mama his Madonna. That's why he fell in love with her. She reminded him of all those paintings of the Holy Virgin that he adores.'

There was something about the way Anna spoke of her mother and stepfather, impatient and unloving, that grated on Simeon.

'Even if what you say is true that still doesn't alter the fact that any union between us is forbidden,' he said carefully. 'Your Church . . .'

'I've given up religion. I'm a Freethinker. And your father is only my half-brother. Come here.'

Slowly, half-convinced by her certainty that what they both wanted so much could not be wrong, Simeon crossed the room to sit by her side. His eyes feasted on the line of her jaw, on the sweep of dark hair by her cheek, on the fullness of her red lips, turned invitingly up to his.

They had kissed before, but always Simeon had made himself hold back. Now, in his desperation, he let slip that careful control and part of him was appalled and part of him exulted in the way Anna responded to his ardour.

It was Simeon who freed himself at last. His whole body was shaking with the effort of putting Anna away from him. Anna, her face turned up to his, her eyes closed, had the blind look of a drowning woman. Her lips moved, still trying to entice him back again, but Simeon, with a strength he had not believed he possessed, held her away from him.

'I must go,' he said, his voice reduced to a thread of sound by the strain he was under.

Anna's eyes flew open. 'No! I won't let you leave me. Listen, my darling: Bradley and his man are out, the servants are safe in the basement and I've sent Hendy to the circulating library. You see how shameless I am? I've planned my own seduction, if you can call it that when the girl herself is asking for love.'

Flushed by the warmth of their lovemaking, the face that was turned towards him was still that of a child, its soft contours unmarked by experience. Anna, in her rapt and blissful vision of their love, had no regard for the consequences of her directness.

'You don't know what you're doing,' Simeon said.

'But I *want* to know. Simeon . . .'

The pleading look she turned on him, the soft pressure of her hand in his as she led him towards the door were irresistible. When, at the top of the stairs, Anna turned on him a face sparkling with mischief, Simeon could not suppress an answering smile. They were two against the world, two who ought not to be kept apart just because of an accidental relationship.

160

Chapter Twelve

'I told you we wouldn't be able to stop,' Simeon said, raising himself up to untwist the sheets that had wound themselves round the two bodies on Anna's bed.

'I don't want to stop,' Anna said lazily. She turned her head to nuzzle his bare shoulder. 'Oh, Sim, Sim, Sim, isn't loving one another the most wonderful thing that ever happened?'

Since the first time they had crept up the stairs to Anna's bedroom they had repeated their adventure many times. They were becoming careless. Simeon knew it and was worried.

'The servants must know,' he said.

'Who cares about them?'

'Bradley . . .'

'No, I don't think he suspects. He's always been out of the way when you've come to me.'

'Miss Henderson may tell him. Worse still, she may tell my parents.'

'Hendy doesn't care what I do. All she wants is a quiet life, good pay and a bottle of whisky in her bedroom.'

Simeon got out of bed and Anna lay watching him as he dressed, adoring his long legs, his firm buttocks and the line of his spine. She knew why he was keeping his back to her when he said, 'You ought to go back to the States when Bradley leaves.'

'I can't do that, not now. You don't want to lose me, do you?'

'Neither do I want the sort of scandal that'll break over us if what we're doing gets out.'

'Everyone will hush it up and pretend it didn't happen,' Anna said, stretching and yawning. 'I suppose I'll have to follow your good example and put some clothes on.'

She sat up, hugging her knees and still watching Simeon until he was fully dressed.

'Tomorrow?' she said.

'No, not tomorrow. Sorry, darling, but there's a big sale of

Chinese art and it'll look odd if I don't attend, given my special interest.'

'And you want to be there,' Anna suggested.

'I do,' Simeon agreed, sitting down on the bed to kiss her goodbye. 'Don't come downstairs. I'll slip out quietly.'

'Day after tomorrow?'

He laid his cheek for a moment against the tumbled mass of dark hair.

'I shan't be able to stay away for more than forty-eight hours,' he said. 'You're a witch, you know.'

'Mm, I spread my wicked spell over you. Love me?'

'I have a decided preference for you,' Simeon said gravely.

He dropped a light kiss on the end of her nose, resisting her efforts to detain him. He did not look back as he left her room, after a cautious glance up and down the corridor, knowing that the sight of Anna still in bed, shamelessly naked and holding out her arms to him, would delay him beyond prudence.

He met Bradley and his manservant on the pavement outside and breathed a sigh of relief that he had left in time. Bradley went out in his wheelchair every afternoon, but he took a determined, ungainly walk round the rose garden in the park each day, and he insisted that he was becoming positively agile.

Simeon stopped for a brief, friendly word. Anna was right, he thought; Bradley did not suspect, otherwise his smile would not have been so open nor his word of regret that he had missed Simeon's visit so spontaneous.

When he was away from Anna, Simeon could acknowledge the folly of their relationship. It was mad and it was dangerous yet he loved her to the point where none of that mattered – not all the time they could keep meeting. On the day of the sale of Chinese ceramics, he put Anna out of his mind and was not sorry to have a respite from the vortex of sex and passion and desperate regret into which she had plunged him.

The articles being auctioned were exactly what appealed to him most in the field of Chinese art – lovely, simple bowls and vases, relying for their appeal on rich plain colours and perfect line.

One of the buyers was already known to Nicholas, a man

called Terence Camperdine, with business interests in the Far East. Nicholas paused after he left the rostrum for a word with him.

'I'm glad you got the Tang Dynasty ewer,' he said.

'It'll fill a gap in my collection,' Mr Camperdine agreed. 'But you pushed it up to a price I didn't altogether enjoy.'

Nicholas smiled, knowing that Terence Camperdine could well afford to indulge his whim for an eighth-century jug.

'I'd like to introduce my son to you, if I may,' he said. 'Simeon shares your passion for early Chinese art.'

'Are you joining the business?' Mr Camperdine asked.

'I'm more or less in it already,' Simeon said. 'I've not yet been assigned to a department, but when I've had a bit more general experience I'm specialising in Oriental ceramics.'

'Have you thought of visiting China?'

'Thought of it, yes, but not made any definite plans. Excuse me, I think I'm wanted.'

'A fine young man,' Mr Camperdine remarked.

Nicholas did not answer. He had been visited by an idea which needed thought, but with his customary decisiveness he said, 'Could you spare me a minute or two? I'd like to consult you about Simeon?'

'I have to wait while the ewer is packed, anyway. I want to take it with me.'

In his office Nicholas said, 'I haven't had time to think this out. It came as a flash of inspiration while we were talking. Simeon wants to go to China and I'm anxious to get him there. I'd like to pick your brains, see if you have any ideas about how and where I could place him so that he'd see something of the life and culture of the country.'

'Do you want me to give him a job?'

'I hadn't got as far as that. Are there are openings?'

'Does he speak Mandarin?'

'Fluently – so far as one can be fluent in the language of a country one has never visited. He studied the language at Cambridge.'

'I could probably use him. You know my business – imports and exports. It's ironic that I'm importing back into China a lovely old ewer that must have been exported here some time in the last hundred years. I can usually find a place for a bright young man, not too onerous but not too well-paid either, because if I take him on he's there to learn.'

'I'd pay all the expenses of his journey, and continue his allowance.'

'I leave for Shanghai in two weeks' time. If your Simeon wants a job he'd have to come with me.'

'That would be highly satisfactory,' Nicholas said. 'Provided, of course, that I can make Simeon . . . I mean, that Simeon agrees.'

'Quite.' Mr Camperdine leaned back in his chair and looked at Nicholas with shrewd eyes. 'Now tell me why you want to get him out of London. He doesn't look like the wild sort. Has he done anything wrong?'

'Nothing that need worry you in employing him,' Nicholas said quickly.

'Then it's a woman.'

'That's right,' Nicholas admitted. 'I'm not supposed to know about it, but of course I do. It's a sad business. Frankly, I'm sending Simeon out to China as the only way of rescuing him from a disastrous affair.'

'We've all been young and most of us have made fools of ourselves,' Mr Camperdine said tolerantly. 'Do you think Simeon will resist your plan?'

'I'm not sure. In his heart he must know that it's got to end. There've been times when I've suspected he might welcome a way out. Can I tell him that you'd be willing to take him?'

'Why not? I'd like to see him again before I really commit myself, but I like the idea in principle. Tell him he can catalogue my collection. That ought to fetch him.'

Nicholas saw exactly how Simeon reacted when he called him into his office and told him about Terence Camperdine's offer – excitement followed by dismay.

'It's wonderful, of course,' he said. 'But . . .'

'But you don't think you can accept.'

'It's so sudden.'

'You sound as coy as a girl considering a proposal of marriage. Actually, I'm not offering you a choice, Simeon: I'm telling you. You're going to China, even if I have to knock you out and put you

164

on board in a sack. "Shanghai" you is the appropriate expression, I believe.'

There was a long silence and then Simeon said, 'You know.'

'Of course I know and so does your mother. In fact, it was she who opened my eyes.'

Simeon drew a long, shuddering breath. 'I can't leave Anna in the lurch,' he said obstinately.

'You can't stay with her, that's for certain. You're a pair of young fools who've got to be saved from yourselves.'

'You don't understand! You don't understand at all. We're in love.'

'In love!' Nicholas snorted derisively. 'You don't know what love is. What you're suffering from is a fever in the blood, easily caught and easily cured, though the treatment may seem harsh to you now. It's time enough to talk about love when you've been married to a woman for twenty odd years, not always happily, not always in harmony; when you've been through good times and bad together; when you've seen her in labour with your child and shared her joy in its safe delivery; when she's comforted you in bereavement and shown you loving kindness after you've made a fool of yourself. That's love, not the kind of infantile passion you and Anna have contracted.'

'Anna and I could have had everything you're talking about, if only . . .'

'Ah, if only! Didn't someone once say they're the two saddest words in the language? If only Giorgio had married Serafina then Anna would have been your cousin and there would have been no bar to your union. As it is, you've got to part.'

'I won't go to China.'

'You will. And shall I tell you why? Because in your heart you know I'm right and because if it wasn't for this entanglement you'd be over the moon at being given such a chance.'

'It would break Anna's heart if I left her.'

'Anna is due for unhappiness whatever you do. Sooner or later the story will come out and the whole of her life will be spoilt. At the moment there's still some slight chance of keeping it in the family. Poor little wretch, I pity her with all my heart. She seems to have no conception of right and wrong and she's had the misfortune to fall in love with a young man who's done nothing to save her from herself. I'm ashamed of the way you've behaved, Simeon. You've ruined – and I mean that in the good old-fashioned sense – a young girl who ought to have been as safe in your company as your own sister.'

Nicholas saw his son struggle with a fierce rejoinder and then subside.

'I put it down to your credit that you don't say that Anna led you on,' he said drily. 'As I don't doubt she did. I trust you've been taking precautions?'

'Of course,' Simeon muttered. 'Nearly always.'

'Nearly always is as dangerous as never. Oh, Simeon, Simeon . . . my dear boy, I do understand, no matter what you may think, and because I can enter into your feelings I *know* that what I'm urging you to do is right. Make the break. Start a new life. It'll be hard on Anna, but time won't make it easier. For her sake, go to China.'

'I must talk to Anna,' Simeon said. 'I can't decide anything – either one way or the other – without discussing it with her first.'

It was an admission that his resistance was weakening, and it gave Nicholas hope.

'We'll say no more for now,' he said. 'I still have to break it to your mother that I'm sending you off to the other side of the world. It'll make her very unhappy.'

The next twenty-four hours were the longest Simeon had ever lived through. What made the time drag as he tossed and turned through a sleepless night was his own divided mind. He was appalled to realise how much he wanted to go to China. His first split-second reaction had been pure pleasure, followed by a terrible realisation of his situation and the treacherous thought – 'If only I were free . . .'

He was not free, not unless Anna released him. How could he be the one to sever the link after his protestations of love and the lust that had ravaged her body? He could not believe that his father had the slightest idea of the strength of the bond between them. He and Anna had shared moments of such passion that more than once she had lost consciousness and he had been almost frightened when he saw the extent of her ecstasy. How ever fond his parents might be of one another, his father was still a middle-aged man married to a middle-aged woman and there was nothing in their affectionate relationship to tell their son that they, too, had known the heights of passionate love.

Simeon went to Anna the following afternoon with his mind still in turmoil, almost persuaded that it would be better not to tell her anything about China for fear of betraying his ambivalent feelings, which she would see as disloyalty, and found that on her side, too, the situation had changed.

'Hendy is trying to get money out of me,' she said. 'I didn't think she'd do that.'

'Blackmail. How revolting,' Simeon said.

'She says she'll tell Bradley.'

'Does he really not know?'

Anna took some time to answer that question. 'He seems not to,' she said at last. 'It's difficult to tell with Brad. He's very deep and keeps his thoughts to himself. I can't believe that if he knew he wouldn't take steps to separate us. He's very fond of me. Too fond, I've sometimes thought. It's pitiful, really.'

'Other people know,' Simeon said carefully. 'Father tackled me yesterday. He . . . he wants to send me to China.'

To his surprise Anna did not blaze into immediate indignation. She was looking pale and sad, with dark smudges under her eyes and a pitiful downward droop to her mouth.

'When would you go?' she asked.

'In two weeks' time. Too soon. I can't tear myself away from you at a moment's notice.'

'Whenever it comes it's going to be hard,' Anna said.

It was the first time, ever, that she had admitted the possibility that they might have to part, and Simeon felt chilled by the resigned way she spoke.

'That horrid blackmailing woman has upset you,' he said, taking her in his arms. 'My poor darling, shall I throw her out of the house for you?'

'You mustn't do that. I'll take care of Hendy.'

'You shouldn't be exposed to anything so nasty. Not that talking to Father was exactly pleasant. He doesn't *understand*.'

'No one does.'

Holding her had awakened his longing for her. 'Is it safe to go upstairs?' he asked.

'Everyone's out,' Anna admitted. 'But . . . no, not today.'

'Sorry, darling. Is it . . . is it the wrong time?'

He held her close, feeling a special tenderness towards her, and Anna stared over his shoulder, her eyes wide with fear.

'Yes,' she lied. 'Leave me now, Simeon. I have to think.'

'There's no need to think about me going off to China and leaving you, you can forget about that,' Simeon said, kissing her.

He spoke with great firmness, but there was a touch of bravado behind his words. He thought Anna detected the false note because she gave him a wretched little smile and said, 'We'll have to see about that.'

Alone in the drawing room which had been the scene of their first tumultuous embraces, Anna smoothed her hand over the cushion which still retained the impress of Simeon's body and something of his warmth. Simeon had been right in thinking that she had been upset by her scene with Miss Henderson, but there was more to Anna's about-face than that. Anna had woken up to the consequences of her headlong passion and she was looking at a future that was bleak beyond anything she had ever foreseen.

It was something Miss Henderson had said that had jolted her into horrified awareness.

'Like mother, like daughter,' the half-drunk woman had jeered. 'You'll end up with a little secret to be hidden away in the country and an even worse parenthood than the one she disowned.'

Anna had smiled contemptuously and then, hitting her like a thunderbolt, had come the thought: her monthly period was five days overdue! At first she could not believe that she had overlooked it, but a hurried calculation as soon as she had dismissed Miss Henderson, with a promise of a settlement which had sent the former governess stumbling up the stairs to her room unable to believe her luck, had confirmed that she was right.

She told herself that it was a mere accident of nature, that the violent lovemaking in which she and Simeon had indulged had upset her body. If she went for a long walk, jumped off the table, took a purge, had a hot bath – for Anna, brought up by servants, knew a servant girl's desperate remedies – then it would all come right, but in her heart she knew that she had conceived and that she would have to go through with the pregnancy.

In the twenty-four hours in which she did not see Simeon she went through her grim little catalogue of 'cures', but even though the purge griped her bowels there was no sign of a menstrual flow.

She might have told him if it had not been for his news about the voyage to China. It was, in a way, an answer to her dilemma. If she told Simeon she was pregnant then he would insist on staying with her. There could be no marriage, but he would take her away somewhere where they were not known and make her live with him. That was what Anna had always insisted she wanted and yet now, faced with the reality, she knew that they would not be happy. Cut off from his family, his work and from his expectations for the future, Simeon would be miserable and might come to blame her.

As for Anna, she still clung to the belief that she would love Simeon to the end of her days, and yet somehow Simeon the prospective father, the 'husband' whose true status must be kept hidden, was not the same as the dashing young lover she had adored in secret. Dragging it out into the open would destroy their love. It had a fairy-tale quality which would not survive in the light of ordinary human existence.

There was one other possibility and it had been put into Anna's head by her conversation with Simeon that afternoon. She took another twenty-four hours to think it over and then, with something of the same coolness with which she had planned her campaign to win him, Anna set about extricating herself from Simeon's love.

She sent for him and gave him an afternoon of unstinting love. That, at least, was something that she would have to remember. Then she told him that he must fall in with his father's plan and go to China.

'How can you say that when we've just . . .' Simeon muttered.

Her hand covered his mouth. 'No, my darling, you mustn't argue with me. I've poured out all my love for you this afternoon because it's goodbye. It's got to be, Simeon, it's got to be.'

He rolled over on his back and stared at the ceiling.

'I know you're right,' he said at last. 'How am I going to bear it?'

Rather better than I am, Anna thought. And that tart little thought carried her through the rest of their farewells.

She told Bradley of her decision to return home with him that evening when they were alone after dinner.

'Shall I be able to get a berth, do you think?' she asked.

'Surely. If necessary I'll delay my own departure so that we can go together.'

'Simeon is going to China.'

'I see. My dear, I've been aware of the attachment between you two and been distressed by it. It's best for you to part.'

'Yes. It went deep, Brad.'

'I'm sorry.'

Anna took a deep breath to steady herself as she reached the crux of the matter.

'I haven't been a good girl, Brad. There'll be consequences.'

She saw shock, compunction and something else, perhaps anger, struggling in Bradley.

'I understand you, I suppose,' he said at last.

'I need a husband, Brad. And soon.'

He looked up at her, a lovely young girl, vivid and taut with nerves, not really believing that he understood her meaning.

'I'm asking, Brad,' Anna said. 'Will you marry me?'

It took a long time for Brad to answer and when he did it was not the reply Anna was expecting.

'If I agree,' he said slowly, 'there's one thing to be made clear right from the start: it's to be a proper marriage.'

Anna would have given a lot to have bitten back the words which escaped her: 'But you can't . . .'

'I can, and occasionally I do. This isn't a conversation I ever imagined having with you, Anna, but I may as well complete your education by telling you that a man with money can always find a willing woman, no matter what he looks like.'

There was a bitter twist to his lips as he watched her. Not realising how closely he observed her reaction, Anna allowed herself to dwell for one anguished moment on the memory of Simeon's body, his long, straight legs, his slim hips and powerful shoulders, the smooth perfection of his skin.

'I shan't bother you often,' Bradley said. 'It seems a small thing to ask in return for my name, my protection – and my silence.'

The alternatives whirled through Anna's mind and she

recoiled at the thought of what discovery would bring to her
'I agree,' she said.

Chapter Thirteen

'It's too cruel,' Julia said. 'No sooner do we get you home from China after *years* of anxiety – and if I'd known they were going to have a revolution I would never have allowed your father to send you there – than a war breaks out in Europe. Not that you're going to be involved in that, of course.'

She looked at her three menfolk challengingly, and was chilled when none of them answered.

'We have an army,' she persisted. 'Surely there'll be no need for civilians to fight?'

'The Germans have been preparing for this for years,' Nicholas said. 'And we haven't started well. Liège and Namur have fallen. I'm afraid before the year's out there'll be a call for volunteers.'

'I've heard it will be over by Christmas.'

'Nonsense, dear. It isn't going to be as easy as that. I agree there's no need for the boys to rush into uniform, but if either of them decides to go and fight then I won't stand in his way.'

'I've seen enough killing to last me a lifetime,' Simeon said.

'You wrote and told us you were safe,' Julia accused him.

'As a foreigner I was safe enough, especially in Shanghai, but outside in the country it was a different story.'

He paused, but the look of revulsion on his face spoke for him. In his nostrils was the remembered reek of freshly spilt blood and in his mind, however hard he tried to forget, the picture of piles of severed heads. Once again he faced the contradiction in the character of the people he had respected and at times loved: the exquisite sensibility allied to an indifference to human life that shocked a European reared in a different culture.

'Would you ever go back?' Martin asked, reading his brother's thoughts more accurately than Simeon had expected.

'Not for a very long time.'

'I should hope not,' Julia said. 'I expected you to be gone for one year, not four. Simeon, dear, we missed you dreadfully.'

The small, remote smile she got from Simeon dismayed her. He was a stranger, a thin, self-contained man of twenty-five who had travelled the world and seen horrors and disasters. Gone for ever was the ardent boy who had thrown himself into a disastrous love affair, and Julia blamed the change as much on Anna as on Simeon's experiences in China.

Some time Anna's name was going to have to be mentioned, but not now, not so soon after his return, when Julia was still having to get to know him again and was grieved to the heart by the necessity.

'We were sorry to hear of Mr Camperdine's death,' Nicholas said.

'Yes, it was a blow and, of course, that was why I delayed my own return for so long. He lingered . . . and suffered. I couldn't desert him, especially once he'd asked me to bring Mrs Camperdine and Jane back to England for him.'

'Poor things, I must call on them,' Julia murmured. 'How old is Jane?'

'About Melissa's age. Father, I brought something else home. Because of all the political unrest, Mr Camperdine's fortune dwindled, but his collection is intact. I've managed to get the whole lot into England and Mrs Camperdine wants Hope & Company to sell it.'

Julia saw the way Nicholas's face lit up and felt a stab of irritation at the way his mind could always be diverted by the idea of a fine auction.

'This is not the best time for a major sale, surely,' she objected.

'Surprisingly enough, the market's buoyant,' Nicholas told her. 'Simeon, this is marvellous news! Some of Camperdine's pieces are museum quality. I'm really excited about handling them.'

'And it's a minor consideration that the owner's dead, his widow and daughter have lost most of their possessions and are having to sell the rest, and there's a war on,' Julia said, and burst into tears.

Simeon jumped to his feet, but his father held up his hand and jerked his head towards the door.

Outside in the passageway Martin let out a long dismayed breath. 'Poor old Ma, she's rather overwrought.'

'I suppose she was bound to be a bit emotional.'

'She's upset because you're not her little boy any more,' Martin said, once again surprising his brother by his perception.

'Neither are you,' Simeon pointed out.

'She's seen me change gradually, but the photograph of you she's kept on her dressing-table is the one that was taken at your degree ceremony and you know, bruv, you're no longer that open-faced child.'

'No.'

Martin gave his brother a sideways look. 'Let's go and have a smoke in the square,' he suggested.

In the middle of Eaton Square was a garden with gravel paths and grass and trees, a place where the boys had been allowed to play decorous games when they were small, something they had soon outgrown.

Simeon breathed in deeply. 'I'd forgotten that damp, green smell,' he said. 'Wet dust, earth, leaves . . .'

'A touch of horse dung and a whiff of petrol.'

'Those too,' Simeon admitted.

'And cigarette smoke. Here, have one of mine. You didn't take to smoking opium in the decadent East?'

'Good grief, no!'

They strolled along the gravel path. They had the gardens almost to themselves. One tardy nanny rolled up her knitting and stowed it in a bag, calling to Master Peter to come and have his tea, and then they were alone.

'You came home via America?' Martin said.

'Yes. We broke our travels on the way, but the train journey was interminable.' There was a long silence and then Simeon continued softly, 'I didn't go anywhere near Minneapolis. Is that what everyone wants to know?'

'Nothing's been said but, yes, I'm sure it's on the parents' minds. Damn it, Sim, I don't want to probe. I couldn't believe what happened to you and Anna and you never talked to me about it.'

'You wouldn't have understood.'

'When I first realised . . . I couldn't see how you could have allowed yourself to drift into such a dire situation.'

'Drift! I dived into it head-first.' Simeon flung his half-smoked cigarette into a flowerbed, where it lay smouldering quietly.

'All that heartbreak, all that passion,' he said. 'It's gone. I've got over it. Of course, the news that Anna had married Bradley

174

helped. One sees why she did it, naturally. Once I was gone and there was no hope left, she took the chance of a wealthy and not too demanding husband. There was always a severely practical streak in Anna.'

'You didn't like it.'

'I certainly did not! I felt sick – and betrayed. I went on an almighty bender and when I'd recovered from that I found myself a Chinese girl.'

'Nice?'

'Delightful.' For a moment Simeon allowed himself to smile with reminiscent pleasure. 'Runliang helped me back to life again. One day I woke up feeling like a man who's just recovering from a long illness; the fever in my blood had gone. Even so, the thought of Bradley and Anna together, with no love on her side – fondness, but no love – still nauseates me.'

There was something not quite right about this. Before he could put his finger on it Martin found himself saying, 'And you know about the baby.'

'Mother broke the news to me. By that time it must have been a year since I'd seen Anna, and Runliang had joined me in my bungalow, but the knowledge that Anna and Bradley had truly been living together as man and wife, right from the start, still gave me a nasty jolt. Stupid – and selfish, considering the Chinese contortions I was enjoying with Runliang – but I'd seen Anna's marriage as more of a business proposition. I didn't think . . . damn it, I didn't think Brad was capable of making her pregnant.'

Martin digested this in silence and with growing dismay. 'I wish I'd never started this,' he said. 'I think I'd like to sit down.'

They found a wooden seat and Martin felt automatically for his cigarette case.

'You smoke too much,' Simeon said.

'I know I do. I'm trying to give it up, but at the moment I need something to steady my nerves. Hell and damnation, Mother's been doing her Machiavelli act. She must have written that letter meaning you to be deceived, but I think you have a right to know the truth.'

'What are you talking about?'

'Anna and Bradley were married by special licence while you

were still en route for China. The baby was born less than eight months later.'

From Simeon's stunned silence it was obvious that this was news to him.

'It's *mine*?'

'So I've always assumed.'

Again Simeon took time to clarify his thoughts before he spoke.

'Mother deliberately gave me the impression that Anna and Brad had been living together for two or three months before she conceived. The actual date of the birth was never mentioned, and what with the length of time letters took to reach me . . . it made for a very convenient vagueness. And all the time Anna was having *my* child.'

'That was why she and Brad were married in such a hurry, of course.'

'I can see that now. Anna must have known . . . When she sent me away, she must have known.'

'Would you have left, if she'd told you?'

'Of course not. I would have had to stand by her.'

'And that might not have been the best thing for any of you, including the child.'

'Perhaps not.' Simeon was pacing to and fro, half a dozen steps in one direction and half a dozen in the other.

'What are you going to do now?' Martin asked.

Simeon came to a halt, staring blindly at the trembling leaves of a young silver-birch tree.

'Nothing,' he said.

'Not even tell Mother you've caught her out?'

'I think not. Poor old love, she meant it for the best and she might even have been right. Look, I don't want to have to go over this again. Could you slip the word to the parents that you've had a chat with me and I'm all cured and over it and don't want to rake over dead cinders?'

'Of course. Sim . . . I'm *bloody* sorry, old chap.'

'Yes. Thanks. One of life's nastier twists. In my meaner moments I've caught myself asking why did it have to be *me*? And the answer is that I asked for all I got, which is not an easy thing to admit.'

'We'd better go in. Actually, there is something else . . .'

'Not another shock, I hope. I don't think my constitution could stand it.'

'It's about this war. One of us is going to have to go and fight. I'd quite like it to be me, but I'll draw straws with you for the chance if you want.' He was walking towards the exit as he spoke, but when he realised that his brother had stopped, he turned round enquiringly.

Simeon was standing in the middle of the path with a look of mingled horror and amusement on his face. 'Martin, really! We can't draw straws about which of us is going to offer to go and get killed.'

'I've no intention of getting myself killed. My word, no!'

'It'll be no picnic. Remember, I've seen war.'

'Don't you come the big brother over me, big brother. I reckon I'll make a better soldier than you; you're too squeamish. So, shall I be the one to volunteer? After all, you've got this big Chinese sale to see to.'

'Father can handle that. All right, I'll pick a couple of pieces of grass and whoever gets the short one departs for the Front.' He held out his hand with two points of grass protruding from his closed fist. Martin took hold of one and drew it out . . . and out.

'Oh, heck,' he said. 'I was sure I'd get the short straw.'

A blade of grass fluttered to the ground and Martin pounced on it.

'You cheat! Both the same length. Do you think I'm going to let you go and get yourself killed just because you don't particularly care whether you live or not? That settles it; I'm the one to go.'

Simeon shrugged. 'I think you're mad.'

'Me and a lot of other young men who're dying to get into the fight.'

As they left the garden Simeon said abruptly, 'What did Anna call the boy?'

'Victor. In memory of Grandfather.'

'Poor little devil. What an ancestry!'

'A very fine fifteenth-century jade bowl decorated with incised fish, the edge of the bowl carved to represent breaking waves,' Simeon said. 'May I say two hundred pounds . . .? Two-fifty . . . three hundred.'

He looked round the room enquiringly, anxious not to miss a possible bid. He had been taken by surprise when his father had said he would like Simeon himself to conduct the sale of the Camperdine Collection. Simeon had expected to be given responsibility for the catalogue, but to take over as auctioneer for the afternoon was a challenge he had almost shirked, since he knew how much depended on a successful sale, not just for Hope & Company's reputation, but also for a comfortable future for Mrs Camperdine and young Jane.

They were both in the Sale Room, and that bothered him, too. If he were going to muff it, he would rather the Camperdine women did not witness his failure. Fortunately, it was going rather well. In spite of the war the room was full and people seemed anxious to buy. So far everything that had come up had exceeded its estimated price.

He dealt briskly with a group of bronzes before turning, with growing exhilaration, to the ceramics which were his own passion.

Simeon felt a pang of regret as he prepared to sell a magnificent covered jar from the first century. The austere decoration and greenish-brown glaze might not be as immediately appealing as the brilliantly coloured bowls of later centuries, but he and one or two other men in the audience valued it to the point of reverence for its antiquity and technical importance in the history of ceramics. He regretted quite fiercely that this collection was being split up, but the decision was not his and Mrs Camperdine had the right to decide that it was to be used to give herself and her young daughter a comfortable life.

To Simeon's surprise one of the strongest bidders for the Han jar was a young woman sitting in the front row. He had already noticed her, but had dismissed her as a probable non-bidder, a young Society woman with nothing better to do than to drop in on a sale. She wore a grey two-piece and a long flat ermine stole which slipped about her shoulders as she raised and lowered her catalogue in the bidding. The brim of her hat dipped to one side so that he could not properly see her face, but from the small portion of cheek which was visible and the glimpse of the hair gathered into a knot at the back of her neck she seemed to be dazzlingly fair, and the hobble skirt of her suit was short enough to reveal a fine pair of ankles in grey silk stockings above her black kid shoes.

An elegant young woman, and presumably a rich one, with a wholly unexpected interest in early Chinese ceramics. Simeon was sufficiently intrigued to make a point after the sale was over of finding out who she was.

'She was bidding for the Hart Museum,' he was told.

'Really?'

Simeon could not conceal his surprise. The Hart Museum was noted for its fine collection of Chinese art and he had visited it many times to study items which were not available anywhere else in the United Kingdom.

'The men are going off to the war and the young ladies are coming into their own,' the porter told him cheerfully. 'Not that it's the first time we've seen Lady Francesca here; she's reckoned very knowledgeable.'

'Lady Francesca?'

'That's right, sir. Lady Francesca Kenrick, Earl Kenrick's daughter.'

Simeon had to break off his conversation because his father came up, escorting Mrs Camperdine.

'A good sale,' Nicholas said. 'Congratulations, Simeon.'

'Thank you. Are you pleased, Mrs Camperdine?'

'Very pleased, Simeon.'

'Well, I'm not!' The fierce young voice broke in on their mutual congratulations. Jane Camperdine, scowling in an effort to hold back her tears, hurried on: 'All Daddy's lovely things being sold and everyone being *pleased*; it's horrible.'

It was no secret that Mrs Camperdine had Chinese blood somewhere in her ancestry; indeed, it was thought that that was what had attracted Terence Camperdine to her. The connection showed in her daughter, although Jane was far taller than any Chinese girl of her age. A black-haired, brown-eyed girl with a complexion of old ivory and exquisite hands, she was both slender and graceful – destined to become a great beauty, but at that moment she was disfigured by her rage and grief.

'The pieces will still be cherished,' Simeon said gently.

'I know, I know, but to sit here and watch it happening . . .' She felt frantically in her pocket for a handkerchief and then accepted the one Simeon silently held out to her and blew her nose in the prosaic way of a young child.

'I'm sure I don't know how else we could have managed,' Mrs Camperdine said.

She was smaller than her daughter, with an air of fragility about her which Simeon knew to be misleading. Behind the big brown eyes which Olga Camperdine had passed on to her daughter was a shrewd brain and considerable determination. Mrs Camperdine had the instincts of a survivor and she knew that she could not afford to be sentimental where money was concerned. She had married a man of immense riches and had seen his empire crumble. To her it seemed only common sense to cash in on what had survived.

To Simeon's relief his father shepherded the ladies away in search of a reviving cup of tea. Simeon, pausing for a word with one or two dealers who were on their way out, drifted towards the spot where Lady Francesca Kenrick was making arrangements about the collection of the fine pot she had purchased.

'A unique piece,' he ventured to remark.

She lifted her head and he saw that her eyes were grey. Because she was so fair he had expected them to be blue. Seen full face she was not strictly speaking beautiful, though her complexion was dazzling. She had a narrow head and a chin that was slightly too long and a sharp, thin nose. A highly bred, fastidious face. In her old age she would be very much a *grande dame*; even now there was something formidable about her.

'I would have liked to bid for the guardian figures,' she said, indicating the fiercely scowling pottery warriors. 'But I spent up to my limit on this one item.'

'It's some years since I last visited the Hart Museum, but my recollection is that you haven't anything similar of this period.'

'No, it will fill a gap.'

'Do you often visit our sales?'

'When I see something worthwhile in the catalogue and can persuade the Curator that we should spend the money. I haven't see you here before, have I?'

'I've been in China.'

'Interesting.'

'Rather too interesting in the last year.'

'Yes . . . I suppose so. And now? You're not planning to go off to the war?'

'My brother, Martin, has joined up. We've agreed that it's my turn to stay at home and mind the shop.'

'I see.' The cool grey eyes looked him over and Simeon realised that he had been weighed up, found wanting and dismissed.

'No doubt we'll see you again when we have anything to offer that's worthy of your notice,' he said with an edge of sarcasm in his voice.

Lady Francesca finished pulling on her grey kid gloves in a leisurely way before she answered.

'This is my last foray for the time being,' she said. 'I'm going to France to drive an ambulance.' She gave him a nod and walked away, spare and elegant as a greyhound.

Going home with his father in the car later, feeling unexpectedly tired but pleased with himself, apart from that one niggling little annoyance, Simeon said, carefully casual, 'I was surprised to find a member of the aristocracy buying for the Hart Museum and a young woman at that – Lady Francesca Kenrick.'

'Oh yes – *that* girl.'

Simeon shifted in his seat so that he could see his father's face. 'Why *that* girl?'

'I've no great liking for Lord Kenrick or his family, for reasons that go back many years. As for Lady Francesca, she ran off with a married man and was named in the divorce case.'

'But they didn't marry?'

'Apparently not.'

'How does she come to be buying for the Hart?'

'Her uncle is one of the trustees.' Nicholas paused and then added grudgingly, 'She's knowledgeable.'

'So I thought. A highly competent young woman.'

'Mm, one can't admire the way she's managed her own life. She's not a girl one could expect your mother to welcome to the house, for instance.'

'She's going to drive an ambulance in France,' Simeon said evenly.

'I daresay she'll find scope for mischief, even there.'

Simeon was not prepared to answer that and they drove the rest of the way home in silence, but the thought that was keeping him quiet was that this was the way people might have talked about Anna if she had not married Bradley. And yet he himself was received everywhere and no one questioned his morals. It was not fair, and Simeon could see that it was not fair, but there seemed to be nothing he could do to change the standards of the world in which he lived, except perhaps to be scrupulously just to women like Lady Francesca, who chose to compete for a living in a man's world.

The first surge of confidence in the art market did not last. Business dropped away as the news from the Front continued to be uniformly bad. The war stretched on for another year and then another. At last, in July 1916, the newspapers reported the start of a new British offensive on the Somme and the ominous headline appeared: '*Fighting Developing in Intensity*.'

It was not realised at first how futile this great battle had been, but as the hot July days crept by, convoy after convoy of wounded arrived in the London hospitals.

'It's been a disaster,' Nicholas said bluntly to Simeon. 'I wish we had some news of Martin. I'm on edge – and not only because we haven't heard from your brother recently. For the first time since I took over from your grandfather we're barely going to break even this year.'

'I'm not surprised. How do we stand? Are our finances strong enough to keep us going?'

'We can ride it out for a couple of years as long as we don't actually start losing money.'

'I see. Father . . . I can't help thinking that I ought not to have had to ask that question. I should be more aware of the company's financial situation.'

They were in Nicholas's office. It was late in the summer afternoon and the sunshine lit up the panelled walls and the leather furniture, slightly rubbed now, which Nicholas had inherited from Vittorio. He took his time about replying and Simeon felt compelled to urge his point.

'I'm twenty-seven – not exactly a child. And I've taken a very full part in running the business for the last two years.'

'You're right, of course,' Nicholas said. 'The thing that surprises me is that you say you aren't fully in the picture. You can see the accounts any time you want.'

'That's not quite what I meant. As I understand it, at the

moment the entire company belongs to you, and Martin and I are your paid employees. Is that correct?'

'Not exactly. Because of the way Papa left things, I actually own five-eighths of the company. The remaining three-eighths are held in trust for Anna and Violetta, and they receive the income from that – which won't amount to much more than peanuts this year.'

'What happens when they die?'

'It passes to their children.'

'Absolutely?'

'So I understand.'

'Violetta has no children as yet,' Simeon said evenly. 'And Anna has only one son.'

There was a brief, uncomfortable silence as both men thought about that son.

'You have three children,' Simeon went on. 'And I presume you would want to treat them all equally. Five-eighths split between three comes out at less than the three-eighths which Anna's boy may one day inherit.'

'Violetta may still have children, which would split the inheritance,' Nicholas protested.

'After six years of marriage one begins to wonder. The day could come when Anna's boy will have a larger stake in Hope & Company than Martin, Melissa and me.'

'Than any of you individually, yes; but as long as you three stick together then no one else is going to rank above you.'

'That's true,' Simeon admitted. 'I suppose it's all right. I don't know why I suddenly felt uneasy about it.'

'Especially since I'm still in my fifties and have no intention of kicking the bucket just yet.'

'I should hope not and I don't want to sound as if I'm harping on your early demise, but Hope & Company really means "Nicholas Hope", doesn't it? We're very much a one-man band.'

'It's the way Papa ran the business once his original partner died,' Nicholas said, not disagreeing, but taking his time to think about what Simeon was saying.

'He didn't have two sons in the business.'

'No, as things worked out, he didn't.'

The telephone rang and Nicholas stretched out his hand to pick it up, not sorry to have a diversion. He had been leaning back in his chair, at ease at the end of a day's work, but suddenly he sat up straight with a jerk, as if an electric shock had shot through him.

'Simeon's with me,' he said. 'We'll both come home straight away. Yes, dearest, yes, I know . . . but he's alive and we'll pull all the strings we can to find out where he is, how badly he's hurt and how soon we can get him home.'

There was no need for him to explain. Simeon was already on his feet, prepared to leave. 'Martin?'

'Yes, wounded. The telegram gives no more than the bare fact. God knows how bad it is.'

It was another three anxious days before they had any further news and then it was by means of a rough note, scribbled in pencil, from Martin himself: '*I caught a nasty one on the 15th. Fortunately only in my left leg and foot, so I'm still more or less in one piece. Hoping to be sent back to England. More news when I know what's happening.*'

It was difficult to get Julia to let that note out of her hand. She clasped it as if it were a lifeline to which Martin was attached, and only her hold on the little scrap of paper could save him.

She took to haunting the railway stations, sickened and appalled by the convoys of desperately wounded soldiers who were carried off the trains from the coast, until Nicholas realised what she was doing and insisted that she must give it up.

'While you're waiting at Victoria, Martin could be arriving at Charing Cross and I found out yesterday that trains were being sent in via Paddington because Charing Cross became too congested. Dearest, the most sensible thing you can do is to stay at home so that there's someone here if he tries to get in touch with us.'

'I haven't been doing enough for the war,' Julia said in a distracted way. 'My Red Cross Committee and Comforts for the Troops . . . it all seems so trivial when you see those poor men on stretchers.'

'You've done what you can and it's been worthwhile,' Nicholas said firmly. He was conscious himself of the inadequacy of his contribution to the war effort and it came as no surprise to find that Simeon was thinking along the same lines.

'I shall be called up,' he said abruptly, while they were waiting for news of Martin. 'On the whole I'd rather go as a volunteer.'

'For God's sake don't do anything about it until Martin has surfaced,' Nicholas begged. 'To lose you just now would kill your mother.'

The message they were expecting came the next day.

'He's at Woolwich,' Nicholas said as soon as Simeon came down to breakfast. 'I'll get on to the hospital and find out when we can see him.'

'Why don't we just go down?' Julia demanded. 'He's so *near*. Surely they'd let us see him?'

Nicholas dropped a kiss on the top of her head as he passed her chair.

'I'll get on the telephone straight away,' he said.

'I'll come and listen!' Julia jumped to her feet.

In spite of war-time shortages there was bacon and eggs on the sideboard. Simeon lifted the lid of the silver dishes sitting on their hot-water containers, but in the end all he could manage was a slice of toast and a cup of tea.

He caught Melissa watching him and grimaced at her. 'I can't eat,' he said.

'Neither can I,' she agreed. 'My stomach feels like a coffee-grinder. Sim, if they say we can visit Martin, you won't let them leave me behind, will you?' Seeing that she had surprised him, she urged, 'I'm not a kid any more. In fact, as soon as I've had my birthday I'm going to make Mother let me go to be a VAD.'

'All of us going off to the war? Mother won't like that.'

'You, too?'

'Yes, especially if Martin is out of it. We drew straws to see which of us should volunteer. It makes me feel sick now to remember how lightly we treated it.'

'You'd only just come home from China,' Melissa remembered. 'You'd been gone for so long – I hardly knew you.'

It occurred to Simeon that they still knew very little of one another, in spite of living in the same house for the last two years. When he had come back from China Melissa had been a leggy schoolgirl with her hair in a plait down her back. Now she was a young woman, with that hair turned up and tied in a big black bow at the nape of her neck. She was very much in the family pattern, a brown-haired, brown-eyed girl, with good bone structure.

'What do you want to do with yourself – apart from being a VAD?' he asked abruptly.

'I'd like to be a doctor,' Melissa said. 'I'm still a bit young to get into Medical School – if they accept me, which is doubtful; it's quite difficult for a woman. So, I thought I'd join another branch of the medical profession, just to ease my way in, you know. And, of course, I'm a suffragette and mean to campaign for votes for women.'

'Shall I come home one day and find you chained to the railings?'

'Don't laugh. I take it seriously.'

'Well, so do I. I mean, I'm in favour of universal suffrage.'

'But you don't do anything about it, do you?'

There was no reply to that, since his support for the women's cause was strictly theoretical.

'I had no idea we were cherishing such a strong-minded woman in the family,' he said.

'You do rather tend to go about with your head in the clouds.'

Before Simeon could find a reply to that criticism, Julia and Nicholas returned.

'Three o'clock this afternoon,' Nicholas said. 'Just Julia and me today, but as soon as we've found out how he is then you children can go and visit him, too.'

'We've got a silver sale this afternoon,' Simeon reminded him. 'Do you want me to handle it?'

'Can you?'

'Of course.'

'May I come and watch?' Melissa asked.

'Glad to have you to swell the crowd,' Simeon said with feeling. 'Business is not exactly brisk at the moment.'

'Shall I run the prices up for you?'

'No! The sight of you bidding will put me completely off my stroke.'

'And anything you buy – accidentally or otherwise – you'll pay for,' Nicholas said. 'Which will put your allowance in jeopardy for many months to come, young lady.'

They were all making jokes, suddenly light-hearted at the thought of Martin back in the safety of England once more.

'But we mustn't forget he's wounded,' Julia said, with one of the lightning swoops of thought to which she was prone.

That was what haunted Simeon all day, even when he was on the rostrum and conducting a decidedly lacklustre auction of some fine English silver. It occurred to him, too late, that this would have been an opportunity to invest in something for his own future, and for a moment he regretted not having given young Melissa a commission to bid for him. Then he remembered his resolve to join up, and put the old silver out of his mind.

Melissa had not come alone to the auction. He recognised immediately the girl who sat by her side, even though, like Melissa, she seemed to have grown up all of a sudden. Melissa had been a very ordinary schoolgirl who had begun to blossom late, but Jane Camperdine had always been a potential beauty and she was now a real headturner. Her Oriental heritage seemed to have been emphasised; even her eyes had an intriguing slant he did not remember them having before.

Simeon had been neglecting the Camperdines. He acknowledged it, and admitted to himself that it was because he had no great liking for Olga Camperdine. All the same, Terence had been his very good friend and mentor, and he ought not to have let the man's family slip out of his mind so easily.

To salve his conscience he went out of his way to speak to the girls once the sale was over.

'Both you and Melissa seem to have grown up while my head was turned the other way,' he said to Jane.

'I wasn't a child when I came back to England,' she said.

'Can I take the pair of you to tea at the Ritz?'

The two girls looked at one another uncertainly.

'We don't really believe in conspicuous consumption while the country is at war,' Melissa explained.

'You can always say no to the cucumber sandwiches.'

'Don't be flippant, Simeon. We're serious,' Jane told him.

Stifling his amusement at their earnestness, Simeon persuaded them out of the building and into Piccadilly.

'If you can't reconcile yourselves to the Ritz there's Fortnum & Mason or Brown's Hotel,' he offered.

'No, if we're abandoning our principles we may as well go the whole hog,' Jane said. 'The Ritz it is, but I wish I'd worn my best hat.'

'What's wrong with the one you're wearing?'

'It's a going-to-an-auction-with-Melissa hat, not a tea-at-the-Ritz hat.'

When Simeon and Melissa went to visit Martin the next day, they found him propped up in his hospital bed with a cage supporting the bedclothes over his injured leg. He looked thin and tired, and there was a nerve in his cheek that twitched involuntarily until he put up his hand and held it still.

'You look pretty awful,' Simeon said.

'Oh, thanks, that's just the sort of greeting to do me good. Actually, I'm not too bad except for my rotten leg.'

'From what Mother and Father said after talking to the doctors yesterday, you were lucky not to lose your foot.'

'They've made a splendid job of sewing it back on, or so they say – it looks pretty gruesome to me. Do you want a peep?'

'No thanks, and I'm sure Melissa doesn't either.'

'I ought to nerve myself because of being a VAD and, I hope, a doctor one day, but it's sort of different when it's your own brother,' Melissa said uncertainly.

'There's nothing to see, really,' Martin said quickly. 'Just a few stitches and a bit of plaster.'

They already knew that there would be permanent damage, but Simeon was not sure whether Martin himself knew this until he went on, 'It's always going to be stiff and apparently I'm likely to be invalided out.'

'My chance next,' Simeon said.

'You don't have to go, Sim, not until you're called.'

'Yes, I do. You know I always meant to volunteer. I'm the eldest, after all, and if it hadn't been for the fact that I'd only just come back from China, I would have overruled you and not let you take my place.'

There was no point in saying that the carnage he had witnessed in China was still a loathsome memory. It would be even worse in France – just looking at his brother was enough to tell him that.

'Why don't you try for the Royal Flying Corps?' Martin suggested. 'It would suit you, tootling around in your own little aeroplane. You've always been a bit of a loner.'

'That's an interesting idea. You're right, the idea of flying is more appealing than slogging through the trenches. I wonder whether they'd have me?'

'Only one way to find out.'

'I'll make enquiries. Melissa, keep this to yourself. Mother is going to have kittens when she knows I've made up my mind to go.'

'And the thought of her little boy in one of those rackety flying machines will be most unwelcome,' Martin said.

'You neither of you understand Mother in the least,' Melissa said. 'Honestly, *men*! You think you're so strong, but we women have got twice your guts.'

'We women! Will you listen to the child!'

'I am *not* a child,' Melissa said, glaring at him.

'Stop teasing her, Martin. And calm down, Melissa. We're supposed to be cheering the boy up, not having a family quarrel.'

Martin looked at Melissa with an unrepentant grin and reluctantly she smiled back.

'How long are you likely to be in here?' Simeon asked.

'Not much longer, but then I've got to go to a convalescent home where they'll make me do exercises to stop my leg shrinking and get my ankle joint working again – as far as that's possible. I'll probably end up with a bit of a limp.'

'Very appealing. There's nothing like an *obvious* wound to bring the girls flocking round.'

'All my girls seem to have deserted me – got married or taken up nursing or become land girls or taken driving jobs . . . That reminds me, Simeon, I bumped into a friend of yours before I caught my piece of shrapnel. Very upper-class and domineering – a Lady Francesca Kenrick.'

'I wouldn't exactly call her a friend. We only met once.'

'You seem to have made an impression. When she realised you were my brother she gave me a message for you.'

'You've taken your time to deliver it.'

'Quite slipped my mind, what with one thing and another – the Battle of the Somme and being wounded – you know, just little things. Besides, I didn't know what she was talking about. Something Chinese about living in interesting times.'

'It's an ancient Chinese curse – "May you live in interesting times", meaning that days of peace and plenty are uneventful.'

'And war is interesting! I see. She said you'd understand.'

'How did you come across her?'

'She was driving an ambulance in our sector. My word, she's a cool lady. I helped her load up some of our chaps and we had a cigarette together before she took off. She asked me what I did in civvy street and I told her and she laughed and said I must be your brother and next time I saw you to tell you she'd found out the truth of this Chinese saying. Then off she drove and I went back into the line and a nasty Hun lobbed a shell at me.'

'Poor Martin,' Melissa said.

'At last, some sympathy! I thought you'd never get round to it. Yes – poor Martin. I need petting and spoiling and cosseting. Haven't you got any nice girlfriends who'd like the job, Melissa?'

'Well, there's Jane.'

'Jane Camperdine? Hm, sweet little thing, as I remember. Trot her out and I'll let her hold my hand.'

'You're in for a surprise,' Simeon said, getting up to go. 'Jane has turned into a remarkably lovely girl.'

'They will do it,' Martin said. 'Even Melissa here isn't at all bad on a dull day with her back to the light.'

'Beast! I'll bring Jane to visit you, but I'll warn her first that you're the worst flirt in the world.'

Chapter Fourteen

The sky above him was blue. Below him was a wisp of cloud, so fragile that it might be dispersed by the wind of his passing. Simeon searched the horizon. German aeroplanes had been seen heading in this direction and he had been sent up to intercept them.

He whistled softly and unconsciously, all his attention given to the business of flying his Sopwith Camel while at the same time keeping a sharp watch to make sure he was not taken by surprise.

Martin was right, the life of a fighter pilot *did* suit Simeon. He picked up the elements of flying in a few hectic weeks of training and had been in action since early 1917. He had come through the month which became known as 'bloody April', when the losses in the Royal Flying Corps were appalling, had earned a word of commendation for surviving one crash-landing and managing to bring his aeroplane back more or less in one piece – though at that point the aircraft were less expensive to replace than the pilots – and he was credited with five definite 'kills' and a lot of useful skirmishing which had driven German aeroplanes away from their targets.

He banked and turned in a long, sweeping circle to check that he was not about to be approached from the rear, and then he saw a dot in the distance, a second . . . and a third. Long odds for a solitary fighter pilot, but if he could take them from above and out of the sun he stood a good chance of making a kill.

The target he selected was a Fokker, and Simeon was on top of it before the pilot knew he was there. Simeon saw bullet holes in the fuselage and then, sickeningly, the pilot slumped in his seat and Simeon knew that he was already dead as his aircraft spiralled down to the ground.

It had been too easy, and the other German pilots were not going to let him get away with it. There were bullets singing through the air all round him as he climbed to evade them. One bullet smacked through the windscreen, but that was minor damage and nothing essential seemed to have been hit.

He dived now for the second Fokker, and heard himself scream in exultation as flames broke out from the engine. He saw a flash of white as he broke away. The pilot had baled out and Simeon was relieved to see his parachute open as he began to drift to the ground.

Checking on that aspect had distracted him for a crucial moment. He had lost height and position, and the enemy pilot of the third German aeroplane must be desperate for revenge. Simeon would have liked to call it a day and turn for home, but first he had to deal with the remaining menace.

For about two minutes, which seemed like eternity, they jockeyed for position. No point in firing when there was nothing in your sights. Where the devil had the bastard gone? A violent shock at the rear of the Sopwith gave Simeon the answer: he was being attacked from behind.

He screamed towards the ground and then went into the steepest climb he had ever attempted, praying that the aeroplane wouldn't stall. The German was coming after him, but Simeon thought he had the greater manoeuvrability. He flattened out and put the joystick over and there was a sudden appalling lack of response. His aeroplane was damaged and he had no idea when it had happened. He was lucky not to be dead already considering the strain he had put on the Sopwith, but he was certainly going to catch it now when the German realised that he was almost a sitting target. Even as he thought this, he was hit by a hail of bullets. He felt a sharp pain, red-hot and piercing, through his right arm and his plane began to lose height.

As the ground came up to meet him Simeon abandoned any hope of using his parachute. His arm was too excruciatingly painful, but if he could get the plane under control and if the German didn't come after him, he still had a chance. *If* . . .

With a terrible shock Simeon realised that he had lost consciousness for a moment, but he was still flying – and the German seemed content to leave him alone to crash. Except that he was not going to crash.

He was still going down, but slowly . . . gliding rather than crashing. He had done this before. If he wasn't careful he'd get a reputation for bringing home aeroplanes that ought to have been written off. He was barely above the trees, then hedge-hopping and then, finally, he put the aeroplane down, nose in the ground and damaged tail at a ridiculous angle, in a soft ploughed field.

Climbing out of the cockpit was an almost impossible feat, and his clumsy tumble down on the ground was agony. He put up his left hand to his mouth and took it away wet with blood where he had bitten through his lip. Laboriously, he staggered a few yards before collapsing. He lay there, too spent to do more, knowing that although the essential effort had been made he was still too near the damaged aeroplane for safety.

Miraculously, it seemed that there was to be no explosion. After lying on his back with his eyes closed for five minutes he felt sufficiently recovered to try to get up again.

He had no idea where he was, except that safety was to the south-east and danger was to the north-west. The little cloud he had noticed when he had first taken to the air had spread itself into a mantle of grey, but he could still see the position of the sun. Doggedly, dragging his feet over the sticky damp soil, Simeon set out to find some sort of habitation.

It took him twenty minutes to locate the farm. By that time rain was falling steadily. He was wet through and he had lost a lot of blood.

There was a farmyard and a house, with an open door, and he could hear voices. Two women, working at a big wooden table in the middle of the room, fell silent and looked round as his arrival blocked out the light.

'*Je suis anglais*,' Simeon said. '*Un aviateur . . .*'

The last thing he remembered was an extraordinary blackness rushing towards him as he fainted, falling on his damaged arm. He thought that he screamed, but the two women heard nothing as they rushed to his aid, exclaiming in horror at the plight of the poor young man.

Simeon was dimly aware of a jolting ride over country roads, of a pain in his arm about which he tried to protest, and then oblivion.

He woke up in a hospital tent and a nurse came to him as soon as she saw he was conscious.

'Lie still,' she said. 'You've only a minor wound, but you're very weak. Be good and we'll soon have you on your feet again.'

He ran his tongue over his dry lips and she raised his head to give him a sip of water.

'My family . . .' he said.

'They'll be told all about it. Don't worry. Just rest.'

It was all very well to say rest, but now that he had come to himself, his arm was extremely uncomfortable and he had a nasty pain in his chest.

'I . . . hurt,' he said.

'I expect you do. You've had a bullet dug out of your arm.'

'Here.' He managed to put his undamaged hand on his chest.

'I'll prop you up a bit higher. Let's see what the thermometer says.'

What the thermometer said was disquieting. The nurse smiled as she gave it a professional flick to send the mercury down again.

'Nothing to worry about,' she said, but as soon as Simeon was settled she went and reported to the Sister.

He had pneumonia, and it was rather more serious than the wound which had put him in hospital. He was weak from loss of blood, he had asked too much of his body when he was in a state of shock, and he had been soaked to the skin before he had received any treatment.

For several days Simeon drifted in and out of consciousness, vaguely aware that people were worried about him and that it was extraordinarily difficult to breathe, and then quite suddenly he knew he was going to get better. It was something he had experienced before. The memory eluded him, since he could never remember having been through a severe illness, and then it came back. It was just the same as when he had realised that he had got over his searing desire for Anna. He had thought then that he was like a man coming out of a long sickness – and he was right. Now he felt the same weakness, the same desire to be left alone to drift through days that were no longer filled with pain, and eventually the same reluctant acceptance that life still had to be lived.

By that time he had been moved out of the Field Hospital and into a nearby town, where he was nursed in a convent. It was on the day that the regretful thought entered his mind that it was just his luck that the nurses were nuns and not pretty young girls that Simeon admitted that he was more or less cured.

He had a visit from two of his squadron, who twitted him, just as he had expected, on his ability to walk away from wrecked aircraft.

'We were quite gloomy about you for a day or two, started calling you Lost Hope, but of course we should have known you'd turn up. By the way, did you know you were a hero?'

'Of course I know,' Simeon said indignantly. 'I was there, wasn't I? Huns on every side of me, bullets whizzing, Fokkers diving and me, cool as a cucumber, putting them down right, left and centre.'

'Two was what we heard.'

'It felt like twenty,' Simeon said with feeling.

'It looks as if you'll get a gong out of it.'

'A medal? Oh lord, I don't want that.'

'Ungrateful hound. Take what your King and Country give you and try to look modest. Actually, we're mildly pleased about it. It was time one of us got something.'

They stood up to go, but before they left they gave him the most welcome news of all.

'You're being sent back to Blighty, lucky devil. Someone thinks you ought to convalesce before you come back and win the war for us.'

The following day he was sent in an ambulance to Calais. He was none too steady on his legs, but at least he was walking, and although his arm was in a sling it was healing rapidly and he would have full use of it, not like some of the poor devils who were sharing his journey.

The driver of his ambulance was a brisk young woman and he asked her idly, 'Have you come across a driver called Francesca Kenrick?'

'Yes, rather. Fran's one of our team. Are you a friend of hers?'

'Just an acquaintance. If you happen to see her you might say that Simeon Hope sends his regards, coupled with the name of Kuan Yin.'

'I'll do that – if I can remember it. Who's Kuan Yin when he's at home?'

'She, not he. Lady Francesca will know.'

He was kept waiting for forty-eight hours in a tented clearing station because of the need to ship more urgent cases back to

England. Indeed, Simeon suspected that his own return owed more to the exploits for which he was to be honoured than his wound. He was passing the time away with a dog-eared Edgar Wallace novel when someone stopped by his chair and, looking up, he saw Francesca Kenrick herself, very trim and not a hair out of place. It was something of a surprise to realise how well he had retained the memory of her sharply cut features.

'Greetings in the name of the Goddess of Mercy,' she said.

'I thought you'd get the point,' Simeon said, struggling to his feet.

'Don't get up and don't offer to fetch me a chair. I'm fitter than you are.'

'Actually, I'm the most terrible fraud,' Simeon told her as she sat down by his side. 'I'm perfectly all right and ought to stay in France and go back to duty.'

'You still look fragile. What's the trouble with your arm?'

'A perfectly clean bullet wound. Unfortunately, I went down with pneumonia, that's why I'm still looking pale and interesting.'

'Take your time, get properly fit. I don't think we're going to have a victory this year, even though the Americans have come in.'

'Have you met any of them yet? I seem never to have been in the right place.'

'Yes, they've been all over my sector. A grand lot.' She paused and smiled. 'A little too sure that they're going to get right in there and win the war in a couple of months, but a bit of battle experience will calm them down.'

'I wish I could see any end to it.'

'That's the weakness of your illness speaking. The end's in sight, truly it is. Not today, not tomorrow, but we will win.'

'The official line,' Simeon murmured.

'Let's talk about something else. What do you think of this?' She felt in her pocket and pulled out a small silken pouch. Untying the cords she removed a piece of jade.

'It's a funeral piece, isn't it?' Simeon said, taking it from her. 'A plaque from one of those wonderful suits of jade found in ancient tombs.'

'That's what I thought. I found it in a tiny junkshop in Amiens and the following day . . . .' She stopped and then said carefully,

196

'We had a bit of trouble on the road and I was lucky to survive. I've carried it ever since as a good luck piece.'

'Were you shot up?' Simeon asked.

'Yes. I'm charitable enough to believe that it might have been a mistake. One of their beastly aeroplanes dived on us . . . Do you really like flying?'

'I love it.'

'It takes all sorts. Well, I'll have to go. I just took a moment between loads to come and have a word with you.'

She was going and he wanted her to stay.

'I mean to go on flying when peace breaks out,' he said. 'One of these days I'll take you up.'

'That might be interesting,' Francesca smiled.

'Look, I can see you're on duty and can't linger, but perhaps when times are better, when we're both back in London, we could meet?'

'Why not? All we have to do first is survive.'

With a cool nod she walked away, and Simeon was left knowing that he had not only come back to life, but that he had discovered a completely new reason for living.

'How's business?' Simeon asked.

'Poor,' Martin admitted. 'We get the occasional war profiteer putting his ill-gotten gains into antique furniture, but on the whole we're doing badly. Father's worried.'

'I started to talk to him once about reorganising the company, but I didn't get very far.'

'He'll have to face up to it if we're to survive, because we're going to need fresh capital.'

'That'll mean bringing in someone from outside the family. Father won't like that.'

'No, but he'll have to come round to it.'

'I suppose there's not much to be done until after the war.'

'We talk about "after the war" as if we were travelling towards some Promised Land,' Martin said. 'If you ask me, "after the war" is going to be almost as grim as "during the war".'

'Not quite,' Simeon said mildly. 'At least we won't be getting killed.'

They were walking slowly along Piccadilly, back to the Sale

197

Rooms, after lunching together. Martin made light of his injury, but he could not walk without the aid of a stick, and Simeon suspected that he suffered more pain than he admitted. Simeon had been released from his convalescent home and was spending a short time at home on leave, during which he would go to Buckingham Palace to receive his Distinguished Flying Cross.

'Mother's in ecstasies about your decoration,' Martin said. 'The only trouble is, she can't quite see why we haven't both got a medal.'

'She's probably right,' Simeon said. 'Knocking aeroplanes out of the sky is spectacular, but you did as much as I did, if not more. She won't be pleased to learn that I go back to France forty-eight hours after the Investiture.'

Julia and Nicholas went with him to the Investiture, Julia in a new hat and Nicholas in a morning suit which he was annoyed to discover had become slightly tight round the waist. Even in war-time, Buckingham Palace was a blaze of gilt and brocade. Simeon, suppressing a nervousness he was ashamed of feeling, got through the ceremony without falling over his own feet or forgetting the protocol. The King, in uniform himself and looking smaller than Simeon had expected, only ever having seen him on horseback or riding in a carriage, spoke a few sentences which Simeon had difficulty in remembering afterwards, and he managed to reply in a way that must have been acceptable because the King smiled and nodded as if he were pleased with him.

'Darling, it was wonderful and I'm so proud I could burst,' Julia said afterwards.

Simeon had vetoed lunch in a public place after the ceremony, but he had agreed to go to Hope's to have a glass of champagne with the staff.

'A lot of them are old hands who've known you since you were a boy,' Nicholas said. 'It'll mean a lot to them if you come in with your medal on your chest.'

The champagne was served in the main Sale Room, still decorated in the sage green Nicholas had chosen to replace the dark red Vittorio had favoured. It was looking shabby, Simeon thought, but of course in war-time that could not be helped. The other thing that struck him, looking round the smiling faces, was that the average age of the firm's employees was well over fifty –

and many of them were in their sixties. Again, that was something that had been brought about by the war, but younger blood would be needed if they were to regain their former position.

'Melissa!' Julia suddenly exclaimed as her daughter made her way through the small crowd of people.

'Matron gave me the afternoon off,' Melissa said. 'She didn't relent until this morning, so I couldn't let you know. And look, I've brought Jane with me. We told Matron she was Simeon's fiancée.'

Simeon could see that his mother was not quite pleased by that piece of deception, so he rushed into speech.

'I wish you'd told me earlier that I was engaged,' he said plaintively. 'I could have done very nicely with a fiancée who looks like Jane.'

He was relieved to see the anxious look in Jane's eyes disappear. She was breathtakingly lovely, a creature of monotones, ivory skin, dark hair, dark eyes, the only touch of colour in her face a mouth the colour of coral. Simeon was conscious of real regret that he had not had the benefit of this beautiful girl's company during his brief leave.

She was smiling, blushing a little at his open admiration, but when Simeon tried to keep her in conversation he noticed that her attention had wandered. He glanced over his shoulder and realised that Martin had walked away and was standing with his back to them, a little too studiously engaged in talking to a clerk from the Furniture Department. Turning back to Jane, Simeon caught a fleeting expression on her face that startled him, a look of hurt, quickly banished, which made him wonder just what had passed between his brother and the girl he had brought back from China when she was no more than a child.

There was too little time for finesse. He tackled Martin about it as soon as he could get him on his own. The pair of them had escaped, as they had so often done in the past, to the garden in the centre of the square, for a bit of peace and quiet and a cigarette.

'We ought to have brought the girls out with us. I daresay they need a breath of fresh air after being cooped up in a hospital day after day,' Simeon said deliberately.

'Mm.' That noncommittal murmur was all the response he got from Martin.

'I always knew Jane would turn into a beauty,' Simeon persisted.

'Your fiancée,' Martin said.

'Young Melissa's got a nerve. I could see Mother didn't quite like it.'

'I expect you could bring Ma round if you decided to make it true.'

'Don't be daft, Martin. It was only a joke, an expedient to get a few hours' leave.'

'Jane went along with it,' Martin pointed out. 'She's always looked up to you, ever since she was a child in Shanghai. If I were you, I'd be tempted to hold her to it.'

'You've got it wrong. Jane's not for me.' As he spoke Simeon was haunted by the memory of another face, fair and clear-cut; not the face of a girl but of a woman, the eyes a little weary, the mouth too tightly set, the face of a woman who had been through the fire and had come out singed.

'I couldn't talk to Jane about my wicked past,' he said. 'I can't marry a woman unless I can be frank with her. Besides, I don't want a girl who's in love with my brother.'

'You're talking nonsense,' Martin said roughly.

'Am I? Just how much did you see of her after I'd gone off to France?'

'Oh . . . quite a bit. Then I started thinking . . .'

'Not a thing you're very good at, bruv.'

'Damn you, Simeon! Look at her! Lovely as a picture. Then look at me. A damaged crock with a stake in an ailing business. Why should she care two pins for me?'

'God knows, but I think she does. It's not like you to be so humble.'

'I took a course in humiliation when I discovered how difficult it was to walk up and down stairs.'

This almost silenced Simeon, but he rallied and pressed on.

'There are going to be a lot of men as badly injured as you, and worse. Are the girls to stay unmarried because there are too few perfect specimens left?'

Before Martin could find an answer to that they were interrupted by Melissa coming into the square to find them. Jane was with her, but it seemed to Simeon that she hung back, as if reluctant to intrude.

'We've only another half an hour before we have to start back,' Melissa said. 'It's been marvellous, and the champagne is definitely going to help me through the rest of the day, but I've hardly seen you, Simeon. Come and talk to me.' She put her hand through his arm and pressed it as if to convey some special meaning, before leading him away to the far end of the garden.

'Why are you dragging me away from my fiancée?' Simeon asked plaintively, amused by these tactics.

'Because I hope a bit of jealousy will have brought Martin to his senses,' Melissa said. 'Jane's besotted about him. Odd, isn't it? She's quite sensible in other ways.'

'That sounds like a girl who's never been in love,' Simeon remarked.

'I know. I feel quite despondent about it because the other nurses seem to be in love with someone all the time. Do you think there's something wrong with me? Oh, dear, they're not even talking to one another.'

'Walk on, out of sight. They can't stand there in silence for ever.'

It seemed like for ever to Martin. Brought face to face with the girl who haunted his thoughts night and day he could find nothing to say, and it did not help that Jane herself stood silent, looking at him with troubled eyes.

'I've been sounding Simeon out about holding you to your engagement,' he said, knowing that it was a silly thing to say. 'How do you feel about it?'

'Simeon is my friend and has been ever since I was a little girl. I wouldn't marry him, though,' Jane said.

'We were saying it was going to be hard on girls like you – young, beautiful, with all your lives before you – having to make do with old crocks like me for husbands.' He stopped and then added hastily, 'Not that you won't have your pick of anything that's going.'

He stopped again, miserably aware that none of that speech was likely to endear him to Jane.

'An old crock like you would do me very nicely for a husband,' Jane said. She waited for this to sink in and then continued, 'Of course, I wouldn't marry a man who didn't love me.'

'Who could help loving you?' Martin said.

'And I wouldn't marry a man I didn't love.'

'You don't,' Martin said uncertainly, 'you couldn't . . . Jane, you don't mean . . . you wouldn't really, would you?'

'If that's meant to be a proposal, then I've got one answer – yes – and one question – *when*?' Jane said.

Then they were clasped tightly in one another's arms, kissing and murmuring incoherently, oblivious to passers-by and to Simeon and Melissa when they strolled back.

'I say, that's my fiancée you're kissing,' Simeon complained.

Martin released Jane and looked round. 'Hands off, this one's mine,' he said with a grin.

'I must say that's most satisfactory,' Melissa said. 'Though it's going to be difficult to explain to Matron that I took you out engaged to one brother, Jane, and brought you back engaged to another.'

When Simeon went back to the Front, everyone took it for granted that there was little hope of him getting leave so that he could be his brother's best man. What no one anticipated was Mrs Camperdine's adamant refusal to consent to Jane's marriage.

'Jane, dear, you're only nineteen,' she said. 'This dreadful war has been going on ever since you began to grow up, and working in that hospital has given you no chance to meet the right sort of man. I really think you should be free to look around before you tie yourself down.'

'There's no point in looking around when I've already seen what I want: I'm going to marry Martin.'

'Of course he's very charming, though it's a pity he limps in that nasty way. He'll never be able to dance with you.'

'I'm not marrying for a dancing partner.'

'No, dear, I hope I brought you up to think more seriously than that.'

Jane looked at her mother disbelievingly as she fell silent. Was she really going to say no more than that?

'What do you have against Martin?' she demanded.

'Frankly, dear, I think you can do better for yourself.'

'In what way? To me, Martin seems an absolutely ideal husband. He has enough money to live on, a career in a family business, he's interesting and everyone likes him – except you, apparently – and on top of all that he loves me and I love him.'

'I don't dislike Martin. As you say, he's a very pleasant young man – but rather lightweight, don't you think? I can't say I've ever seen any signs of him working very hard.'

'That's Martin's way,' Jane said quickly. 'In fact, he takes his responsibilities very seriously.'

'Well . . . I'll have to take your word for that. But for all his good points I think you should wait until the war is over before you marry him.'

'I can't shake her,' Jane said to Martin in despair.

'She thinks I don't deserve you, and you know I agree with her over that,' Martin said.

'It's not a question of deserving, not when it comes to love,' Jane said sadly. 'What are we to do?'

'Be patient, I suppose. It's going to be hard, and I don't like it, but I can't very well run off with you.'

'Why not?' Jane muttered.

'Because it would be a bad start for us,' Martin said, kissing her. 'What we have to do is to tie your mother down to a promise that we can get married when the war is over.'

'You think that'll be before I'm twenty-one?'

'I'm sure of it. Within the next year, without a doubt. If the war is still going on by Christmas 1918 then we'll take off for Gretna Green, you and I.'

'Oh, lovely!'

'In the meantime, there's no reason why we shouldn't consider ourselves engaged. Try this on and see if you like it.'

Jane held out her hand. 'Put it on for me.'

She looked so long at the ruby set in diamonds and gold that Martin said anxiously, 'If you don't care for it the jeweller is perfectly ready to change it, but when I saw this ring I thought it looked right for you.'

'I love it,' Jane said, looking up and smiling through a dazzle of unshed tears. 'And I love you.'

When Simeon heard that Martin's marriage had been delayed he was philosophical. His brother was lucky to have secured a lovely girl like Jane. He had her promise and Simeon doubted whether she would go back on it. As for Olga Camperdine, her attitude did not surprise him since he had suspected she was hungry for social success and could imagine that she had hoped for a grand marriage for her beautiful daughter.

Simeon was feeling melancholy. He still enjoyed flying, he was doing some useful sorties, but he never again reached the heights of daring that had won him his Distinguished Flying Cross. He had to admit that what had unsettled him was Martin's engagement: his brother's happiness showed up a little too plainly the emptiness in his own life.

'Cheer up, chum. You've got a face like a wet week,' one of his squadron told him. 'What do you think of this – we're invited to a New Year's party at the local château. The old Comte's opening it up because he thinks this'll be the last year of the war. There'll be girls! Just think of it. You remember girls, don't you?'

'My memory does go back that far,' Simeon agreed.

In his present mood the thought of a party, with or without girls, was not particularly enticing. He toyed with the idea of volunteering to remain on duty, but in the end he let himself be persuaded to go along.

The château was a jewel of a house and fortunately only slightly damaged by shelling in the earlier months of the war. It dated back to the late seventeenth century, and Simeon loved the strict classical lines on which it was built. He had visited it more than once, but now the windows had been unshuttered and the house had come alive.

There were a few of the family heirlooms on view, too. Simeon, a glass of wine in his hand, paused to consider something in his own line, a large powder-blue vase decorated with leaping fish.

'Kangxi period, I think, don't you?' a voice behind him remarked.

Simeon turned quickly. He always remembered the way Francesca looked at that moment, amused at having taken him by surprise, raising her glass to her lips and smiling at him over the rim. She was wearing a pre-war evening gown of pale green satin sewn with crystal beads. Not that he was aware of the details, only that she looked like a water creature with her fair hair and white skin and the shimmering material slithering round her long limbs.

'Undoubtedly Kangxi,' he said. 'How very nice to see you again.'

'Thank you. You recovered completely from your wound?'

'I told you I was a fraud.'

'Congratulations on your decoration.'

'Oh . . . that. Thanks.'

Francesca's smile deepened at his embarrassment. 'There's a most curious carved box over in the corner,' she said. 'Come and have a look.'

She led him to the corner and together they examined the intricately decorated box.

'Japanese, do you think?' Francesca asked.

'Mm . . . I'd hazard a guess at Korean,' Simeon replied.

'Let's ask our host. Antoine . . .'

The Comte came towards them, smiling at Francesca, and Simeon admired and was slightly intimidated by the way she immediately slipped into perfect French to put the question to him.

Simeon spoke the language sufficiently well to gather that his identification of the piece had been correct.

'Congratulations again,' Francesca said. 'My own specialisation has been too narrow, I know. I wish I had your wider knowledge of Oriental art.'

'After the war . . .' Simeon said automatically.

'Yes, perhaps. My old uncle has died and I don't know whether the Museum will go on employing me without him to turn the screw.'

'You'll have to come to me for a job.'

'I might do that. Though, actually, dear old Uncle Mark has seen me all right and left me a decent amount of money. The family is furious.'

'So you don't have to earn a living any more?'

'No, but that's not to say I might not want to.'

'We never met in London,' Simeon said abruptly.

'I don't think I've been home since we ran into one another in Calais. I've had leave, but I spent it in Paris.'

Alone? Simeon had almost asked the question aloud before he realised that he had no right to know.

'That's the trouble with war-time,' he said instead. 'One meets people one would like to see again and circumstances make it impossible.'

'True. Tell me about your time in China.'

They stayed together, talking with concentrated absorption, for the rest of the evening.

'I almost didn't come,' Simeon said as midnight drew near.

'You're glad you did?'

'Very glad.'

The old Comte thumped on the floor with his stick and held up a hand as the clock began to wheeze in preparation for striking midnight. As the cries of 'Happy New Year' and '*Bonne Année*' broke out Simeon turned to Francesca and took her in his arms. The kiss he pressed on her lips was no mere gesture of goodwill, but the lingering kiss of a lover.

He thought when he let her go that she was looking pale.

'Watch your step, pilot,' she said in a voice that was unconvincingly facetious. 'I'm not good news. Fly away from me.'

'Nonsense! I'm not letting you go tonight without getting your address, and the sooner we can meet again the better I'll be pleased.'

Chapter Fifteen

'What we need is a complete reorganisation.'

'I agree, and now that you and Martin are safely home from the war, I mean to put it in hand. In fact, I put out a feeler to see whether there was any hope of acquiring the part of the company owned by Anna and Violetta. After all, Papa can never have anticipated that his second wife and both his daughters would end up living on the other side of the Atlantic and, what's more, all married to rich men.'

'That would have made you absolute owner of Hope's,' Simeon said.

'I meant, of course, to pass their three-eighths on to you boys, to give you a suitable stake in the business. However, that idea has been scuppered.'

'They wouldn't sell?'

'Violetta was interested, but before I could take the matter any further, Anna stepped in. She had information which I lacked: Violetta will never have any children. Anna has done a deal with her sister by which the holding in Hope's passes to Anna and ultimately to her . . . children.'

Martin took a look at his brother, but Simeon was doodling with his pencil on the pad in front of him and refused to look up.

'There is only the one child, isn't there?' Martin asked.

'She and Brad had a daughter who died at birth,' Nicholas said. 'Apart from that there's only Victor.'

'I don't altogether like it,' Martin said.

'Neither do I,' Nicholas agreed.

'She won't do us any harm,' Simeon said, still intent on his drawing.

'Probably not, but it's a big holding for one person with no interest in running the business, and it spoils my plan for giving you and Martin a share in the company.'

'It was a generous idea, but neither of us has enough money to buy our way in and that's what's needed – fresh capital.'

'And fresh blood,' Martin said. 'Our staff are growing old. We need people with good contacts and a bit of drive who will seek out business instead of waiting for it to come to us.'

'I think we should become a private limited company, with a share issue on offer to a few selected partners,' Nicholas said.

'Where does that leave Martin and me – and, come to that, Melissa?'

'Melissa is enrolling in Medical School and I take it that neither of you two means to go on living at home indefinitely?'

'Now that we've stopped fighting the Germans I'm turning the guns on Mrs Camperdine,' Martin said. 'Jane and I will be married very soon and then, of course, we'll want a home of our own.'

'Simeon?'

'I'll be looking for a place of my own, too.'

'So, you see, we don't need that great house in Eaton Square any more. Once that's disposed of and I've found a more modest home, I'll have sufficient capital in hand to secure you both a holding in the firm.'

'That's very generous of you,' Simeon said.

'Nonsense! I need your help. What I'd like from you now is ideas about possible new partners. Do you know any rich, well-connected young men who might like to join us?'

'I have one idea . . . though it's not a man,' Simeon said. 'I think she might be interested – I'd certainly like to persuade her. Lady Francesca Kenrick.'

He was aware of his brother's quick, interested look, but most of his attention was focused on his father. Nicholas's reaction was more than negative, it was hostile.

'She's knowledgeable and she's certainly well-connected,' Simeon pointed out.

'I was under the impression that her family had thrown her out,' Nicholas said drily.

'Not all of them. One of her uncles not only found her a way of earning a living, but when he died he left her his fortune.'

He waited until at last Nicholas burst out, 'It's not just the girl herself, it's the whole family. I don't like them.'

'Why not?'

'Their morals . . . It's ancient history, I know, but Lady Francesca's grandfather jilted your grandmother.'

'Really?' Martin sat up, looking interested. 'I say, the things we don't know!'

'And her father was Serafina's lover.'

That silenced both his sons.

'I didn't know that,' Simeon admitted. 'All the same, do we have to hold the sins of the father against the daughter? It's not very logical.'

Uneasily, Nicholas realised that part of his distaste arose from the guilty knowledge that both he and his father had benefited from the secret hoard of diamonds which should, strictly speaking, have belonged to the Kenrick family. No one was going to find that out, not at this late date, but the recollection made him uncomfortable.

'I'd better break it to you that I mean to marry Francesca,' Simeon said. He had finally put it into words, the decision that had been forming at the back of his mind for months.

'I didn't realise you knew her so well,' Nicholas said, startled.

'I don't. We met in the Sale Room and a couple of times in France and I've seen her once or twice since I was demobbed. I've said nothing to her and I don't know how she feels about me, but I mean to make her my wife if I can.'

Watching his father and seeing his dismay, Simeon went on quietly, 'I'm thirty, Father. I've knocked about the world, I've fought in the war and I've been through a devastating emotional experience in my younger days. I know what I'm doing. Francesca is the only woman I could think of marrying.'

'My dear boy . . . it's your life and, of course, you're capable of running your own affairs. I don't like it, I can't pretend I do, but I don't know your Francesca, except . . .'

'Except by reputation,' Simeon said evenly. 'That's what worries you, isn't it? Pretty unfair, don't you think, to forgive my lapse and hold hers against her? You don't know the circumstances.'

'No. No, that's true.'

'And she had a pretty heroic war,' Martin put in.

'Of course, that's a great point in her favour,' Nicholas said unconvincingly. 'May I tell your mother?'

'Are you capable of keeping it from her?' Simeon asked with a smile.

'Probably not,' Nicholas admitted. 'Damn it all, I've never preached to you boys – at least, I hope I haven't – but the best thing I can wish for you is a good wife and a solid home life, and when I see you taking a risk I can't help feeling anxious. Simeon, I'll reserve judgement until I've met your Lady Francesca.'

'I think you'll come to value her.'

Simeon and Francesca dined at the Savoy, something that would hardly have been possible before the war for a young unmarried man and woman. Now, they passed unnoticed amongst the other diners and dancers.

'You dance divinely, Simeon,' Francesca remarked.

'Thank you, but I'm only as good as my partner,' he said with a smile. 'Francesca, I want to talk to you – seriously, I mean. May I come back to the flat?'

'Dear me, it must be important! You've always been so scrupulous about dropping me at the door!'

She was mocking him, but he had learned to know her well enough to realise that she had turned defensive, ready to repel him if he became what she called sentimental.

'It's a business proposition,' he said calmly.

'That'll be a change! I'm intrigued. Let's go.'

Back at the flat, she moved restlessly about the room, fetching him a drink, making one for herself and looking through the pile of gramophone records which stood on a side table.

'Don't turn on the gramophone. Come and sit down,' Simeon said.

She dropped down obediently at the other end of the large sofa on which he was sitting.

'Do you want a cigarette?' she asked.

'No, I do not want a cigarette. I want you to listen to me.'

'I'm listening.'

'Would you be interested in investing in Hope & Company and coming into the firm as a working partner?'

He guessed from her sudden stillness that this was the last thing she had expected.

'I've taken you by surprise?' he asked.

'You certainly have! I don't know what to say. Interested? Yes, very.'

'That's all I need to know, really. I can't talk facts and figures because it's a very new idea.'

'When you say a working partner . . .'

'Cataloguing, valuing, advising generally. You'd have a seat on the Board.'

'A woman?'

'Why not?'

'Why not indeed. The more I think about it, the better I like the idea. I've got plenty of money, thanks to Uncle Mark, but I'm at a loose end. Even if the Museum wanted me back, which they don't, I'd be reluctant to go. It's too much of a backwater.'

'Hope's must move into the twentieth century. I think you could do a lot for us.'

'Does your father agree?'

'He's doubtful, but not actively hostile. I think once he's talked to you he'll come round.'

Francesca was not given to showing excitement, but there was an unaccustomed flush along her high cheekbones and a sparkle in her eye that pleased Simeon.

'That's one hurdle crossed,' he said. 'I'm afraid I may fall at the second. Will you marry me?'

Francesca put her glass down on the table with a crash that nearly shattered it.

'Damn you, Simeon! Just as I was feeling happy! Does coming into the firm depend on being your wife?'

'No.'

'You must see that if I turn you down I can't very well be your business partner.'

'Why not? I shan't hold it against you. Of course, I shall keep on asking you, which you may find tiresome. Perhaps we could reach some agreement about it. I'll pop the question three or four times a year for five years. After that, if you're still adamant, I'll give up.'

In spite of her agitation, Francesca could not quite suppress a smile at his reasonable tone.

'Fool! Do you really think you'll be faithful that long?'

'Oh, yes. You're my woman. I only wish you would admit that I'm your man.'

'I like you. Sometimes I almost think I might fall in love with you. I'll be your mistress if you like.'

'Don't sound so bleak about it! If I thought it'd lead you into marriage I'd be tempted to close with that offer, but it would be an awkward situation – working together and sleeping together with no formal link between us. Sorry, it's marriage or nothing.'

'Then it's nothing. And I won't come into the company either.'

'Suit yourself.' Simeon drained his drink and stood up.

'You've heard about my lurid past,' Francesca said abruptly.

'I know you had an unfortunate love affair. So did I.'

'Oh, you! No one cares what men do.'

'My affair was a bit out of the ordinary. Perhaps I'd better tell you about it.'

He sat down again and Francesca shot him a quick look, knowing that he realised she had meant to delay his departure.

'It's something that has to be kept secret,' Simeon said. 'Not for my sake, but because there's a child involved and because Anna . . . poor Anna . . . was young and foolish and badly brought up.'

'As I was,' Francesca said evenly.

'But even you didn't bear a child to your own half-nephew.'

Very simply he told her the story of that summer before the war, not excusing his own madness.

'It was wrong, and I knew it was wrong,' he concluded. 'I've paid for it, not just from remorse, but because I've never been able to commit myself permanently to any other woman. You're the first one to whom I've been able to talk frankly.'

'Knowing that I'm a bit damaged myself?'

'Knowing that you'd understand. Why didn't you marry the man with whom you ran away?'

'Because in the months that I lived with him I found out that his wife was right: he was a brute.'

'My dear . . .'

'So I ran away again, but my family wouldn't take me back. You wouldn't have thought a little adventure like that would have troubled them, especially my father. He had affairs all over the place and he's got at least one bastard tucked away in a cottage on the estate.'

She found a handkerchief and blew her nose vigorously. 'If it hadn't been for Uncle Mark I would have been destitute. He found me somewhere to live and made the Museum give me a job.

I'd always been interested in ceramics – such a nice hobby for a girl, you know – and I became quite the little expert.'

'Your mother?'

'Completely under Papa's thumb. She hasn't spoken to me since I left the house with Rolf. I tried . . . both my brothers were killed in the war . . . I wrote, I even went to see her, but she wouldn't talk to me.' She was openly crying now, though from her frown Simeon knew that she was angry with herself for showing weakness.

'I love you,' he said. 'I haven't said that before because I didn't think it would be welcome, but I love you with all my heart. Your courage, your gallantry, your cleverness, your looks . . .'

'Simeon, please don't, please don't.'

'You can't stop me loving you by asking me not to. I want to make you my wife.'

Francesca shook her head.

'What you need,' Simeon said, moving to her end of the sofa, 'is a much larger handkerchief and someone to hang on to.'

'I'm not a hanger-on. I stand on my own two feet. And I don't cry – not normally.'

'This isn't a normal situation. Dry your eyes, darling. I can't kiss you while you're mopping and mowing.'

'You really do love me, don't you?' Francesca said wonderingly.

'I do, I do.'

He waited until she stopped crying and gave him an uncertain smile, then he kissed her. Her lips tasted of salt and her response at first was uncertain, but before he moved away Simeon had felt her stir in his arms and when he looked down he saw that her eyes were closed and her lips slightly parted.

'And you're going to love me, too,' he said.

'I don't know . . . perhaps. You broke me down, you wretch. Simeon, is it possible? If you knew how frozen I've been.'

'I do know.'

'There've been other men,' Francesca said, speaking quickly and not looking at him. 'Two, during the war.'

'I haven't led a celibate life, either. I had a Chinese mistress in Shanghai.'

'What fun for you.'

They sat together quietly, not speaking, until Francesca turned her head.

'Kiss me again,' she said.

'If it requires a big wedding in St Peter's, Eaton Square to reconcile Mrs Camperdine to Jane and Martin's marriage then I don't blame them for falling in with her plans, but not even Westminster Abbey would bring my mother round, so Simeon and I are free to slip quietly into the Registry Office and tie the knot with no fuss,' Francesca said.

Julia suppressed a sigh. She was trying very hard to be pleased about Simeon's engagement, but Francesca's attitude made it difficult. She was so offhand and uncaring, not even apparently very much in love, although Simeon seemed perfectly contented with the scant attention he got from her.

'The news of your marriage might be just the chance your mother is waiting for to make up the quarrel,' she suggested, not very hopefully.

'Hardly!' Julia winced at the derisive note in Francesca's voice. 'Mama doesn't like the Hope family – or, at any rate, not the Speranza side of it. Mrs Serafina Speranza was Papa's favourite lady for years and, of course, one has always speculated whether the by-blow brought up by the Woods might not have been her child.'

'You know about that?' Julia said faintly.

'Of course. I was intensely interested in the rumours when I was a child.' For a moment Francesca's careless manner wavered. 'Mama lost two sons in the war,' she said quietly. 'It must be hard to see the little bastard still flourishing, as I presume he does.'

'I don't know. I've never seen him or had any knowledge of him . . . My dear, I am so sorry about your brothers. You've never said anything, so I didn't know whether you cared . . .'

'*Cared?*' For one moment Francesca's face was ravaged by grief and anger. 'Of course I cared.' She turned away with a gesture of her hand as if to repel unwelcome memories.

'You don't like to show your feelings,' Julia said.

'I've learnt that it's better to keep them under control. Simeon understands.'

'Yes, I see. I was so afraid you didn't love him enough, but I think I may have been mistaken.'

With her back to her future mother-in-law, in a voice still shaken by the emotion she repudiated, Francesca said, 'Simeon is my hope of salvation.'

'Oh, my dear, no! Don't put all your faith in one person. It's not fair to him.'

'In my saner moments I know that,' Francesca admitted. 'I've been self-sufficient for so long and now . . . he's undermined all my defences. Oh God, I shall regret talking to you like this! Pure *Peg's Paper*. Do forget it, please.'

'It may make you squirm, but it's made me a lot happier,' Julia said briskly. 'And, of course, I entirely understand about the Registry Office and I won't be tiresome about it any more. What will you wear?'

'I think Simeon is expecting me to turn up in the grey tweed suit I wear to the office, but actually I'm going to be thoroughly bridal in shell-pink crêpe-de-Chine and a straw hat trimmed with roses.'

'That sounds charming.'

'Sentimental,' Francesca said gloomily. 'Pink silk roses – I'm ashamed of myself.'

Before the end of the year both the boys were married and the new Hope & Company was set up. In addition to Francesca they had recruited the son of a merchant banker who preferred antiques to working in the City and a well-connected schoolfriend of Martin's who had a great deal of money and a surprisingly wide knowledge of old silver.

By the middle of 1920 it was obvious that business had emerged from the gloom of the war and Hope & Company was enjoying its most prosperous year ever.

'What would you like for a first anniversary present?' Simeon asked Francesca. 'We're doing so well I can almost say name it and you shall have it.'

'What I'd really like is what Jane's already got,' Francesca said. 'She's expecting a baby, did you know?'

'Martin told me today. Well, darling, I have been working on it, as you may have noticed.'

'Indefatigably,' Francesca agreed. 'And it's most agreeable. Sometimes I almost think you might still be in love with me.'

'Disgraceful, isn't it, after nearly a year of married life. Sorry about the baby. I didn't realise you were so keen.'

'Neither did I until I came over all envious when Jane told me her news. I'd love a little Simeon.'

'Or a little Francesca. We'll just have to keep on trying.'

'As to anniversary presents, when you've seen what I've bought you, I think you'll say I've been extravagant enough for two and refuse to buy me anything more.'

'Sounds intriguing. What is it?'

Francesca shook her head and refused to give in to his teasing questions. 'I'll take you to see it on Sunday,' she said.

She drove him out of town the following Sunday, heading south.

'A country cottage?' Simeon guessed.

'No, you're not even warm.'

'A caravan? A boat? If so, I have to break it to you, darling, that I'm not terribly happy on the water.'

'No.'

Half an hour later Simeon said, 'This is the way to Croydon.'

'So it is.'

'And Epsom. You haven't bought a racehorse?'

'No.'

They reached Croydon Airport and turned in at the gates.

'I'm beginning to have an inkling,' Simeon said faintly. 'Though I can't really believe . . . Francesca, you haven't?'

His wife drew up outside a hangar. 'A two-seater Avro 504N, which I'm told is very safe. You liked flying, didn't you?'

'I did, and I've missed it badly, though I'd never want to fly a fighter again. My dear girl, you were certainly right when you said you'd been extravagant.'

'It didn't cost much more than a really good car, and with our joint income I think we can afford the upkeep.' She burst out laughing. 'Simeon, if you could see your face! Like a child who's been given free run of the sweet factory. Come and see your flying machine, little boy.'

For the next hour she watched in tolerant amusement while Simeon crawled all over the gleaming aeroplane in the company of a mechanic as enthusiastic as himself.

When he finally rejoined her, speechless with bliss, and with a smear of oil on his cheek, Francesca said, 'The aircraft company recommended that you went up the first couple of times with one of their instructors, just to be sure that you know the ropes – if that's the right expression to use about flying a plane.'

'Darling, it's just a newer version of my old RFC trainer.'

'Please, Simeon. I'd be happier. This is a very dangerous toy I've given you, buster.'

'Not in the right hands. I'm a good pilot, though I say it myself. Are you going to take flying lessons?'

'You know, I do like you,' Francesca said. 'Of course I've been thinking about it.'

'You drive a car at least as well as I do, if not better. No reason why you shouldn't be an equally good pilot. My anniversary present to you, then, shall be a course of flying lessons. And hands off my aeroplane until you're qualified.'

'I know it's a thoroughly modern thing to do,' fretted Julia, 'but the thought of them both up there flying about over our heads makes me feel quite ill. I'd much prefer Francesca to keep her feet on the ground and have a baby like Jane.'

'No sign of that?' Nicholas asked.

'Apparently not, and not likely to be while she's going up and down in an aeroplane. I can't think it's right for a woman.'

'You'll be worrying about the speed of the trains upsetting the cows in the fields next,' Nicholas said, looking up with a smile.

'Meaning I'm old-fashioned? True, I'm afraid.'

They were at breakfast and as she spoke the maid came in with the letters.

'Oh, dear, there's one with a black edge,' Julia said. 'Now, that *is* old-fashioned. Who can it be?'

Nicholas watched as she slit open the black-bordered envelope and guessed from her slight relaxation that it was no one very close.

'Maurice Coppett has died,' she announced. 'Poor Serafina is a widow again. How very sad. Of course, he was years older than her. Still . . . she's obviously very upset.'

Nicholas was looking thoughtful. 'I wonder what'll happen to his picture collection,' he mused.

'Nicholas, that's really very heartless, to start thinking about business as soon as you hear someone's died!'

217

'I didn't know the man all that well,' Nicholas said. 'And his collection is really very good. I expect he's left it to an American gallery.'

That was only partly true, as Nicholas discovered a few weeks later.

'The Minneapolis Institute of Art has been given the choice of any three of Maurice's pictures and the rest are left to Serafina unconditionally,' he told Martin and Simeon.

'I wonder which of the pictures the Institute will take?' Martin asked.

'The Raphael, the Giorgione and . . . I don't know about the third. If it's a choice of three works of art then I'd expect them to take the Donatello bronze, but if the bequest is confined to paintings then there are two or three they might want.'

'You've never seen the Coppett Collection, Father, but you seem to know it extremely well,' Simeon said.

'I saw many of the items he purchased in Europe, but my knowledge comes from the beautiful catalogue Maurice commissioned. I must have a copy of it somewhere.'

The following day Nicholas dropped a cream-bound book on Simeon's desk.

'The Coppett Collection,' he said. 'Complete with photographs. The catalogue is a work of art in itself. Look after it because if Serafina ever decided to sell . . .'

'We might get the business?'

'I'd like to think so.'

Simeon took the catalogue home with him and leafed through it idly that evening after dinner.

'Look, that's the Raphael Father thinks the Minneapolis Institute will choose from the collection,' he said to Francesca. 'I wish the photograph were in colour.'

'Lovely composition. It reminds me of a similar picture I've seen somewhere else.'

'I believe one or two artists painted the Madonna and Child.'

'Idiot. I mean I've seen something very similar . . . I know – it's a dim old painting hanging in Uncle Mark's dining room.'

'Might be a copy of this very painting. Where is it now?'

'Still in the same place. Uncle Mark's old housekeeper and butler have the right to go on living in his flat until they die and, if

you ask me, they're going to live for ever. Not that I begrudge
them a roof over their heads because they looked after the old
dear for years, but when they eventually go I get the flat.'

'And the contents?'

'It's full of the most gruesome old furniture. No Chippendale or
Hepplewhite there, I can assure you.'

'Do you ever go and visit your property?'

'Not as often as I should. I drop in for a cup of tea occasionally.'
Simeon waited hopefully and Francesca laughed. 'You want to see
my apartment, don't you? You're in for a hideous surprise. Uncle
Mark had no taste at all. Sporting prints . . . oh, curses!'

'Quite, dear heart. We sold a set of sporting prints for several
hundred pounds last week. If you had the contents properly
valued you might get a shock.'

'I couldn't do that while the Brookmans are still alive,'
Francesca said slowly. 'They'd think I was planning to sell up and
turn them out, and I wouldn't worry them for the world. But I
could take you round to meet them – they'd like that.'

'Saturday afternoon? I'm tied up in the Sale Room for the rest
of the week. And on Sunday we'll take a flip over to Deauville.'

'It's a bargain.'

Simeon was amused by the brisk way Francesca dealt with the
two old servants when they called at her late uncle's flat in Prince
of Wales Drive, an enormous mansion apartment on the fifth
floor.

'I've never seen you doing your feudal act before,' Simeon said.

'I try to keep it under control, but it comes out occasionally,'
Francesca admitted. 'I let Mrs Brookman know we were coming
so she's sure to have been baking all day yesterday. I hope you're
up to eating a large tea.'

'I'll do my best.' Simeon looked round critically. 'You were
right, this is a gloomy place and I wouldn't give the furniture house
room.'

'I did tell you. Come and look at the pictures.'

'I'm already looking. There's not much of interest, but that one
there might just be a Stubbs. It'd be worth having it properly
examined.'

They wandered through into the dining room and there, over

219

the sideboard, was the painting Francesca had compared with the Coppett Raphael.

'I was right, wasn't I?' she asked.

'Absolutely. It's undoubtedly a copy of the *Madonna of the Lilies* – and a very good one, as far as one can judge through the grime.'

'I suppose the smoke from the candlesticks at either end of the sideboard, not to mention the fumes from the dishes of food and Uncle Mark's cigars, have been wafting over it for years and years.'

'You ought to have it cleaned. It's a well-executed, decorative item and even as a copy it would be worth a bob or two.'

The old butler appeared in the doorway. 'Tea is served in the drawing room, milady,' he said with a touch of reproach.

'Do you know anything about this picture, Brookman?' Francesca asked. 'It's always been here and I've never thought about it before, but it's not quite Uncle Mark's taste, is it?'

'You mean the gambling picture, milady?'

Francesca cast a startled look at the sweet-faced Madonna. 'No, this one of the Virgin and Child.'

'Mr Mark always said that his grandfather took it from his brother-in-law in payment of a bet, and he called it the gambling picture, milady.'

Simeon and Francesca wandered back to the drawing room.

'Cucumber sandwiches, shortbread, scones, fruit cake and madeleines,' Francesca murmured. 'Thank goodness we're not dining out tonight.'

'Looks good to me. Who was your Uncle Mark's grandfather's brother-in-law?'

'What a highly complicated question! I don't know. Who was he, Brookman?'

'That would be the French duke, milady.'

'Oh, yes, I've got him now. Uncle Mark was mama's brother – a great deal older than her, though – so they had the same grandfather,' Francesca explained. 'He was, of course, my great-grandfather and he married the sister of the Duc de Rocheville-sur-Lac and apparently went in for betting games with his brother-in-law. They did a lot of gaming in those days, didn't they, Brookman?'

'So I understand. Is everything satisfactory, milady?'

'It all looks absolutely splendid. Mrs Brookman has been working far too hard. I must have a chat with her before we go.'

As she poured the tea Francesca remarked, 'One thing I am looking forward to having one day is Uncle Mark's tea set.'

'Rockingham, isn't it?'

'Yes. What are you looking so thoughtful about?'

'That picture. Doesn't it seem odd to you that a duke should pay off a gambling debt with a *copy* of an Old Master?'

'Perhaps it was a very small gambling debt. Perhaps Great-grandfather took a fancy to the Madonna.'

'Would it upset your old retainers if we took it away?'

'They'd be pleased to see me taking an interest. You wouldn't ever want to live in this mausoleum, would you?'

'No, thank you. I prefer our nice airy modern flat. May I have a piece of fruit cake?'

'You're being quite piggish and Mrs Brookman will love you. That picture – you're not really thinking what I think you're thinking, are you?'

'Not seriously, but even in a poor light and obscured by grime it's got quality. I'd like to have it cleaned and examined by an expert.'

When they left, the painting went with them, carefully wrapped in an old curtain provided by Mrs Brookman.

'I'll take it round to the office and lock it up for the rest of the weekend,' Simeon said.

'You've got a feeling about it, haven't you?'

'When we took it down from the wall and I saw it in a different light I got goose pimples all over.'

'How very unattractive. You're imagining things, you know. It couldn't possibly be the original. What about the painting Mr Coppett bought?'

'What indeed! Did he get an expert opinion or did he rely on its impeccable provenance? He bought it at auction, at a sale of the contents of the Paris house of the last remaining member of the ducal family "who had had it in their possession for over two hundred years". I read it up in the catalogue.'

*

By the end of the following week Simeon and Francesca, Martin and Nicholas were all standing in front of the newly cleaned picture, displayed on an easel in Nicholas's office, and absorbing in silence the richness of the colour that had been revealed, the purity of the Virgin's face and all the exquisite details surrounding her, right down to the dusting of golden pollen on the white of the lilies at her feet.

'If we didn't know about the identical picture in the United States . . .' Nicholas said.

'If it weren't for that then I'd sell it without hesitation as a Raphael,' Martin said.

'And I think you'd be right,' Simeon said. 'I had Oldroyd from the Courtauld here this morning and he nearly swooned. He's about ninety-eight per cent convinced that this is the original.'

'What will you do?' Francesca asked.

'It's up to you; you own the picture. My feeling is that we ought to get another independent opinion and then try to bring the two copies together for comparison.'

'Would Duval come over from France?' Martin asked.

'He's an awkward cuss, but if there's a controversy he'll want to be in the middle of it.'

'Let's get in touch with him,' Francesca suggested.

'You do it, darling, your French is impeccable and you can wave your title at him. Mention your connection with the Duc de Rocheville-sur-Lac and he'll probably swim over!'

Monsieur Duval, the renowned art historian and expert on Raphael, proved to be less easily persuaded to cross the Channel than Simeon had anticipated.

'He writes that he suffers from *mal de mer*,' Francesca reported. 'He suggests taking the picture to him, which I'm sure you won't want to do.'

'I'm not going through all that fuss with the Customs. Tell him I'll fly over and collect him and return him the same day – or when he wants to go.'

'*Chic, alors!*'

'Let's hope Monsieur Duval thinks so.'

On that basis the Frenchman agreed to visit London to give them the benefit of his opinion. In the meantime, two more British experts were allowed a sight of it, and a buzz of excitement began to go round the art circles of London.

'As a matter of courtesy we ought to warn the Minneapolis Institute of our suspicions,' Nicholas said.

'They've chosen the Raphael from the Coppett Bequest?'

'Inevitably. They don't possess one and it's a real prize – if it's genuine.'

'Which I'm increasingly convinced it's not. I must be off to the aerodrome at Croydon. We should be back here in time for lunch, if Monsieur Duval feels like eating. With as much wind as we've got today he may find the air passage as trying as it would be by sea.'

Simeon put his head round the door of Francesca's office to say goodbye. She was making a telephone call, but she blew him a kiss and he went off.

By the end of the morning they were all a little on edge, waiting for Simeon and Duval to put in an appearance.

'Simeon will have been battling with a head wind all the way over the Channel,' Francesca said, drawing on her scanty knowledge.

'Is that dangerous?' Martin asked, not thinking about what he was saying.

'It can be . . . no, no of course not. Simeon is an experienced pilot. If he thought the wind was too strong he wouldn't have taken off.'

They waited another few minutes in uneasy silence and then Francesca said, 'I'm going to telephone Croydon Airport.'

Her call elicited only the fact that Simeon had taken off at the prearranged time.

'The force of the wind has increased since then,' she reported. 'It may be that they're having difficulty getting away from France.'

'We'll wait another half hour and then we'd better have lunch,' Nicholas said.

Before the hour was up, they were interrupted by the arrival of a telegram. Nicholas tore it open.

'Has Simeon had to make a forced landing?' Francesca asked. 'Poor dear, he'll be so cross.'

'It's from Duval, asking why Simeon hasn't arrived,' Nicholas said in a shaky voice.

'Shall I get on to Croydon again?' Martin asked.

'I'll do it,' Francesca said. 'I know who to speak to, what to ask.' She looked with a strange feeling of detachment at Simeon's father and brother; nice men, both anxious, but without the feeling of cold horror that was attacking her.

She asked for the number with a steady voice and put the necessary questions without faltering, but when she turned back to the two waiting men she could only shake her head.

'They have no news?' Nicholas asked.

'He set out on course but he never arrived. That's all they can say at the moment. The coastguards will be alerted and shipping will be warned to look out for . . . for wreckage. There's nothing we can do except wait.'

They waited all through the long afternoon, only remembering Monsieur Duval when a second querulous telegram arrived. It was Martin who drafted a reply to that: *'Greatly fear accident to aeroplane . . .'*

'I must go home and tell Julia,' Nicholas said at last. 'Francesca, my dear, will you come with me? You mustn't be on your own at a time like this.'

Francesca looked at him strangely, but she did not speak the thought in her mind, that she had always been on her own – except when Simeon had come into her life.

'I must be at the flat in case Simeon telephones,' she said. 'I'll be all right.'

Martin took her home, but she refused to let him go in with her. In the face of her obstinacy there was nothing he could do except drive away and leave her on the doorstep.

Francesca let herself into the flat and looked round, not believing that everything could seem so normal.

'A nice airy modern flat,' she quoted out loud. 'I think I need a drink.'

She made herself a whisky and soda, but when she tried to drink it her hands were shaking so much that the glass rattled against her teeth and the liquid slopped over the side. She managed to take a gulp, choked and subsided on to the sofa, her eyes tightly closed, fighting for control. When Simeon came home he would expect to find that she had kept cool, she told herself fiercely. *When Simeon came home . . .*

After a few minutes she forced herself to go into the kitchen. She cooked a poached egg on toast, then threw the egg away and ate the toast.

That left the rest of the evening stretching before her emptily. She turned on the wireless, caught a gale warning and switched off again immediately.

I'm suffering from shock, she thought. I ought to be given hot drinks and reassurance. It's my fault that I'm not with people who'd give me both, but I couldn't bear it. I could have some tea, though. She thought about putting on the kettle for quite ten minutes before she was able to get her reluctant limbs to move, but when it was made the hot tea was some comfort.

Francesca curled up on the sofa, the same sofa on which Simeon had kissed her for the first time, but that was not a thing to be thought about, not unless she wanted to drive herself mad. She sat without stirring while the light faded, until she was in complete darkness apart from the glow of the street lamps outside.

Towards midnight she dozed off and woke some hours later, cramped and cold. For a moment she was too disorientated to remember why she was so uncomfortable, then realisation came back. It was difficult to move, but she managed to get to her feet and to stagger on numb legs to the bedroom. She undressed, dropping her clothes on the floor, and crawled under the bedclothes. Her hand went out to the empty space by her side.

Simeon's pillow was there, smelling subtly of his presence. Francesca took it in her arms and hugged it to her and like that she eventually drifted into a troubled, dream-haunted sleep.

Chapter Sixteen

'The Minneapolis Institute want us to send our *Madonna of the Lilies* over there so that they can compare it with their copy,' Nicholas said. 'Francesca, would you be willing to take it over?'

Francesca came to with a start. It was the first Board Meeting she had attended since Simeon's disappearance. Someone had been sensitive enough to remove the chair he had always occupied, but that left a gap on Nicholas's right hand which riveted her attention and prevented her from taking in what was being said.

The wreckage of his aeroplane had been found, but Simeon's body had never been washed up and the lack of any grave, any settled point of mourning, was more of a deprivation than she would have thought possible, she who had always derided the outward trappings of grief.

Her immediate reaction to this suggestion was the thought 'Suppose Simeon comes home?' – and the reason she failed to reply was because she was thrown back into the abyss of realising that Simeon would never come home now.

'Never, never, never, never . . .' she said out loud, and then saw from Nicholas's surprise that he thought she was refusing his request.

'Sorry, not attending,' she said. 'Yes, I'll take the picture to Minneapolis, if you like. It'll be the first thing I've done to earn my keep for the last three months.'

'My dear, we none of us blame you for that,' Nicholas said gently. 'The voyage and change of scene will do you good.'

Francesca smiled and agreed, knowing that nothing could do her good, nothing could ever restore to her what she had lost.

She was ashamed of the thought that came into her mind – 'Thank God, I'll be out of the country when Jane has her baby' – but she knew it would be a relief not to join in the congratulations, lacking a child of her own to remind her of Simeon.

*

Francesca sailed for New York, passing the voyage in the solitude that had become habitual to her, and earning herself the reputation of being a snob who thought herself too good to mix with her fellow passengers. It would have surprised her had she known this but it would not have touched her. Nothing reached Francesca nowadays.

The picture, insured for a sum Nicholas thought appropriate, travelled in conditions of the utmost security until at last Francesca gave permission for it to be unpacked by the administrators of the Minneapolis Institute of Art.

They took it out and stood it on an easel, side by side with the Coppett painting.

'If it's a copy then it's a remarkable one,' the director said eventually.

'Could they both be by Raphael?' Francesca asked, feeling a faint stirring of interest.

'Possibly – if they weren't both so exactly the same . . . No, I think one is by the Master and the other is a later copy.' He turned miserable eyes on her. 'As soon as I had Hope's first letter I examined our Raphael more closely than I ever had before, and I must admit to doubts.' He sighed deeply. 'We have experts arriving from all over to look at the two side by side. You're authorised to leave it with us?'

'It belongs to me,' Francesca said. 'I can do with it what I like. Keep it by all means. I know you'll look after it.'

'Indeed I will! Lady Francesca, I'm truly grateful to you for making this trip, especially at such a difficult time . . .'

'I must go,' Francesca said, interrupting him ruthlessly. 'Mrs Coppett is expecting me for dinner.'

It had never occurred to Francesca to go into mourning, but Serafina was draped in black from head to toe, presumably for the loss of her husband rather than for her step-grandson, Francesca thought dispassionately. Serafina did not remember, but Francesca had seen her many times at Mercia House, at the height of her beauty. She had put on weight since then and Francesca suspected that the black of her hair owed something to the dye-pot, but she was still a striking-looking woman.

So, too, was Anna. Francesca greeted her coolly, unaware that

227

the question in her mind was much the same as the one in Anna's head. Could this dark, lush beauty really have aroused Simeon's desperate love? What could have made Simeon choose this cold, blonde aristocrat to be his wife?

As for Bradley, Francesca had been warned about his disability, but she was unprepared for the crawling slowness with which he dragged himself forward to shake her hand. He was on his feet and walking, but the effort it cost him was all too obvious and she was shocked by the clammy coldness of his hand.

'And I thought you would like to meet my son,' Anna was saying. 'Victor, say good evening to your . . . aunt.'

Francesca stood so still that the boy looked at her questioningly. She could neither greet him nor conceal her shock. No longer a baby, but not yet adolescent, he had the touching awkwardness of an undeveloped animal. *And he was Simeon*. In all the lineaments of his face, in the turn of his head, in the tentative smile that wavered as she stared at him, he was Simeon come back to life.

She lifted her eyes to look at Anna and saw, with fierce resentment, the complacency in her smile. Anna was triumphing over her. She had Simeon's son and Francesca had nothing.

Turning away, too distressed to know what she was doing, Francesca found Bradley by her side. Unexpectedly, he put a hand under her elbow and held her in a firm grip.

'Your discovery of the Raphael has caused a sensation,' he said.

Francesca made an effort to respond to his well-meant kindness. 'It was Simeon's discovery,' she said.

She had managed to bring out his name. It dropped like a stone into a pool of silence. Only the boy was unaware of the ripples it caused. Serafina must know, surely? But it was Serafina who eased the tension by saying, 'He was a clever man. I feel for you in his loss, I who am also a widow twice over. I had two dear, good, kind husbands; I know how hard it is to be left alone and comfortless.'

'Now, Mama, you mustn't be morbid and you can hardly call your situation comfortless,' Anna said.

There was a hardness in the way she spoke that grated on Francesca, but what surprised her was the way Anna looked at Bradley as she spoke. There was impatience and dislike and a sort of nervous dread in that look. Anna, too, it seemed, was afraid of being left alone, even though she obviously had no love for her husband.

228

It made Francesca examine Bradley more closely, and this time she saw signs of ill-health that went beyond the strain of his crippled state.

The following week passed in a blur for Francesca, lit up only by the moments when she was able to see Victor. She knew she would do the boy no good by arousing his suspicions, and neither to him nor to his mother did she drop the slightest hint that she recognised him as Simeon's son, but she did tell him that he would always be welcome to visit her in England, and was pleased to see a spark of interest in his eyes.

'I'd like to join the family business one day,' he confided. 'Mom says there's no need because I'll always have enough money not to have to work, but if that was what she intended she shouldn't have named me after my grandfather. It was Vittorio Speranza who started Hope's, you know.'

'Not quite,' Francesca said. 'There was a man called Charles DuFrayne who came before him.'

'Sure, but it was Grandfather Vittorio who made the firm what it is today. I'm really interested in art and antiques and all that. Aren't you just thrilled that the Raphael you've discovered may turn out to be the real thing?'

Francesca, who was almost totally indifferent to the authenticity of her Raphael, smiled and agreed that it was most exciting, and invited the boy to go with her to hear the experts' verdict.

As she had expected ever since she had seen the two paintings together, the answer was that the real Raphael had been acquired by her great-grandfather in somewhat dubious circumstances, and the erring duke had substituted a copy which had never since been questioned.

'It makes us all look fools,' the director of the Institute said. 'Now, of course, we can see the points of weakness. When it wasn't queried we accepted the picture on its face value and everyone was blinded by "knowing" that it was a Raphael. I could weep.' He looked hopefully at Serafina, but she had no intention of making good such a monumental mistake.

'You chose this Raphael – and I am still not completely convinced that it is *not* authentic – and you must keep it as one of the pictures left to you by Maurice. My husband was cheated. If he were alive he would be most displeased.'

The director accepted this with an obvious effort. 'Lady Francesca, do you intend putting this painting on the market?' he asked. 'I don't know whether we can afford it, but if it's up for sale then I guess we'll do our utmost to bid for it.'

'You can have it if you like,' Francesca said. 'My ancestor seems to have behaved in a most underhand way and I think it's up to me to put it right. If you're satisfied that my painting is the authentic *Madonna of the Lilies* then I'll exchange it with you for the copy which is what I always thought I had.'

For the first time for many months she felt a stab of pleasure at the sensation this speech caused. The director was incoherent with delight, Serafina looked sour, Anna looked angry, as if Francesca had scored over her in some way, and Victor laughed out loud and almost skipped over to Francesca to grasp her hand.

'Aunt Francesca, you're the tops,' he said fervently. 'I think that's just the most generous thing anyone ever did. And I can come to the gallery every day to look at the Raphael if I want to.'

'And remember me,' Francesca said. 'I'd like you to do that, Victor.'

'You gave away the original Raphael?'

Nicholas sounded stupefied, but he was thinking not so much of the value of the gift as the loss of publicity for Hope's. Unconsciously, he had been looking forward to an immensely important sale, with all the great names in the art world competing to secure the treasure his clever son – his dear, dead, clever son – had unearthed.

'Perverse of me, wasn't it?' Francesca asked in her most annoying drawl.

'I'm disappointed,' Nicholas admitted. 'I'd hoped to put it up for sale and to make a really grand occasion out of it. Silly of me, perhaps, but I saw it as a sort of memorial to Simeon.'

'The Institute is cataloguing it as my gift in memory of Simeon.'

'I see. Well, what can I say, my dear? It's wonderfully generous of you and, as you say, Simeon has got his memorial.'

Francesca accepted this without comment.

'It was a good trip,' she added. 'I made contact with one or two people who'll certainly pay more attention to auctions at Hope's in future. Is Julia in this afternoon, do you know? I thought I'd call in to see her.'

It grated on Nicholas, the way Francesca had adopted the casual habit of calling him and Julia by their Christian names. Jane called them Mother and Father, which seemed more fitting, but of course Jane was a much younger woman and of a different stamp altogether.

'You did know Jane and Martin have had a son?' he enquired.

'Martin told me. It's splendid news,' Francesca said.

She repeated that when she met Julia half an hour later. 'I must think of a suitable christening gift,' she said.

'I believe Jane means to ask you to be godmother,' Julia said.

'It's lovely of her, but I think I'll ask to be excused. I have a vague feeling that there might be a God somewhere, but I couldn't be called a true believer. Certainly I'm no churchgoer. Not at all a suitable godmother – all those promises and certainties. Not my style at all.'

'If you feel like that then you're right to refuse,' Julia said quietly. 'Tell me about your visit to America. Nicholas has already telephoned me so I know about your gift of the Raphael. I'm very happy that Simeon's name should be associated with such a splendid gesture.'

'That's more than Nicholas is! He tried to look pleased, but I could see the effort it cost him.'

'Poor dear, he was looking forward to getting up on the rostrum to sell that picture. He would have done it beautifully.'

'I suppose so. Well, it's done now and I can't say I regret it. The visit to America . . . it was interesting, even exhilarating at times. I'd like to go back again.'

'You're looking better.'

Julia examined her daughter-in-law carefully. She was still too thin, but there was slightly more colour in her cheeks and an alertness in her manner that made Julia think that Francesca had recovered from the terrible lethargy into which she had fallen after Simeon's death.

'I've decided I must start living again. I mean to pull my weight at Hope's. After all, with Simeon gone I'm the best we have in the way of an Oriental specialist. A poor best, but if I apply my mind I hope to prevent us from making too many expensive mistakes.'

The jeering way she spoke grated on Julia, but she recognised the desperate hurt behind her daughter-in-law's words.

'How did you find Serafina?' she asked.

'Opulent, in every way. She sent the usual messages to you. I didn't meet Violetta because she lives too far west, but I saw Anna, of course.'

'And Bradley?'

'He's a sick man. I think Anna is destined to be a dashing young widow like her mother.'

'You didn't like her.'

'How could I? She spoilt Simeon's youth and she's got his son; the son I should have had.'

Francesca felt in her handbag for the photograph she now carried with her all the time. Wordlessly, she held it out to Julia. Watching her mother-in-law, she saw her experience the same shock of recognition she herself had felt when she had met Victor.

'He's darker than Simeon,' Julia said finally.

'But apart from that . . .'

'His living image.' Julia put down the photograph and felt for her handkerchief. 'I'm sorry, but it was a shock, seeing a face that might have been Simeon as a schoolboy looking up at me.'

'I should have warned you.'

'It must have been even worse for you, meeting him in the flesh.'

'Worse . . . and better. He's a delightful boy. He was thrilled when I gave my Raphael to the Institute.'

'Was that why you did it?' Julia asked quietly.

'No. I was thinking more of giving Serafina a lesson. She was so ungenerous. Such a bourgeoise mentality.'

'Between ourselves I'm prepared to admit that I never liked Serafina – and with good reason. Anna . . . well, I was sorry for Anna, in spite of what she did to Simeon. She had an ardent spirit that had never been disciplined. I wonder how much of it she's passed on to Victor.'

'Very little, I hope! Not that I'd want him to be a namby-pamby boy, but I could see a lot of Simeon's levelheadedness in him.'

'Simeon was as levelheaded as a see-saw when it came to dealing with Anna,' Julia commented drily. 'Obviously you're very taken with the child, which is understandable, but don't start seeing him as a paragon.'

'Of course not,' Francesca said unconvincingly. 'I'm hoping Anna will bring him over for a visit to London. Fortunately, he already has a real interest in antiques and history.'

'I think that would be most unwise,' Julia said deliberately. 'Far better for him to remain in America and learn how to take over his father's business interests one day.'

She knew that her suspicions had been right when Francesca's head jerked up.

'His father?' she said. 'But . . .'

'Bradley is his legal father, and I presume he has made Victor his heir. There'll be plenty to keep the boy in America. Enjoying antiques may turn into an interest for him, as it did for his grandfather – Maurice Coppett, I mean – but I doubt whether it will ever be his main concern.'

Francesca took hold of the photograph of Victor and held it tightly in both hands.

'You're trying to hurt me,' she said.

'I'm trying to make you take the common-sense view. My dear, the day may come when the boy learns the truth about his parentage, but at the moment he's a very young child who couldn't cope with such a revelation. It would be cruel to thrust it on him, and if he comes to England someone is sure to blurt out something about the remarkable family resemblance. You must bear your own hurt so that he can survive.'

'Don't you want to see him?'

'Of course I do. A small part of Simeon, still surviving . . . Francesca, I understand exactly how you feel. Do look outside yourself for a minute and *think*. You are desperately sad that you never bore Simeon a child, but consider what it is like to have borne a child and to have lost him. You had a short time with Simeon and he was your loving husband and I'm grateful to you for making him happy, but I had him inside my body for nine months. I suffered when he was born, I suckled him, I brought him through childhood illnesses and agonised when he was sick. I saw him grow splendid and tall and brave. I went through the war waiting every day to hear that he had been maimed or killed. I miss him every waking moment of every day. He has been torn away from me with more agony than it cost me to bear him.'

Julia spoke in staccato bursts, breathing with difficulty, and the tears ran down her face unheeded. For a moment Francesca sat quite still and then she went over and knelt by her mother-in-law's side.

'I'm sorry,' she said. 'I'm . . . I'm not good at sharing emotions. Only with Simeon. That was what he did for me. With him I could share anything. I've been selfish and I'm ashamed. I'm not cold, please don't think that. I understand everything you say. I just don't know what to say in reply.'

Tentatively, Julia put her hand on the sleek blonde head bowed down by her side. Francesca leaned against her and they shared a moment of communion that neither of them ever forgot, then Francesca moved away and got to her feet, dabbing at her eyes.

'What a carry-on,' she said. 'How Simeon would have laughed. Very well, I won't urge Anna to bring Victor to London, but I can't help taking an interest in him and I mean to keep in touch, to see how he turns out.'

Chapter Seventeen

'All that remains for me to say is congratulations, Martin. I hope you will be as happy in your chairmanship of Hope & Company as I have been over the years. I think I can congratulate the company, too, on gaining a Chairman of first-class ability.'

Nicholas leaned back in the heavy chair which stood at the top of the table in the Board Room; it was the last time he would sit in it, the last time he would preside at a meeting. He tried to tell himself that he was looking forward to retirement, but the truth was that he still thought himself young enough at sixty-five to carry on. It was Julia who had pointed out, when he had objected that Martin was too young to take over, that at thirty-nine Martin was older than he himself had been when he acquired the company after Vittorio's death.

Now, looking at Martin's gratified face, Nicholas knew his wife had been right. Their son was ready to take charge and it would have fretted him to be kept waiting any longer in the wings. Besides, if one started to look upon oneself as indispensable, where did it end? He might have soldiered on until he was doddering. Better to go now while there were still people on the Board who were regretful about his decision.

'I'm saving my speech for the party this evening,' Martin said. 'All I can do now is to thank you all for your confidence in me. I'll certainly do my best to deserve it.'

'I only wish I were bowing out at a more prosperous time,' Nicholas said. 'This wretched Depression is going to affect business for some time.'

'Plenty of house sales, but fewer buyers,' one of the directors agreed.

'Now's the time to invest,' Martin said. 'I'd like to run a campaign to persuade people to put their money into antiques. I'm convinced they'll hold their value better than stocks and shares have recently.'

'It's a selling point, but not a very dignified one,' Nicholas objected.

'Survival first, dignity second,' Martin said.

'That's what my father seems to think,' Francesca said. 'He's closing Mercia House and selling off the bulk of Grandfather's collection of Greek and Roman marbles.'

'Any chance of Hope's handling the sale?' Martin asked.

'I'm afraid not. He's already given it to Sotheby's.'

'Pity.' Martin looked round the table and asked, 'Has anyone else heard talk of an amalgamation between Sotheby's and Christie's?'

'It's certainly rumoured,' a director replied.

'Their combined organisation would be a formidable rival.'

'Unwieldy.'

'Perhaps.' Again Martin looked round the table. His father was amused, regretful and perhaps slightly envious as he saw that Martin was already behaving like the Chairman of the Board.

'It's not on the agenda for discussion today, but as a matter of interest, what would our reaction be if we were approached about a merger?'

'Wholehearted resistance, I hope,' Nicholas said.

'I'd certainly be against it,' Francesca agreed. 'Hope's is Hope's: smaller than the giants, but with a very special place in the market. I'd hate to see us lose our identity.'

'But in order to survive?'

They tossed the idea about for a few minutes, but it was obvious that, without exception, the Board members would regret anything that would impinge on Hope's unique position.

'In that case, we're going to have to work very hard indeed if we're to make any sort of profit at all this year,' Martin concluded.

'Any other business before I close the meeting?' Nicholas asked.

'One very small thing and perhaps it's not really necessary to bring it up now,' Francesca said. 'I'd like to introduce a young recruit to work here for a few months during the summer. I thought it might interest everyone to know that he's a descendant of one of our founders – Victor Coppett, the American grandson of Vittorio Speranza.'

There was a buzz of interested comment, but neither Nicholas nor Martin said anything. Their eyes met and they were both thinking the same thing. Damn Francesca, she'd deliberately announced Victor's arrival at a Board Meeting so as to make it impossible for them to object.

'How old is he?' someone asked.

'Nineteen, and such a delightful boy. He's very much a Speranza; you'll be amazed by the family likeness.'

That was clever of her, preparing the way for Victor's resemblance to Simeon. She had thought it all out and both Martin and Nicholas were suspicious of her forethought.

'His father died last year,' Nicholas said for the benefit of the other Board members. 'As heir to the Coppett interests I'm surprised young Victor can spare time for dallying with the auction trade.'

'He won't be staying long,' Francesca said. 'Just during his long vacation. He's an undergraduate at Harvard.'

'And his particular interest?' Martin asked.

'Renaissance painting – as you might expect because of his contact with the Coppett Collection.'

'Your field then, Bob,' Martin said, turning to the friend he had introduced to the Board ten years earlier. 'You can use him?'

'Certainly. Provided he's prepared to do the menial tasks, you know.'

'He knows what's expected of him,' Francesca said. 'He'll be staying with me, of course.'

'And is Anna coming too?' Nicholas looked round and apologised. 'I'm sorry, everyone, these are family matters and not worth keeping you sitting round the table for.'

Everyone began getting up as Francesca replied, 'No, Anna feels she must stay in Minneapolis.'

From her look of satisfaction it appeared that this did not displease Francesca, but Nicholas glanced up quickly from the papers he was shuffling together as she went on, 'Her mother's health is causing concern.'

'Serafina? She's younger than I am! What's wrong with her?'

'Her heart, I believe. I noticed last time I was in the States that she was very short of breath, but I thought it was because she was so overweight.'

'It's difficult to think of Serafina . . . of course, I haven't seen her for years,' Nicholas said vaguely.

What was it he was feeling? Regret, almost sadness, at the

237

thought of Serafina, that lush seductress, reduced to a fat and ailing old woman. The passing of the years . . . it brought home his age to him, even more than his retirement had done.

'The Coppett empire crashed badly last year,' Martin said to Jane as they made ready for his father's retirement party. 'Young Victor may be looking round for fresh fields to conquer, especially if his interests lie in the arts rather than in business.'

'In England? Would he want to uproot himself?'

'If the inducement were strong enough perhaps he would.'

Jane leaned forward, carefully applying the deep red lipstick which complemented her dark, exotic looks. She was wearing a gown of jade-green slipper satin, cut very low at the back, with a jade pendant on a gold chain round her neck.

'That's a very becoming frock,' Martin remarked.

'Thank you, darling.' Jane smoothed the cross-cut satin gown over her hips as she stood up and took a satisfied look at herself in the mirror. 'What sort of inducement could Francesca offer a young American to get him to desert his native land?' She asked the question idly, not expecting a serious answer, but Martin's reply jolted her.

'Her shares in Hope & Company.'

'But surely Francesca wouldn't . . .'

'To get Simeon's son into the company? Would she not!'

'Martin, you're not seriously worried, are you?'

'Not yet, it's too soon. But I can't help remembering that Anna has a substantial holding in Hope's, which presumably will go to Victor one day. Add that holding to Francesca's own shares, plus the ones she inherited from Simeon . . . yes, I might be worried if an unknown young man were in a strong position to interfere with the policy of the company.'

He shrugged himself into his jacket as he spoke and Jane picked up the long-fringed silk shawl which matched her gown, ready for the party but with none of the unalloyed pleasure she had felt before.

'I wish this hadn't cropped up on your triumphal day,' she complained.

'The party is for Father's retirement, not my accession,' Martin reminded her.

'Yes, of course, but there've been all sorts of messages of congratulation since it was known that you were taking over.'

Jane was looking forward to being the Chairman's wife. She might have rebelled against her mother's plans for her before her marriage, but Jane had inherited Olga Camperdine's social acumen and once she was established in a stable, happy marriage to a man with an assured position she had begun to show considerable flair as a hostess. Martin indulged her, and appreciated the way she managed her parties. They worked as a team and Martin knew that if he told Jane that he was anxious to meet a potential buyer or someone with an interesting collection, then he could rely on her to arrange a congenial meeting. It was her career, just as dealing in fine arts was his.

'There's Quentin to be thought of,' Jane said.

'Plenty of time to start worrying about our son's position,' Martin said. 'Put it out of your mind, darling. And whatever you do, don't say anything about it at the party. Have you heard whether Melissa is putting in an appearance?'

'Yes, she's managed to get a free evening. I hope she won't be wearing that prune-coloured gown, but I expect she will.'

'You know Melissa has a mind above frocks.'

'Silly girl. She could be so good-looking if she'd only take the trouble.'

Jane gave a last pleased look at her own reflection. Not an ounce of spare flesh, a smooth unblemished skin and hair with the sheen of a bird's wing. No wonder Martin slipped an arm round her waist and kissed her before they left for the party.

Melissa, on the other hand, was the despair of her female relations. She was a qualified doctor and she had given herself up entirely to her specialisation in paediatrics without a thought, to her mother's regret, of producing any children of her own. She was on friendly terms with the male doctors at her hospital, but Julia had never heard of any romance in her life. Julia grieved over it, but Melissa went on being the same bright, sunny-natured girl she had always been. She was thirty-two, the same age as Jane, but she had a youthful quality that was not at all the same thing as Jane's careful retention of her looks. Melissa was untouched, in spite of the experience and knowledge she had gained in her profession, and it was this slightly suspect immaturity that worried Julia.

That evening at the party she was, of course, wearing the prune-coloured gown which Jane despised. There was nothing actually wrong with it, but neither was it particularly becoming. A suitable gown for a middle-aged woman, which Melissa was far from being.

'Hello, old thing,' she greeted Jane affectionately. 'I say, you look stunning.'

'That's more than I can say about you. Before the evening's out I'm going to spill a glass – or preferably a bottle – of red wine over that horrid dress. I do think you might have sported something new for such a special occasion.'

'Never mind, ducky, you look good enough for two and so does Francesca. Even Mother is as fine as ninepence.'

'Which shows you up all the more, you wretch.'

'Don't scold, there's a pet. It's ages since I saw you. Is Martin very cockahoop at taking over from Father?'

'He is, but he's already reminded me that this is Father's evening, not his.'

'Poor old Father, I can't imagine what he's going to do with himself. Hope's has been his life.'

If Nicholas had similar qualms he was able to hide them that evening. He accepted the presentation of a piece of very fine Georgian silver and made a graceful speech assuring everyone that Hope's would survive the present troubled times and go on to even greater triumphs 'under the guidance of your new Chairman, my son, Martin'.

Julia smiled and smiled and no one looking at her radiant face would have guessed that she had as many doubts about the future as her daughter. She and Nicholas were leaving for a cruise within the week, but she had considerable misgivings about keeping Nicholas amused when they returned.

By the time Julia and Nicholas returned from their lengthy break, Victor was installed in Francesca's flat and going to Hope's with her every day. This was to last for two months and then he and Francesca were going to Italy for a fortnight.

Martin, calling round to welcome his parents home, reported that Victor was immensely popular.

'He's hardworking, knowledgeable, keen to learn, and terribly, terribly polite to his elders.'

Nicholas was watching his son closely. 'Just a bit too good to be true?' he suggested.

Martin grimaced. 'The thought has crossed my mind. I don't know why, because it's impossible to fault him in any particular.'

'Does he still look like Simeon?'

'Very much so,' Martin said, turning to Julia. 'Simeon before the war. I'm afraid it may come as a shock to you, Mother.'

'I'm prepared. Does Victor know about his real parentage?'

'I think not, but if anyone tells him then it will be Francesca. She's quite foolish about him.'

'Yes . . . poor Francesca. As soon as we've unpacked and settled down I'll arrange for them to come to dinner. You and Jane must come, too, and Melissa if she can get away. We'll make it look like a welcome for Anna's son.'

Martin was wrong in thinking that Victor did not yet know about his parentage, but right in his assumption that Francesca was the one to tell him. She did it in a way that allowed Victor to ask questions or not ask questions, just as he liked.

It was the morning after his arrival. He came out of his room to join Francesca for breakfast carrying a silver-framed photograph in his hand.

'Why did you put this in my room?' he asked.

'It's Simeon – my husband.'

'So I guessed when I took in the uniform. Before I noticed that, I thought it was a picture of me.'

'You're very like him.'

'You can say that again! My colouring's darker, I think, as far as one can tell from a black and white photograph. I get that from Mom, I suppose. I might be a shade taller. Apart from that . . . we've certainly got the same features.'

'Yes.'

'Is that why you've always favoured me, Francesca? Because I remind you of your dead husband?'

'Partly.'

'What a blow to my ego! I thought you loved me for myself alone.'

'I do.'

Victor took another long look at the photograph. 'It's uncanny.'

'Not really. Think, Victor.'

'Are you trying to tell me something?'

'Not unless you want to know.'

'I want to know.'

'When she married Bradley your mother was already pregnant. You're Simeon's son.'

'Did Dad know?' Victor asked, after a silence.

'I imagine so. Apparently the marriage was very sudden – as it had to be – and I doubt whether Bradley would have agreed unless he knew the reason for the urgency.'

'But why . . . oh, gee, these complicated relationships. Of course, they couldn't marry, could they?'

'Simeon and Anna? No. Victor, I don't want you to think badly of Simeon. He went off to China because Anna urged him to go, and without knowing she was pregnant.'

'What a predicament! Well, for heaven's sake! I always thought Mom must have married Dad for the money. I mean – what else could there have been?'

'Bradley behaved very generously.'

'Did he? I'm not so sure about that. They weren't happy together and he was never what you might call a loving father to me. I had a little sister who died as soon as she was born and he was grief-stricken about that, but to me he always seemed cold. Of course, now, knowing about this, I can see why he acted the way he did. It's no fun, I can tell you, growing up with a father who doesn't seem to like you. Mom should have told me.'

'It's a difficult story for a mother to tell her son.'

'I suppose so.'

'And she won't approve of me telling you.'

'No – she didn't want me to come on this trip.'

'I'm not surprised. Anna's always been afraid I might entice you away from your home. In the past she's been able to hold on to you because of the vast Coppett fortune waiting to come to you one day.'

'That's taken a considerable tumble in the past year. It killed Dad. He blamed himself, even though the same thing was happening to everyone all round him. I doubt whether the Coppett fortune is worth a tenth of what it was when he inherited.'

'You're still a lucky man.'

'I suppose I am. I've enough money, even if it isn't multi-millions any more. I've got brains . . .'

'And looks.'

'Yeah, they come in useful too, sometimes.' Victor shot Francesca a mischievous look. 'I've got friends, like you, Francesca. I guess I can make my way in the world.'

'I've made you my heir, of course.'

'That's very kind and generous of you.'

For once Victor looked faintly embarrassed, but Francesca went on deliberately, 'Keep on the right side of your mother, Victor. The one thing I want, more than anything else, is for her to leave you her shares in Hope & Company – or even hand them over to you early, as I may decide to do with mine.'

'You're saying . . .'

'Control of the company. You're Simeon's son. It's your right.'

With this on his mind it was not surprising that Victor went around with an air of suppressed excitement. His enthusiasm for his exceedingly menial tasks at Hope's took everyone by surprise. Nothing was too small for Victor to do, and his brisk efficiency produced a favourable impression throughout the building. The men liked him, the typists sighed for him, and the man in charge of European paintings spoke of him with particular favour.

'If you decide to take your nephew into the firm you'll gain a real asset,' he reported to Martin, who smiled and made a non-committal answer about letting Victor complete his studies before any decision could be made.

On the evening of Julia's dinner party everyone was on edge. Apart from Francesca, only Martin had met the young man and Julia, Nicholas and Jane all knew that he had reservations about him. Julia was tensed up and nervous, but when Francesca and Victor appeared she went forward immediately, her hands outstretched.

'How very nice to meet you,' she said. 'Anna's boy! After all these years! Bend down, my dear, and let me kiss you.'

Her apparent spontaneity set the tone for the rest of the evening and only Victor knew that the hands which had taken hold of his with such friendliness had been cold with nerves.

He found himself seated at dinner between Julia and her

daughter, Melissa. Presumably they all knew that he was the dead Simeon's son, but none of them betrayed their knowledge by so much as the flicker of an eyelash. That was British reserve for you. Though, come to think of it, his mother, for all her Sicilian heritage, had kept the story from him for nineteen years. It was going to be difficult returning home and not confronting her with it. But Francesca was right, he must keep on the right side of Mom, now that he knew that the prize of Hope's might be his one day.

'I've sort of lost count,' he said. 'Are there any younger members of the family I haven't met?'

'Only Quentin – Martin and Jane's son,' Melissa said. 'He's . . . let me see. How old is Quentin, Jane?'

'Your godson is nine years old,' Jane replied. 'He sometimes asks whether, once upon a time, he didn't have an aunt called Melissa.'

'Would you call that a hint?' Melissa asked Victor.

'A decided hint,' Victor agreed. 'You've been neglecting your little nephew.'

'Not so little,' Jane remarked. 'Quentin's a big boy for his age.'

Victor could not resist teasing them. 'And all set to follow in his father's footsteps one day?' he asked.

'I hope so,' Jane said. 'One would like to see the continuity of the company secured.'

'I guess there's more than one way that might happen,' Victor said. He had caught their attention. He looked round the table and smiled happily.

'After the great time I'm having in the old firm I might be tempted to ask for a job. Permanently, I mean. That would secure the succession, too. Through Grandfather Speranza, I mean.'

'Get your degree first,' Martin said. 'Talk to your mother. And think hard about uprooting yourself. It doesn't always work.'

'You weren't particularly subtle,' Francesca said, sounding cross.

'I couldn't resist shaking them up,' Victor confessed.

'You did that all right, just by walking through the door. I thought Julia was going to faint, even though I'd warned her about your likeness to Simeon.'

'She hid it pretty well. They all did.'

They were driving back to Francesca's flat in her car.

Tentatively, Victor put his hand over hers as it lay on the steering wheel, but when Francesca shook him off he sat back in his seat and kept silent.

'The evening's been a strain for me,' Francesca said at last. 'I'll be glad to get home and have a strong drink.'

'I'll fix it for you,' Victor promised. 'You know I mix a mean martini.'

Back in the flat he set to work immediately, pouring the gin into a jug. Francesca picked up an envelope and glanced at it.

'A cable,' she said. 'For you.'

She took over the mixing of the drink while Victor tore open the cable.

'Bad news?' she asked. 'Nothing wrong at home, I hope?'

'Bad news, but not unexpected,' Victor said slowly. 'Grand-mother has died.'

'I'm sorry,' Francesca said automatically.

'I feel sort of sad about it. On the other hand, she's been suffering quite a bit.'

'How will this affect your plans, Victor?'

'I guess I'll have to go home.'

'You can't get there in time for the funeral.'

'Even so . . . it's the right·thing to do.'

'I suppose so. Damn. I so much wanted to get you established as an asset to Hope & Company and I'm dying to show you Italy.'

'Why not bring the trip forward?' Victor said. 'We could travel overland to Italy, take a flying look at, say, Rome and Florence and Venice, and I could sail from Genoa.'

'Splendid idea! I'll get on to Cook's in the morning.'

The visit to Italy was, from Francesca's point of view, a great success. Victor was a perfect travelling companion and with every ancient church and picture gallery they visited she felt her hold on him tighten. Just let Anna try to keep him in America after this! Europe had got its hooks into Victor and Francesca was sure that he would not be able to keep away.

By the time Francesca returned to England the news of Serafina's Will had been received.

'Perverse to the last,' Nicholas said. 'Oh, Serafina, Serafina! What a nuisance you are, and always have been.'

'What's she done?' Francesca asked. 'Not cut Victor out, surely?'

'Not entirely, though I think he's going to be savage when he realises how his inheritance has been reduced. Serafina has opened up a very old scandal. She's left Maurice Coppett's art collection to her illegitimate son.'

'You don't mean the son she had by Father?'

'Yes, indeed. "*My son, Hugo Wood, living on the estate of Earl Kenrick.*" Would you credit it?'

'She must have been out of her mind.'

'No doubt Anna and Violetta, who get nothing – not to mention Victor – would like to think so, but they'll have a hard job proving it. The Will was made years ago.'

In spite of himself, Nicholas could not keep a quiver out of his voice. Francesca, too, although she cast a regretful thought towards Victor's disappointment, had to bite her lip.

'Father will be most disconcerted,' she said. 'Mother will pretend to know nothing, which is how she's survived all these years. Anna, of course, will be furious.'

'Even Julia is rather put out and Jane is distinctly sniffy.'

Francesca gave a snort and then both she and Nicholas burst into uncontrollable laughter.

'Oh, dear, what a couple of fools we are,' Francesca said, wiping her eyes. 'It's going to cause endless trouble. Does anyone know where the boy – or man, rather – is to be found? He can't be living on the estate after all these years.'

'Apparently he attended the Slade School of Art in London which, if Serafina knew about it, may have given her the idea, but when last heard of he was in Paris.'

'I must say I'm agog to make the acquaintance of my half-brother. I wonder whether he'll put the collection up for sale? If so, it might still be possible to secure something for Victor. Poor dear, he must be desperately disappointed to think of his cherished pictures going to an unknown by-blow of the British aristocracy.'

'Francesca, don't let your generosity run riot.'

Francesca frowned at the warning, ready to defend her right to make Victor a present of at least a small part of his lost inheritance.

'Don't make an enemy of Anna,' Nicholas said unexpectedly. 'Victor is her son, not yours. I don't think she's had an easy life. It would be cruel to take her son away from her.'

'He should have been mine,' Francesca muttered.

'But he's not. As for buying pictures for him, Anna might choose to do that herself. Come to that, Victor might want to invest some of the money from Serafina's estate in art.'

'Giving the money to this Hugo Wood? I doubt whether either of them would care for that idea!'

'Nothing can be done until he's located, anyway,' Nicholas said. 'And in the meantime the two of us had better keep our ribald amusement to ourselves. No one else seems to share it!'

They had to wait several weeks before Victor wrote to inform Francesca that Hugo Wood had been traced, living in considerable poverty in Paris.

'Quite the Bohemian artist, apparently,' Francesca told Julia. 'In some ways that's the strangest thing in this whole affair. What on earth in his upbringing could have turned him into an artist? I would have expected him to be a gardener or a tractor driver or something of that sort. An artist! It can't be heredity, can it? Father's the biggest Philistine ever and I never heard that Serafina cared for anything about pictures except their price.'

'Where did your own interest in ceramics come from?' Julia asked.

'I suppose it might all go back to Grandfather Kenrick and his acquisitiveness on the Continent. Anyway, Victor writes that the news of his good fortune has been broken to Mr Wood. I should think Father must be wishing the chap was legitimate; he might have diverted some of his new wealth towards the family estate!'

'Nicholas estimates that the value of the collection must be around five hundred thousand pounds, even though the three most important paintings did go to the Minneapolis Institute of Art at the time of Maurice's death.'

'Enough to put a new roof on Mercia House and a penny or two left over,' Francesca commented. 'How is Nicholas facing up to his retirement?'

'Better than I'd feared. Melissa has got him involved in a

children's charity and he's planning to hold an auction to raise funds for them.'

'Well done, Melissa!' Francesca hesitated and then said, 'Melissa's always been a bit of a mystery to me. I mean, I can understand her wanting a career and, of course, what she does is very worthwhile, but she doesn't seem to want anything else.'

'I know.' Julia sighed. 'It seems as if the clock stopped for Melissa somewhere in her early twenties. She never gets any older. She still looks and sounds like a young girl. She's like someone standing by the side of the track watching the trains go by, perfectly contented but not taking part in life, in spite of the work she does. She's wonderful with children.'

'Perhaps because she's stayed so young.'

'Yes, they sense that she's on their wavelength. I wish something would happen to give her a jolt.'

'Get her back on the line, give her engine a kick-start?'

'Something of the sort,' Julia admitted. 'How unkind it is to want to disturb her serenity just because the rest of us feel that we're living a better life than she is. Francesca, dear, since we're talking in this way, may I ask you something? Have you ever thought of getting married again?'

'No, never.'

'It's more than ten years since Simeon died and you're still a young woman.'

'That depends on your definition of young. I'm forty.'

'That's young,' Julia said with a smile. 'I'd like to see you with some companionship.' She paused and then added deliberately, 'Someone to keep your mind off Victor.'

'Nicholas has been talking to you.'

'We think the same way about this. The boy belongs in America with his mother. You should make a life for yourself that doesn't include Victor, except as an occasional visitor.'

'You may be right.' Francesca's smile was all sweetness, but she only agreed with her mother-in-law in order to be allowed to drop the subject.

Chapter Eighteen

'Lady Francesca Hope? My name is Hugo Wood and I understand I'm your brother.'

'For heaven's sake!'

Francesca had gone to the door wearing lounging pyjamas, expecting the caller to be nothing more interesting than the boy with the evening paper wanting to be paid. Instead, there in the brightly lit hallway of her second-floor flat was a dishevelled figure of a man, looking at her with a hint of a smile that would become a broad grin given the slightest encouragement.

'You'd better come in,' she said.

'Thanks a lot.'

He followed her into the living room, decorated in yellow and white and pale grey, and cast an expert eye round the room.

'Nice place.'

'Thank you. It's modest, but it's home. Sit down. Would you like a drink?'

'I would that, and I expect you could do with one after the shock of me turning up on the doorstep.'

'It was a surprise,' Francesca said.

'I half-expected you to call the porter and have me thrown out.'

'Oh, I wouldn't do that – not to a member of the family.'

He laughed at that, a laugh that creased up his face and almost made his eyes disappear. There was nothing of Francesca's cool blonde beauty in him. He was a bronzed creature, like someone reared in the open. His hair curled crisply, brown with golden highlights, though it was far too long and needed washing. Only his hands betrayed his origin.

As she handed him the whisky and soda for which he asked Francesca remarked, 'I see you've inherited the Kenrick hands.'

'Beautiful, aren't they?'

'They'd look even better clean.'

'How nice, already you're talking to me like a sister.' He was

249

laughing again, with an impudence that won an answering gleam from Francesca.

'Do stop wandering round the room and sit down,' she commanded.

'I'm looking at all your pretty things. Is this bowl Chinese?'

'Yes, a present from my late husband. If you drop it I won't call the porter, I'll throw you out of the window myself.'

'I wouldn't drop such a beautiful object.'

He sat down on the nearest chair and looked at her expectantly, inviting questions. Francesca asked the most obvious one.

'Why have you come to me?'

'Well, now, you've heard about the inheritance from my mysterious mother?'

'I have indeed.'

'I thought you would have. You could have knocked me down with a Tintoretto when I heard about it. Such riches! And me without a bean to my name.'

'Come to the point.'

'Naturally the first thing I did was to pen a line to the lawyers and ask for a sum in advance.'

'Of course.'

'I knew you'd understand. I winkled a measly dollar or two out of them and then I got to thinking. Of course I've always known who my father was – the boys in the village school put me on to that as soon as I was old enough to understand. And I knew your brothers – God, I cried pints when they got themselves killed in the war: they were like gods to me. Somehow I never came across you, but I knew you'd married into the Hope family. So, tell me, how do I go about getting these damn paintings shipped over here and put up for sale?'

'That's what you've decided to do?' Francesca asked, to gain time while she thought furiously.

'What else? Some of us can afford to keep our capital tied up in Chinese bowls, but others need the money to eat, not just for ourselves, but for the starving wife and child, too.'

'You're married?'

'One of the follies of my youth. No, I shouldn't say that. Fay's a lovely girl and the wee babe is the light of my life. But all the same . . .'

' "He travels fastest who travels alone"?'

'You're in the right of it. I'm an artist and I ought to have stayed single. I can make do with a crust or beg a bite from a friend, but a baby needs feeding on proper food. She's four years old now and we have to tie her to the leg of the table to stop her messing with my paints. It's no life for a child. Even I did better than that.'

'Do you make money from your paintings?'

'Never a penny. Not from my original paintings, that is. I sometimes sell a copy of something someone fancies in the Louvre – which reminds me, where do you keep the famous Raphael?'

'The *famous* Raphael is in Minneapolis; the copy is in my bedroom.'

'I'd like to see it before I go – if I go. Could you give me a bed for the night?'

'You've got a nerve!' Francesca exclaimed. 'We've not been acquainted five minutes . . .'

'Rather more than that, and blood is thicker than water. Tell you what, I'll do a sketch of you and sell it for the price of a good meal and an hotel room.'

His dancing eyes were irresistible. Francesca burst out laughing. 'You're on,' she said.

When Hugo arrived he had been carrying a brown leather hold-all like a workman's tool bag. He snapped it open and pulled out a sketch-pad.

'Turn your head, I'll do you in profile,' he said. 'No, not so much, just half a turn.'

For the next few minutes he worked in silence and his concentration impressed Francesca.

'You're serious about being an artist, aren't you?' she asked.

'I'd kill for it if necessary. Keep still.'

She knew he had finished when she heard the sound of the sheet of paper being torn out of the pad. Cautiously, she turned her head. Hugo was looking critically at his drawing.

'It's not bad,' he said. 'Not good, but not bad.' He held out the sketch and Francesca took it.

'It *is* good,' she said. 'Thank you, I'm pleased with it.'

'Hang on to it. It may be worth a fortune when I'm dead.'

'You haven't signed it.'

'I only do that when I get the money.'

'I presume you want cash? Is twenty pounds enough?'

'Jesus, girl, that's twice what I was going to ask. But I'll take it, oh yes, I'll take it.'

'About selling the pictures,' Francesca began. 'Nothing can be done until Probate is obtained, which may take six months or more.'

'Hell's bells, I can't wait that long! I need the money now.'

'I can give you an advance, but I want two things from you. First, a commitment to sell the collection through Hope's and second, I'd like to buy one picture from you privately. There's a Titian – *Portrait of a Young Man with a Feathered Hat* – I'll give you five thousand pounds for it, half now and half when I receive the picture.'

'It's worth more than that.'

'It might be, but the market's depressed. That's my offer, take it or leave it.'

'You're a hard woman.'

'I'm in the trade,' Francesca said drily.

There was a short silence and then Hugo said, 'I can't afford to refuse. You'll have to pay me in cash; I don't have a bank account.'

'Obviously I can't do that tonight.'

'Can I come with you to the bank tomorrow?'

'I suppose so. Now, I'll give you a sight of the Raphael copy and then you'll have to be on your way.'

Hugo stood in silence in front of the *Madonna of the Lilies* for a long time.

'A lovely picture and a very good copy,' he said. 'Almost as impressive as a Hugo Wood version. Was it a deliberate forgery?'

'We've very carefully avoided using that word. My own belief is that it was never intended to deceive, not in the first place. It was merely done to fill up the gap on the wall when the original was lost for a bet. I don't suppose my disreputable ancestor – not yours, by the way, because he was on Mother's side – advertised his folly and the substitution was quite simply forgotten.'

'Hm, that's taking the charitable view. I think it's too convincing to have been commissioned as a bit of decoration.'

'Does it make you regret selling the rest of the collection?'

'Not really . . . no, not at all, actually. I admire the Old Masters for their technique and the historical interest of their paintings, and I can see the emotional appeal of a picture like this Madonna, but I couldn't live with a collection of Renaissance art because I look at things in a totally different way, with modern eyes.'

'Fortunately, not everyone thinks like that or we wouldn't make many sales,' Francesca commented.

'Fortunate for you, unfortunate for me,' Hugo retorted. 'If people weren't blinded by the past they might buy my paintings.'

'I'd like to see your work some time.'

'How polite of you! That's the correct thing to say to an unknown artist, isn't it? You can see my work any time you like to come to Paris.'

'You mean to go on living there?'

'I can't see myself settling in England, no matter how much money I have. Are you sure you wouldn't like to put me up for the night?'

'Quite sure. You've got twenty pounds. That should keep you for long enough to get our other business carried out.'

'You've been treating him like a friend. How could you, Francesca? Mom and I regard him as our direst enemy.'

Victor and Anna had come to England for the sale of the Coppett Collection. As Francesca had anticipated, it had taken well over six months to arrive at the point where the pictures could be released for sale in England, a process which had not been expedited by Hugo's habit of being absent from his only known address every time his signature was required. It was the spring of 1931, and in spite of the continuing recession the imminent sale of such an important collection of paintings was arousing excitement.

'Hugo's my half-brother, even if it is on the wrong side of the blanket,' Francesca pointed out in reply to Victor's protest. 'I couldn't help being interested when he turned up on my doorstep. I think he's probably a bit of a rascal, but I suspect he has talent, and he knows how to make himself liked.'

'Obviously.'

'Don't be churlish with me, wretched boy, or I won't give you the nice present I'm planning for you.'

'Sorry.' Victor gave her a shamefaced grin. 'It's just that I see red every time Hugo Wood's name is mentioned. Tell me about my present.'

'I've made a down payment on the Coppett Titian. Hugo has promised to keep it back from the sale. I mean to give it to you, to make up for your disappointment over the rest of the pictures.'

'Francesca! Wow! That's generous beyond belief. My favourite picture – after the Raphael, which has already gone from the collection. I was planning to make a bid for it myself, but now I can spend the money on something else.'

'The nucleus of your own collection?'

'You could be right about that. I might specialise in drawings. I covet the Dürer that's in the sale and Mom has a lovely drawing of a kneeling saint – unattributed, but certainly fourteenth century – which she's promised to give me.'

'Did I make a mistake in asking Hugo for the Titian?'

'No, no! That's the thing I want most.'

'Where will you hang it? Your college rooms will hardly be suitable.'

'My "collection" will have to stay at home for the time being, of course.'

'I could house anything you bought.' She spoke casually, but they both knew that this was a crucial matter which required a decision.

'It's a long way to come to look at a picture,' Victor said. 'I'd like to be able to gloat without having to cross the Atlantic.'

'No chance of your settling over here?'

'Not for a year or two.'

'But eventually?'

'Could be.'

Victor was looking disturbed. With an effort Francesca remembered that although he had had a birthday since they had last met he was still only twenty.

'I have to graduate,' he said. 'And then I thought I'd maybe join a museum or gallery, or perhaps the American Art Association, and get some experience behind me.'

'You'll visit Europe?'

'Every year, I hope.'

He took her hand and squeezed it.

'And this will always be my first port of call.'

The sale brought Hugo and his wife and child over from France. Fay apparently had been making a precarious living as an actress when she met Hugo, and still had ambitions to make her mark on the stage. She was pretty in a fragile way, with a mop of bright red curls, a very white skin with a dusting of freckles on her nose, and big grey eyes. When Francesca first met her she was wearing a blue cotton skirt sprigged with flowers, boy's boots, a long blouse in a different flowered cotton worn over the top of her skirt and confined at the waist by a wide leather belt, a fringed scarf round her shoulders and a straw hat.

'She could pose for Augustus John without changing a thing,' Martin breathed in Jane's ear.

'Is she coming to the sale like that?'

'Why not? It'll add colour.'

They had met at Francesca's apartment, mainly because Francesca wanted reputable witnesses to her transaction with Hugo over the Titian. Melissa was also there.

'She just happened to drop in to see Jane, so we brought her along,' Martin explained. 'Watch what happens with the child. It's a most uncanny thing.'

Melissa, in the sensible navy blue suit and white blouse which was her professional uniform, had seated herself a little away from the other four people. She looked her usual calm, cheerful self, saying little but looking at Hugo and Fay with unabashed curiosity.

The little girl, a scrap of a child with her father's brown eyes and hair of an astonishing dark red, was shy amongst these unknown people and clung to her mother's skirt, half-hidden. She peeped out and her gaze settled on Melissa. She released her clutch on the folds of blue cotton and walked across the room, straight towards Melissa, who was apparently taking no notice of her until Lynette put a hand on her knee to attract her attention, then Melissa looked down and smiled, a warm, uncomplicated, loving smile. Lynette looked at her solemnly and then climbed up and sat on her lap.

'There now, she's taken to you,' Hugo remarked.

'Put Melissa down in a roomful of children and one by one

they'll stop what they're doing and go and stand round her,' Martin said. 'It must be a sort of magnetism. How do you do it, Melissa?'

'They're important to me and I suppose they know it,' Melissa said.

'Lynette is usually bashful with new people,' Fay said. 'I'm afraid she's not very bright. Not imbecile, or anything serious, just rather backward.' She spoke quite dispassionately and a faint frown appeared on Melissa's face.

'How old are you, Lynette?' she asked.

Lynette looked uncertainly from Melissa to her mother.

'She doesn't speak an awful lot of English,' Fay explained.

'*Quelle âge as-tu, mignonne?*' Melissa repeated.

'*J'ai presque cinque ans.*'

'*Aimes-tu l'Angleterre?*'

The little head was shaken with determination.

'*Non?*'

'*Non. Jeanne n'est pas ici. Et mon bébé non plus.*'

'Oh, that *bébé*!' Fay exclaimed. 'She means her doll. We left it behind and we had the most hideous journey when Lynette missed it.'

'And Jeanne?'

'Our concierge's daughter. She looks after Lynette while Hugo and I are working.'

Lynette sat quietly, allowing the grown-ups' talk to carry on over her head. Looking at her inattentive face Francesca could see why Fay had described her little daughter as backward. She seemed quite content just to sit. It made for a restful, uninterrupted conversation, but it was surely not natural for a four-year-old to be so docile.

Without making any special movement towards her, Melissa spoke to Lynette again. The child did not look up, nor did she respond.

'You see, she just doesn't pay attention,' Fay said.

'I suspect a slight deafness.'

'Oh, surely not!' Fay leaned forward and spoke directly to the child, raising her voice. 'Lynette?'

Lynette turned her head straight away.

'You see? There's nothing wrong with her hearing.'

'I said slight. Enough for her to become confused when she's surrounded by several adult people all talking above her head and in a language she imperfectly understands. May I examine her? I've got my bag with me.'

'A free consultation? How kind. Yes, of course, if it'll make you feel better.'

A few minutes later Melissa came back from washing her hands.

'I'd like her to see an ear, nose and throat specialist,' she said. 'But I'm sure he'll agree with my diagnosis. Chronic secretory otitis media, popularly known as "glue ear". She may need a minor operation. Fortunately, there's rarely any permanent deafness.'

'Oh, dear, what a bore! Poor little thing. Hugo, remember to get something done about it when we get back to Paris.'

Hugo, who was talking animatedly to Martin about a recent exhibition at the Musée d'Orsay, looked round impatiently and said, 'Lynette's your department. Surely you can organise a visit to the doctor for her? If you'd checked to see that Jeanne was washing her ears out this wouldn't have happened.'

'That's got nothing to do with it,' Melissa said quickly. 'Why can't Lynette be treated in London?'

'How long will it take? As soon as Hugo has got the money from the sale we're going to Morocco.'

'Marvellous light,' Hugo put in. 'I've been wanting to get to North Africa for years.'

'Sunshine . . . servants . . . oh, it's going to be bliss,' Fay said.

'What about a school for Lynette?'

'Oh, I can teach her. And she'll be picking up the most wonderful education in *life*, won't she?'

'Not if she can't hear what's going on,' Melissa said drily. 'If I can arrange for a colleague to see Lynette tomorrow, will you allow this quite minor operation to be carried out in the next few days?'

'Will we have to pay for it?'

Again that look of controlled distaste passed over Melissa's face. 'As I understand it, you and your husband are about to become quite seriously rich. Surely you can afford to spend a few pounds on your daughter's health?'

Hugo turned his head and spoke sharply. 'Fay, don't be an idiot.

Of course we must have Lynette's ear seen to. Thank Dr Hope properly and get it fixed up.'

Fay subsided, looking sulky. Lynette peered from Melissa to her mother, her face anxious. Melissa smiled at the child and put her down.

'I'll use the telephone in your bedroom, if I may, Francesca,' she said.

There was a slight awkwardness in the air and to relieve it Francesca began asking Fay where she and Hugo were staying in London.

'A friend of Hugo's has lent us his flat in Bayswater. Actually, he's gone ahead to Morocco to find somewhere for us all to live when we've got our lovely money.'

'That reminds me of a favour I was going to ask you, Francesca,' Hugo said with a smoothness which Francesca found slightly suspect. 'Would you let me savour the pleasure of being the owner of a Titian just for a week or ten days? It's the only picture not going into the sale so presumably it could be released to me.'

'You want to keep a Titian in a flat in Bayswater?' Francesca asked.

'Just for a short time until we leave for Morocco.'

'It's half mine,' Francesca pointed out.

'And you're getting it at a bargain price.'

'I'm not so sure about that in the present financial situation,' Martin intervened. 'Francesca is paying you a fair price and in her place I'd not be too keen to let the picture be taken out of safe-keeping. What about security? What about insurance?'

'You see?' Hugo said to Fay. 'Haven't I always said it's a mistake to have possessions? You have to start worrying about keeping them.'

'Why not let me have the Titian straight away and then I can be the one to do the worrying?' Francesca suggested.

From the sullen look on Hugo's face it seemed that this idea did not appeal to him.

'I could change my mind and put the painting into the sale after all,' he said.

'Not without repaying me my two and a half thousand pounds – immediately,' Francesca pointed out.

Hugo suddenly changed tactics. With a smile of enormous

charm he said, 'Ah, let me have it! I'll sit indoors and look at it all day and every day if that's the only way you'll feel secure. And I'll pay for the insurance. How about it?'

Francesca was looking at him in a curiously speculative way. She started to speak and then seemed to change her mind.

'I'll do it,' she said. 'Martin will arrange the insurance through the company's usual contact and I'll deduct the premium from the payment I still have to make to you.'

The sale of the Coppett Collection was a major event. In spite of the depressed state of the market it aroused great interest amongst dealers. The Sale Room was crowded and Francesca felt the familiar thrill of excitement. How Simeon would have enjoyed this occasion – and that was a thought that had not come to her for a long time. Strange, the way one recovered from an apparently crippling blow. She still missed him, but she had made a life for herself, and a good life, and she had the thought of Victor to sustain her. One day it would be Victor who stood at the rostrum and looked round to command silence as the sale commenced.

Victor was there, sitting between Francesca and his mother. He was planning to bid for the Dürer drawing, some animal sketches by Pisanello and a wonderful engraving by Schongauer.

Hugo, to Martin's horror, had insisted on not placing reserve prices on any of the works of art on sale.

'I want to sell everything,' he said. 'I've told you I don't like being cluttered up and I need the money. Let the things go and if some lucky person gets a bargain who am I to quibble, who've been the luckiest person in the world? Let the paintings be bought by people who take the conventional view of the value of the Old Masters, which I don't.'

'Except for Titian,' Francesca remarked.

'Ah, that was just to let me anticipate the pleasure of being a rich man,' Hugo said, but there was a mischievous sparkle in his eye which Francesca profoundly distrusted.

Victor obtained all the items he wanted and at a little below the limit he had set himself, which brought a satisfied look to his face. It was to Francesca that he turned with a delighted smile when the Dürer drawing was knocked down to him.

'The thing I most wanted,' he said.

'It should all have been yours,' Anna said, not bothering to lower her voice. 'Francesca, is that man here?'

'To your right, two rows ahead,' Francesca said. 'The dark young man with the red-headed girl.'

Fay, she saw, had undergone a transformation. From being a gypsy she had become excessively *mondaine*, in a sleek black dress with clips at the neck which were too large to be diamonds, even allowing for Hugo's sudden wealth. A tiny black hat clung to one side of her head and she had matched her scarlet lipstick to her long nails. With her change of clothes her manner had also altered. Her hands fluttered nervously and she moved her head with birdlike movements as she kept up an animated conversation. Fay, as Francesca suddenly remembered, was an actress and these chameleon changes were part of her repertoire. It must make her singularly unrestful to live with, but perhaps Hugo found it interesting.

Hugo himself was unchanged. He was wearing a suit, of sorts, and he seemed to be keeping his trousers up with braces instead of the old tie around his waist which he had worn when he had first visited Francesca. Apart from that his disreputable appearance was the same and he tilted back on his chair and gazed around him with the air of one prepared to be amused, not at all like a man in the act of acquiring a fortune.

'Would you like to meet him?' Francesca asked Victor.

'Yes, I would.'

'Victor, no!' his mother protested. 'He's a person in whom we can take no interest.'

'Now, don't be stuffy, Mom. Surely you want to speak to him? After all, he's your half-brother, just as he is Francesca's.'

'That's something I prefer to forget. And so would you if you had my memories. Mama . . . but I mustn't speak ill of the dead.'

'Why not? They're the least likely to answer back. Grandmama, as far as I can make out, was shockingly fast. Well, I find that interesting. Having lived a blameless life yourself, darling, you don't understand the fascination of sin. I'd love to know all about Serafina's reckless past and I only wish I'd had the chance to talk to her about it while she was alive.'

Francesca was studying her catalogue, carefully avoiding

looking at Anna. Victor was being naughty . . . a blameless life . . . when he knew very well that Anna had a past which was at least as interesting as her mother's. The fact that he dared to tease her in that way indicated that Anna was still not aware that he had been told the truth about his father. It would come as a shock to her if she ever discovered that he knew.

'Come and say hello,' Francesca said. 'Anna, I quite understand how you feel, but Victor is old enough to resist contact with a bit of raffishness.'

Everyone was standing up, exchanging greetings and moving slowly towards the doorway. Hugo and Fay were still seated, but Hugo got up in a leisurely way as Francesca approached him.

'Congratulations,' she said. 'A very good sale, considering the financial climate. I was keeping a running total and I think it works out at around four hundred and eighty-six thousand pounds. Add on the five thousand for the Titian and you've netted over four hundred and ninety thousand.'

'Less commission,' Hugo said.

'Yes, of course. It's still a tidy sum. In fact, by anyone's standards, it's a fortune.'

'Especially to a man who yesterday had nothing. And who may this be?'

'May I introduce Victor Coppett – Maurice Coppett's grandson.'

'And my half-nephew. You bought the Schongauer engraving. A fine piece of work.'

'It is indeed. I'm looking forward to having the Titian, too, when you can be induced to part with it.'

'Francesca's giving it to you?' Hugo glanced at Francesca with interest. 'There's a generous auntie. Well, now, about the Titian. I've grown fond of it and that's the truth. However, needs must when the devil drives. We'd be off tomorrow if we could lay hands on our money and our child, but I'm told it'll take a day or two for the funds to filter through the system and Lynette doesn't get released from hospital until tomorrow, so we're kicking our heels for a while.'

'I'm not kicking my heels,' Fay said. 'I had a film test this morning and I'm told it was really promising.'

'You can't pursue a career in films and go to Morocco,' Francesca pointed out.

Fay pouted, the very image of a spoilt young thing, whereas the last time Francesca had seen her she had been the epitome of the free soul, untrammelled by convention. It was confusing, but it was also fascinating.

'That's what Hugo says,' she complained. 'Of course, Morocco will be heaven and I die for it, but apart from sitting for Hugo and his friends there'll be nothing for me to do, nothing creative, that is.'

Victor was growing bored with this posing. 'About the Titian . . .' he hinted.

'As I was saying, I like having it around.'

'You've got to part with it eventually, so why not now?' Francesca asked.

'I haven't *got* to do anything,' Hugo said softly. 'Don't use that word to me; I don't like it. You can have your Titian next week. Call for it with the money and your armed guard, or whatever you think appropriate, at three o'clock in the afternoon a week from today.'

'Hugo's a nuisance,' Victor grumbled. 'Collecting the Titian next week barely gives me time to have it properly packed and processed for return to the United States.'

'Leave it here,' Francesca said.

Victor picked up her hand and kissed it lightly. 'No, darling, I want it with me. We've been through this already. I'll be back, but not until I'm ready. If I make a move too soon Martin will oppose me and I can't defeat him, he's too deeply entrenched. But if there's a move to replace him with young Quentin . . .'

'That can't happen for *years*!'

'All the better. I'll be prepared and ready to pounce. Leave it to me, darling. I'm much more of a jungle cat than you are.'

'You've barely found your claws. All right, I'll not press you. Hugo's up to something, by the way.'

'Is he? How do you know?'

'He's too damn pleased with himself.'

'Any man might be pleased with nearly half a million pounds in cash.'

'It's more than that. You'll come with me next week?'

'Of course. Hugo fascinates me and as for Fay . . . is she really as bogus as she seems?'

'Totally, but I think she might be quite a good actress. Frustrating for her to be whisked off to Morocco when she might be making a name in films.'

The Bayswater flat was spacious, and although it had a cluttered air it was cleaner than Francesca had expected.

Lynette was out of hospital and came skipping to the door when Hugo opened it.

'Tante Melissa?' she asked.

'No, Melissa isn't with us,' Francesca said. 'That's a very nice doll you've got there, Lynette.'

'She is my new bébé. Tante Melissa gave her to me because I was a good girl. I am being in hôpital because my . . . my ear was fulled up with nasty.'

'You're better now?'

Lynette nodded, full of the importance of having been in 'hôpital'.

'I am all good now,' she said.

'What a little poppet,' Victor said idly as she ran away. 'Now can I see my Titian?'

'In here.'

Hugo led them into the drawing room, full of red plush furniture, with heavy lace curtains at the windows. The room faced east, so that the afternoon light was comparatively dim, especially filtered through the lace.

'Isn't this a gem of a room?' he asked. 'My friend inherited the place from his grandmother and he's kept it as a Victorian relic.'

The painting stood on an easel at an angle to the door. It was just as Francesca remembered it, a fine portrait of a young man, with a mobile face just on the point of breaking into a smile. The tilt of his head and the stare of his hazel eyes challenged the onlooker. In one hand he carried the feathered hat which gave the picture its name. A fine leather gauntlet had been thrown down on a small table while the other was still on the hand he rested on his hip.

'Look at him, isn't he a fine young fellow?' Hugo said softly.

'I've always had a weakness for him,' Victor said. 'I wish we could establish his identity.'

'There's nothing in the archives?'

'Nothing at all. Grandfather employed an art historian to look into it, but he never came up with a solution. Just "a young man with a feathered hat".'

'The painting's magnificent,' Hugo said. He glanced at Francesca, who had been wandering round the room instead of standing still in front of the portrait like the two men.

'It's very good,' Francesca said. 'Nearly as good as the original.'

There was a moment's stunned silence and then Hugo burst into laughter.

'You've guessed,' he said. 'I had a bet with myself that I could fool you, but you saw through me, clever girl.'

'How far would you have let it go?' Francesca asked in a voice of cool curiosity. Victor appeared to have been deprived of the power of speech.

'Would I try to pass off a forgery on my own sister?'

'You might. I can't help wondering why you went to the trouble of putting your copy into the original frame.'

'To make it look right, of course.'

'I hope you haven't damaged the painting,' Victor said quickly. 'If you have I'll hold you responsible.'

'No fear of that. I'm the expert, remember.'

'Indeed you are,' Francesca said. 'Indeed you are.'

'Tell me now, what was it gave my little joke away? I swear it wasn't the quality of the painting, and in this light I'd defy a world authority to be sure after the quick inspection you gave our young man and without the benefit of a paint analysis.'

'You should have inspected the back of the canvas as carefully as you did the front.'

'You put a secret mark on it?' For a moment Hugo looked ugly. 'You never trusted me, did you?'

'Not one inch,' Francesca said. 'Not one tiny inch. How long will it take for you to replace the true Titian in the frame?'

'Give me half an hour. I'll fetch my tools.'

As he left the room Victor said, 'I'm almost speechless. Whatever made you suspect him enough to mark the canvas?'

'I never liked him having the picture and Hugo couldn't resist laughing to himself about the way he meant to outsmart us. I've seen that look before – I had two brothers, remember, who were also Hugo's half-brothers – I knew it meant mischief.'

'Was it a joke, as he says?'

'I doubt it. If he could have got out of the country with the original Titian then no doubt Hugo would have sold it abroad.'

'But he's already netted nearly half a million!'

'When a man's been living on his wits for the better part of his life, as Hugo has, the habit of making an extra profit dies hard. It's not just the money, it's the satisfaction of getting the better of someone who's had advantages that were denied to him.'

'Is he to go unpunished?'

'What punishment is appropriate for a legpull? Let it go, Victor. We need never see Hugo again and I, for one, won't be sorry.'

'Nor me.' Victor hunched his shoulders, looking disgruntled.

'Don't let it rankle,' Francesca said.

'It irks me that you spotted the fraud and I never suspected,' Victor burst out. 'I'm the one who's been studying Renaissance art, I'm the one who's had that picture in front of my eyes for years and yet you walked straight in and saw that it was wrong and I never noticed a thing.'

'I'm more than twice your age and while you've been studying art I've been finding out about human nature,' Francesca said. 'I've been on the alert ever since Hugo walked into my flat six months ago. I knew he'd pull a fast one if he could. It's the nature of the beast. And I saw him studying my copy of the Raphael – that's what gave him the idea. Too clever by half, our Hugo.'

In sudden impatience she added, 'Hugo's such a *fool*. If he'd taken as much trouble over painting an original picture and shown it to me I might have bought it, and surely that would have given him more satisfaction than passing off a spurious Titian on me?'

'Have you seen any of his work?'

'No, I haven't and that's what makes me furious. He says he's a serious artist and he's certainly proved that he's got technical ability. He should have been straining every nerve to sell his own work, not wasting time on an elaborate fraud.'

'I wonder how they'll make out in Morocco. That little kid's going to have a funny upbringing.'

'Indeed she is. Poor Lynette.'

Chapter Nineteen

Melissa put down her pen and leaned back in her chair, stretching out her arms and turning her head from side to side. It had been a long day and a tiring one, but she was free now to leave the hospital and go home to her own small flat. She would have a leisurely bath and something simple to eat – an omelette and some fruit perhaps.

There was a tap on her door and she suppressed a sigh before saying 'Come in.' Under the desk she crossed her fingers in a childish wish that the visitor would not bring her any more work that evening. To her relief it was Stefan Bowman who put his head round the door. They were colleagues, though they only came into contact with one another when she referred one of her small patients to him for advice on an ear, nose or throat problem. It was Dr Bowman who had attended to little Lynette's 'glue ear' some three years earlier.

'Finished for the day?' he asked.

'Yes, thank goodness. You've only just caught me.'

'And you are hoping that your tiresome colleague is not going to bring you another problem. I am, but it's nothing to do with the hospital.'

'Sounds intriguing,' Melissa said. 'Sit down.'

'No . . . please. I am going to ask of you a favour and in order to persuade you I wish to buy you a meal. Will you come to Luigi's with me?'

The suggestion was so unexpected that Melissa hesitated. She had worked with Stefan Bowman for years without feeling that she had ever come to know him. He was a German, and when Melissa had first met him his name had been 'Baumann', but he had since Anglicised it and become a British citizen. The most important thing about him, as far as Melissa was concerned, was that he was an excellent children's doctor.

'I was going home to a simple omelette,' she told him, 'but I'm willing to settle for spaghetti instead, especially since you've aroused my curiosity.'

'Then let us go.'

He was a tall man and too thin. As they sat opposite one another in the small restaurant, Melissa thought to herself that Stefan looked as if he could do with a good bowl of pasta or two. His dark hair lay limply against his skull and he had a nervous habit of pushing back with one long finger the strands which fell over his forehead. His eyes were very dark and their expression was sombre. This unsmiling impression, and the long lines carved in his face from his nose to the corners of his mouth, had given Stefan the reputation of being 'sour', but to Melissa he had never been anything but an unfailingly courteous colleague, and when she thought about him at all she liked him.

'Now, tell me what you want me to do for you,' she said when they had chosen from Luigi's simple menu.

'Is it possible for you to use your influence with your brother?'

'Martin? I don't know that he ever listens very much to anything I say, but I'll do my best.' She was still completely in the dark, as Stefan seemed to realise.

'To begin at the beginning, I am half-Jewish – that is, I had a Jewish father and a Christian mother. Poor Father was quite thrown off by his family for "marrying out" and I do not practise the Jewish religion or, indeed, any religion at all. I have made my home in England, but my family still live in Munich.'

'You're not married, are you?' Melissa asked.

'No, no – there has never been time.'

'That's what I say, but my family don't believe me.'

His smile was perfunctory and she saw that he was impatient at being side-tracked.

'I have settled in England and as things now are in Germany, I am glad of it. Jews are being persecuted in my home town.'

'But you're not a Jew, not a real one,' Melissa pointed out.

'No, I am not, not in my own eyes, but I'm quite sufficiently Jewish to be prevented from working in Germany if I had any idea of returning, which I do not.'

'Is it really as bad as that?' Melissa asked incredulously.

'You are as blind as all the English,' Stefan said bitterly. 'Yes, it is that bad.'

'Is there anything anyone can do?'

'There is something you can do. I am still in touch with friends and relations back home and I mean to return for a holiday this summer. Some of them hope eventually to reach England, but they are afraid that if they try to leave, their property will be confiscated and they will arrive here penniless. We have a plan. They will sell everything they can that is not portable and turn the money into works of art, jewellery – anything that can be easily taken out of the country. I will bring back as much as I dare. Will you enlist your brother's help in selling these things for the best price that can be obtained?'

'Suppose you get stopped at the frontier? You might lose everything if the Customs officials turned nasty.'

'It has been known to happen,' Stefan admitted. 'It's a risk we must take.'

Melissa slowly sipped her red wine, her mind turning over the problem.

'Martin will help,' she said certainly. 'But I think you need more than one smuggler, to spread the risk. Someone like me, terribly respectable-looking.'

'What are you saying?'

'I'm offering my services as a courier. Should we travel together, do you think? Or would it be better if we went separately?'

'You don't understand! The risk . . .'

'Very small, surely. The greatest risk will be coming through British Customs with a load of jewellery on which I have no intention of paying duty. There must be some way round that. Perhaps I can twist some official arm. I tell you what, we'll recruit Francesca. She looks like the sort of person who'd travel with a jewel case and she's got a title, which comes in useful sometimes.'

'But you're involving the whole family!'

'Why not?'

Stefan gave an excited, disbelieving laugh. 'This is more, far more, than I dared to ask. Dr Hope, you don't know what this means . . .'

'It means you've got a friend, several friends. You're right, I've been blind and so, I think, have the rest of my family, but now you've made us see, we'll stand by you through thick and thin.'

She insisted on taking him to see Francesca that evening.

Francesca, informed by telephone that Melissa was bringing a man along to meet her, was all agog, since this was a new departure for her sister-in-law.

From that point of view, however, the meeting with Stefan Bowman was a disappointment. Clearly there was no romantic element in his relationship with Melissa, not yet. Francesca, taking in his air of seriousness, his elegant hands and the endearing way his hair strayed over his forehead, thought that Melissa might do a lot worse for a lover, though she could see that such an idea was far from Melissa's mind.

She listened in dismay to Stefan's account of the difficulties his friends and family were enduring.

'We must try to do something to help,' she agreed. 'This man Hitler who's come to power . . .'

'It's a very, very bad development,' Stefan said. 'I fear the worst results from Fascist rule in Germany.'

'We have our own Fascists here and everyone thinks they're a bit of a joke,' Melissa commented.

'I think you would not laugh if Sir Oswald Mosley were to be your Prime Minister.'

'Well, of course, that's impossible!'

'We did not think it possible for a ranting little man with a silly moustache to become Chancellor of Germany, but Adolf Hitler has achieved this. I must plead with you to take this threat seriously.'

'I do! Francesca, will you come with me to Munich? We can have a short holiday and undertake our mission to bring out anything reasonably portable that can then be sold to provide funds for people to live on when they leave Germany.'

'As it happens, I do have a reason to go to Germany – though I wasn't going to follow it up until you put this idea to me. Not Munich, but Frankfurt. Hugo is having an exhibition there and he's had the nerve to send me an invitation.'

'What a cheek!' Melissa said, much diverted. 'Let's both go. I've always wanted to see what sort of work Hugo did.'

She turned to Stefan and explained, 'Hugo Wood is a . . . a family connection.'

'He's my bastard brother,' Francesca said crisply. 'He's a rogue and the last time he was in England he tried to pass off a forgery on me. All the same, I agree with you, Melissa, I'd love to see his paintings. Can you get away for a fortnight next month?'

'I think so. I'll look at the leave schedule tomorrow.'

A month later, Melissa, Stefan and Francesca caught the ferry to Hamburg. They had agreed that Melissa and Francesca would travel on to Frankfurt while Stefan went straight to Munich, to supervise matters there. They were to split up the valuables between them and travel home on different days in order to lessen the danger of discovery.

The two women ran into no particular difficulties on their journey. The country seemed to be quite normal, although they did see a number of people wearing the Nazi armband.

'Can it really be as bad as Stefan suggested?' Melissa wondered. 'Do you think he was exaggerating?'

'There's a feeling of something under the surface,' Francesca said. 'Perhaps I'm imagining things, but I don't feel completely at ease.'

In Frankfurt they saw a poster advertising Hugo's exhibition. It showed one of his paintings, which looked like nothing more than a confused jumble of swirling lines.

'Perhaps it will make more sense when we see it in colour,' Francesca said.

'Are we likely to meet Hugo?' Melissa asked.

'Probably not, as we've missed the Private View. I don't know that I particularly want to see him, the wretch.'

'I'd like to know how little Lynette is getting along. She was an appealing child.'

The gallery was very modern, white and stark, which suited the paintings Hugo had on view. Francesca's remark about the black and white poster had been apt. As they walked through the door their eyes were assaulted by a blaze of colour.

'Hugo's style is what you might call *vigorous*,' Francesca said. 'He seems to lay his paint on with a trowel.'

'You can certainly feel the heat and the intensity of the light,' Melissa enthused. 'Were they all painted in Morocco?'

'Let's buy a catalogue and find out.'

They wandered around separately. Francesca admitted the strength of the paintings and she could see the effect at which

Hugo aimed, but to an eye trained to appreciate the cool restraint of Chinese art these pictures were too undisciplined to be appealing.

Melissa, on the other hand, was fascinated. Over and over again she returned to two paintings; one was of a child in a courtyard garden with a well, a fig tree and a flight of white stairs leading to the upper floor of the house behind. The child was no more than sketchily suggested, but there was no mistaking that red hair, and the rag doll she dragged behind her might well have been the very one Melissa had given Lynette in London.

The other painting was more difficult to sort out; its riot of colour gradually resolved itself into a market scene – a stall piled high with citrus fruit, white-robed figures with dark faces, a man in indigo blue in the foreground, arches leading to dark cavities, and an iron balcony with a veiled woman leaning over it. Once she had begun to see the details, Melissa felt as if she had stepped into a different world, a place where the light stung the eyes and the sun beat down on an unprotected head, where the shadows were as blue as the robed man and the patch of sky was the same rich colour.

'I'm tempted to buy this,' she said.

Francesca cast a dubious look at the painting. 'Could you live with it?'

'I'd have to get rid of my patterned wallpaper, but it'd be worth it. I'd feel invigorated every time I came home and saw that heat and light. I've made up my mind: I shall buy the painting of Lynette out of sentiment and this one because I can't resist it.'

'Good news for Hugo, as he doesn't seem to have sold anything else,' Francesca said.

'I wonder if he's here in Frankfurt? I'd like to meet him again now that I've seen his paintings.'

They enquired at the desk, but the bored-looking young woman who had been surreptitiously reading a novel told them that Herr Wood had left the city. She began to discuss arrangements for shipping the paintings to England, but Melissa said, 'No, I shall return here soon, pick up my pictures and take them home myself.'

'You'll find them terribly cumbersome,' Francesca protested.

'Plenty of taxis, plenty of porters. Provided they're well

packed I have no qualms about taking the pictures on the train and ship.'

She waited until she and Francesca were on their own before she added, 'Besides, think what a splendid cover they make. I'm a buyer of modern paintings, not an exporter of Old Masters.'

' "Exporter" is good,' Francesca grinned.

'Well, I refuse to look upon myself as a smuggler!'

In those early days of their adventure it was not too difficult for people wishing to leave Germany to abandon their homes and start afresh in other countries, but even by the following year when Melissa and Francesca made another visit, it was noticeable that the situation was deteriorating. They travelled together and Francesca made use of her aristocratic connections and the cool blonde looks she still retained to take them into government circles. She had a great success with Nazi officials, a success she exploited to divert attention from the activities which would not have been popular with her hand-kissing admirers.

As far as Melissa was concerned, the only restriction on her visits to Germany was the amount of leave she could obtain from the hospital. The same difficulty applied to Stefan, but in the summer of 1934 they both managed to get themselves invited to a medical conference in Munich.

'I shall take you to visit my family, as a valued colleague,' Stefan announced. 'We will have our own conference, to discuss how to get even more people out of my unhappy country.'

'Is it your country?' Melissa asked.

'I should not say so when England has been so good to me,' Stefan said quietly. 'But the heart is still German.'

They had become warm friends though, to Francesca's regret, they appeared to be nothing more than that. The only thing that made her sometimes wonder whether her sister-in-law would like a closer relationship was that Melissa had learnt German with ferocious concentration during the past year. She would have been encouraged to know that Melissa had indulged in not only a new suit for the conference days, but also an evening gown in sapphire blue which was by far the most becoming garment she had had in her wardrobe for a long time.

The day before she and Stefan left, Melissa had her hair cut and

273

washed and told herself that it was because she wanted to be a credit to her hospital at the medical conference; at the back of her mind, however, there was a touch of excitement which she tried to stifle, because she was completely ignorant of Stefan's feelings towards her.

He called at her flat to collect her before they departed, a flat which had been transformed since Melissa had acquired her two Hugo Wood paintings. She had got rid of the flower-sprigged wallpaper and had the walls painted white. The result, with her plain dark furniture, grey upholstered sofa and nondescript carpet, had still not satisfied her until, with a sudden access of belief in her own taste, she had had some cushions covered in lemon yellow, orange and blue silk. All of a sudden the room came to life. Melissa was happy with it and all the happier because Stefan shared her taste.

As always when he came to visit her he went to stand in front of the market scene.

'You really like that painting, don't you?' Melissa asked.

'I admire it enormously. You bought well. I think Hugo Wood is a painter for the future.'

The journey was uneventful and the conference went well.

'I can't honestly say I'm learning anything I didn't know before, but the contact with overseas colleagues is always stimulating,' Melissa remarked.

'You'll come with me to meet my parents this evening?'

As they made the short taxi journey Melissa asked, 'Stefan, why haven't your own mother and father left Germany?'

'Ach, if only I could persuade them! They think our fears are exaggerated. Father has his business – he makes optical lenses – and Mother will not question his opinions.'

The Baumanns lived in a spacious apartment in a good residential district. They received Melissa courteously, but she sensed as soon as she and Stefan stepped inside the flat that there was something wrong. Frau Baumann was obviously distressed and Herr Baumann seized hold of his son's arm as if he were grasping a lifeline. She could see by the worried looks they cast at her that they wanted to talk to Stefan, but not in front of a stranger.

'Shall I go?' she asked quietly in English.

Stefan spoke to his parents, so rapidly and idiomatically that she had difficulty in following him. When they replied, both speaking together, she knew that she had been right in thinking that they were in deep distress.

'Go into the drawing room,' Stefan said. 'I'll give you a glass of wine and as soon as I've properly understood I'll come and explain.'

Melissa was settled in the drawing room, with its good old-fashioned furniture and white crocheted antimacassars, which had almost disappeared in England, and obediently sipped her glass of chilled white wine.

When Stefan joined her, his obvious concern echoed his parents' despair.

'My Uncle Friedrich and his wife Miriam have been arrested,' he said. 'For no reason that we can discover except that Uncle Friedrich has a prosperous business – he is one of the town's most respected opticians – and his premises are wanted "for expansion" by a non-Jewish company. Uncle Friedrich refused to sell, so he has been thrown into prison. Aunt Miriam made such a fuss they took her into custody, too, though we have hopes that she will be released.'

'Stefan, how terrible! This is your father's brother?'

'Yes, and he has always continued to be a practising Jew. I'm desperately worried because Father is associated with him in the business. Father's factory actually makes the spectacles which Uncle prescribes. It's my belief that the Nazis mean to close down his business, too.'

They were interrupted by Frau Baumann and this time Melissa understood what she said.

'Stefan, your Cousin Lisl is here.'

The young woman who hurried into the room held out her hands to Stefan. He took them and then leaned forward to kiss her on both cheeks.

In the hubbub of German conversation that followed Melissa knew that she would have to go. She stood up and caught Stefan's eye. He gave a little shrug and then nodded. Frau Baumann and Cousin Lisl hardly noticed as Melissa moved towards the door, but they met Herr Baumann in the hallway and he exclaimed in distress at Stefan's friend being hurried away.

'I hope to meet you again in happier circumstances,' Melissa said carefully.

He smiled and patted her hand, but it was obvious that he was as distracted as his wife.

'If I find you a taxi do you mind returning to the hotel alone?' Stefan asked.

'I can call my own taxi. Don't be silly, Stefan. I'm a middle-aged professional woman and used to looking after myself.'

'You are not in the least middle-aged. Melissa . . . I didn't mean it to be like this.'

They stood for a moment in silence and then Melissa touched him fleetingly on the arm and moved away.

'Go back to your parents,' she said over her shoulder.

Melissa did not see Stefan again until the next morning. He looked like a man who had not slept all night, but in the crowded conference hall she could do no more than glance at him with concern.

He smiled, but so unhappily that she feared something had happened to his parents overnight. To her surprise, when they broke for coffee Stefan walked away from her.

'Stefan, what's wrong?' Melissa demanded, darting after him.

'It's better if we're not seen together too much.'

'What rot! I'm British and, come to that, so are you. We can talk to one another until the cows come home and the German police can do damn-all about it.'

Her vehemence raised a faint gleam from Stefan.

'I'm going to ask you to take the risk of carrying all my mother's jewellery out of the country,' he said abruptly. 'I've persuaded them that they must leave, and soon.'

'Good. What about your uncle?'

'There's no news of him, nor of Aunt Miriam. It begins to look extremely sinister. Lisl is greatly disturbed because she believes that it is her anti-Nazi activities which have put them in danger. She stayed last night with Mother and Father because she dared not go home. Obviously this puts them, too, in great danger.'

'So it becomes urgent to get them out of the country?'

'And Lisl, too, if it can be done.'

'There must be a solution . . .'

'There is. Mother thought of it. She wants me to marry Lisl.'

Quite dispassionately, Melissa noted her reaction. So it really did happen: actual physical pain as a response to emotional shock. She felt as if her entrails were being put through a wringer. In a cool and level voice she said, 'That would give her, too, the right to live in Britain?'

'Exactly.'

'And it could be done – quite quickly?'

'Yes, it could be done, provided we can keep Lisl out of the hands of the police for a few days. Melissa . . . it wouldn't be a proper marriage.'

'That would be for you and Lisl to decide.'

'Mother hopes . . . but I have other . . . Melissa, it's you I love.'

It was like a balloon exploding. The great weight of depression in the middle of Melissa's chest dissipated as if it had never existed.

'Oh, Stefan,' she whispered, with tears starting into her eyes.

'This marriage with Lisl, I have to do it; you do see that, don't you? But afterwards . . . I'll end it as soon as I possibly can.'

'Yes, yes, my dear. Oh, I'm making such a fool of myself, in broad daylight, in public.'

She wiped away her tears with the back of her finger and then smiled at him with blinding happiness.

'A married Jewish doctor with a horde of relatives hanging round his neck,' Nicholas grumbled. 'I thought my little Melissa would do better than that.'

'She's not your little Melissa. She's thirty-six and she's in love – thank goodness,' Julia said. 'I was afraid she'd never come to it.'

'I've known something was going on ever since she bought those peculiar pictures.'

'Yes . . . well, I have to agree with you about the pictures. But Stefan is perfectly acceptable, provided he can free himself from his wife. What a strange, quixotic thing to do – to marry a girl just to give her a passport. Poor Lisl.'

'Why do you say that? Lucky Lisl, I would have thought.'

'I've seen the way she looks at Stefan,' Julia said. 'I think Lisl would not object to the marriage being a true one. It's as well that she and Stefan are living separately.'

277

'You're saying she might try to seduce him?'

'Of course. Lisl has been through too much to have scruples.'

'If Stefan starts playing fast and loose with Melissa . . .'

Julia smiled at Nicholas's indignation. 'Stefan can be trusted,' she said.

It was a situation that Melissa had already faced. Loving Stefan herself, it seemed only too likely to her that any woman might feel the same way about him, especially one whose life he had saved.

She spoke about it, very tentatively, to Stefan and found him blankly astonished at the idea that Lisl might feel anything more than gratitude towards him.

'No, no, Melissa, you are imagining it,' he protested. 'Lisl is no more than my little cousin who has always looked up to me, though she was scathing when I changed my nationality and my name.'

'As she has now done herself.'

'At that time she thought we who disagreed with the Nazis should have stayed in our country and fought against them. She realises now how helpless we are, and always have been.'

Melissa smoothed out the harsh lines on his forehead.

'Don't fret, darling. Everything is going to work out. Tell me about your parents.'

'They have succeeded in travelling to Holland and by next week they will be in England. I am so thankful.'

Melissa, too, was thankful, but when the Baumanns arrived in England she could see that they were going to be a considerable financial burden on Stefan in spite of the funds provided by the sale of Frau Baumann's jewellery. Neither of them spoke English, and until that could be remedied there was little prospect of Mr Baumann obtaining work. He was bitter about losing the factory. It had not been a large business, more of a specialised workshop than a big manufactory, but it had been in his family for three generations and he had been proud of his good standing in the community and the loyalty of his workmen – until the blight of anti-semitism had changed everything.

'I wish I could afford to set Papa up in business again,' Stefan said to Melissa, after they had sat through a long diatribe from Mr Baumann about the way he had come down in the world.

'He needs to be employed,' Melissa agreed. 'So does your

mother, come to that. She misses her friends and her coffee mornings and running a home. Looking after your flat is not the same thing at all, my dear.'

'It's a pity we're not true Jews,' Stefan said. 'I think we'd get more help from the Jewish community if we were.'

'I might be able to help,' Melissa said thoughtfully. 'After all, my family is well-to-do . . .'

'No! You have done enough. Charity I will not accept.'

'Don't fly off the handle.' Melissa watched with affectionate eyes as Stefan paced restlessly round her living room. 'Come and sit down,' she said.

He dropped down on the sofa by her side and she moved closer to him.

'Do you love me?' she asked.

'You know I do.'

He turned and put his arms round her and kissed her. Melissa had learnt a lot since the early days when she had felt herself to be awkward and unknowing in Stefan's arms. She fitted her body to his and her fingers played with the soft hair at the nape of his neck as her lips and tongue ceaselessly engaged his. She felt the anger go out of Stefan and then the beginning of the tension of mounting desire.

'Darling, how long is it going to take for your annulment to come through?' she whispered.

'I don't know, it seems to be taking years,' Stefan said.

'I think we've waited long enough,' Melissa said. 'If I asked you nicely, would you take me to bed?'

'If you asked me . . .' Stefan smothered a laugh against the side of her neck. 'There is nothing I wish for more, my darling. Many times I have been on the verge of suggesting it, but I was afraid you would not want to anticipate our marriage.'

'You do have the silliest ideas,' Melissa said. 'We love one another and we're going to be married and it's only because of your kindness and generosity that there's a hitch preventing us from tying the knot tomorrow. I'm miserably inexperienced, my dear, but I do want to show you how much I love you and that's the best way, isn't it?'

'Indeed yes! Come, I want to make love to you now, this minute. I want to hold you naked in my arms . . .'

'All right, darling, there's no need to spell it out. I know what you want and I'm more than ready to give it to you.'

Two tumultuous hours later Melissa held Stefan as he dozed lightly in her arms. She must not fall asleep because it was necessary to wake him up and send him home. Appearances must be preserved; that was necessary for their reputations as doctors. She felt dazed with love, surprised in spite of her theoretical knowledge at the way her body had responded to Stefan's ardour. A little sore – she moved her thighs and grimaced in the darkness –sticky, heavy and overwhelmingly sleepy, but she had achieved what she had intended. Stefan was hers. There was no point now in Lisl putting herself in his way. Melissa had cemented the bond between them and Stefan would stand by her.

'Barring any last-minute hitch, Stefan and I will be getting married three weeks from today,' Melissa told her mother some months later.

'My dear! But that gives us no time at all to make any arrangements,' Julia exclaimed.

'Nonsense, there's plenty of time. It's to be at the Westminster Registry Office and I don't want anyone there except my own family and Stefan's parents and Lisl. Surely there's still time to make a booking for lunch at the Savoy or somewhere?'

'I suppose so, but it's not what I would have liked.'

'It's my wedding,' Melissa pointed out.

Julia sighed. 'What are you going to wear?' she asked patiently.

Melissa looked sheepish. 'I've had a silk suit made at Hardy Amies,' she said. 'I don't know what drove me to be so madly extravagant, especially when I know I won't be able to wear it for months to come.'

'Melissa . . .'

'I'm pregnant. Not very, so it won't show on the day. Yes, I know it's a terrible bit of mismanagement by a couple of doctors and you'd think we'd know better, but there it is.'

'Was it?' Julia asked drily. 'Mismanagement, I mean.'

'Well, since you insist on knowing – no. As soon as there was definite news of the annulment I stopped taking precautions. I haven't got a lot of time left if I want a family – and I do, so I have to start now.'

'And you wanted to hurry Stefan into marriage.'

'Not because I doubt that he loves me and wants to marry me,' Melissa said quickly. 'The trouble is, he's got scruples about money.'

'With some reason. You won't be able to work and he's committed to helping his parents. Really, Melissa, for a woman of your age you've been extremely irresponsible.'

'A woman of my age has to make sure of her happiness while she can. As for money, my plan is to ask Father to buy back from me the shares in Hope's he gave me when he retired. It was good and kind of him to want me to have a share in the family firm even though I didn't work in it, but what I need now is some capital.'

'I don't doubt that your father will indulge you if you put it to him – especially with the prospect of a grandchild coming along – but if you insist on selling them surely the person to consult is Martin?'

'I'm in a quandary about that,' Melissa said. 'You see, it was Francesca who put it into my head that I could set Mr Baumann up in business by selling out of Hope's.'

'Does she know about the baby?'

'You're the only person I've told apart from Stefan, but I think perhaps Francesca guessed there might be some urgency about getting to the altar.'

'And she offered to buy the shares from you.'

'How did you know? Yes, she's offered me a very good price, but there was a condition attached which I didn't quite like. She says she'll withdraw her offer if I tell anyone in the company what I'm planning to do.'

'You're telling me,' Julia pointed out.

'You're not in the company and neither is Father, not any more. All right, it's splitting hairs, but I think I can square it with my conscience and look Francesca in the eye and say I've kept the secret.'

There was a long silence and then Julia said, 'You're not easy in your mind about it, are you?'

'No, I'm not,' Melissa agreed.

'She'll pass the shares on to Victor,' Julia said with conviction.

'He's her substitute son, isn't he? Poor Francesca. She should have married again. You do like Victor, don't you, Mother?'

Again there was silence.

'In appearance he's Simeon reborn,' Julia said slowly. 'But in his character I see Anna's ruthlessness and it makes me afraid. *I'll* buy your shares, Melissa, matching the price Francesca would have given you, and eventually I'll pass them on to . . . I was going to say my grandson, but in view of your news I suppose I should say my grandchildren!'

'That's right,' Melissa said cheerfully. 'Now that I've got started, who knows how many I may present you with?'

Chapter Twenty

'Two wars in one lifetime,' Julia said. 'I can't bear it.'

Nicholas looked at her anxiously. Since they had entered their seventies Julia had grown increasingly frail. The anxiety of the Munich Crisis the previous year had oppressed her more than it should have done, and now the reality of war between Great Britain and Germany had reduced her to a shaken old woman.

'Martin's too old to go,' Julia said, trying to reassure herself. 'But Quentin . . . oh, Nicholas, not Quentin!'

'He's nineteen, just the right age,' Nicholas replied heavily.

'He's doing so well at Cambridge.'

'That's the last thing in Hitler's mind, or Mr Chamberlain's, come to that,' Nicholas said, trying to get her to smile.

'He'll volunteer,' Julia prophesied. 'Just like our boys did in the last war. Poor Jane, poor Martin . . . I know only too well what they'll go through.'

'It may be over quickly,' Nicholas said.

'Don't be silly. I remember all that "over by Christmas" talk last time and look what happened – four long years of fighting and hundreds of thousands of young men killed. The only way for it to be over quickly would be for us to be defeated – and that's unthinkable.'

'Of course it is.'

Searching for some way of putting her into a better frame of mind, Nicholas went on quietly, 'We have to carry on, treat each day as it comes, that's the only way we can survive. Martin is going to keep Hope's operating, although there's likely to be little in the way of business.'

'I know. Jane was on the telephone to me yesterday. She means to stay in London with him even if there are air raids. And Melissa . . . oh, Nicholas, I wish I could persuade Melissa to come into the country with us. Her place is with the children.'

Melissa, to her own unbounded amusement, had given birth to twin boys, now nearly five years old. As soon as she was fit she had engaged a nurse for them and gone back to practising medicine. Now that war had broken out, she and Stefan had made up their minds that they must stay on duty in their hospital, but she was determined to get the children out of London. Between them, she and Nicholas had concocted a plan to take a house in Cornwall where Julia could look after the boys.

'You know you'll enjoy having Nigel and Thomas to yourself,' Nicholas said now.

'Sometimes I wonder whether I'm up to coping with a couple of five-year-olds,' Julia said ruefully, but at last her face softened into a smile. 'Such little pickles,' she said fondly.

'They'll be starting school in the New Year.'

'The village school . . . I suppose it will answer.'

'Come, come, is this my democratic teacher? I thought you were all for children mixing together, regardless of class?'

'I am, of course. I was thinking about the quality of the teaching.'

'You can offer their teacher the benefit of your own experience.'

'What a long time ago that was. When I think of my young ladies with their long skirts and their earnestness . . . goodness me, what a set of prigs we were! What on earth made you marry me, Nick?'

'I can only think it was love. Do you remember the Harlequin and your dismay when I told you it was worth a lot of money?'

'I remember you making excuses to come to Greenwich to see me,' Julia said. 'We've had some good years.'

'And plenty more to come,' Nicholas said.

They left for Cornwall the next day, with Melissa snatching a few days to go with them to settle the boys in.

'I don't think they'll give you too much trouble,' she said optimistically. 'They're a pair of rogues, but good children on the whole and you manage them so well, Mother. Better than I do, really.'

'Nonsense, dear, you're a very good mother.'

'Don't sound so surprised. After all, I was trained to take a special interest in children.'

'Yes, dear, but that's a very different thing from having two of your own,' Julia retorted.

'The involvement's different,' Melissa admitted. 'I'll miss them.' For a moment she sounded desolate.

'You won't change your mind and move to Cornwall with us?'

'I can't do that. We'll be needed in London.'

'How is Stefan?'

'Very despondent. He can't see any good outcome to this war. I keep telling him that we'll beat Hitler in the end, but that doesn't stop him feeling miserable. Of course, he's still got family in Germany and his parents are in despair over them.'

'They mean to stay on in London?' Julia asked.

'Oh dear, I wish you hadn't brought that up! I can't see any help for it now that Papa Baumann is doing so well, but Mama nearly has hysterics every time an aeroplane flies over. She's convinced we're going to be bombed to smithereens.'

Julia remained silent. The house Melissa had taken in Cornwall was big enough for Julia and Nicholas and the children, and a middle-aged servant who had eagerly accepted Julia's offer of a home in the country. There was a spare bedroom for anyone else who cared to come on a visit and Julia was determined to preserve that haven for her own children, not to clutter it up with Melissa's rather tiresome mother-in-law, who still, after five years in the country, spoke English with a thick accent and a limited vocabulary. She braced herself to be discouraging if Melissa suggested it, but it was a relief when her daughter returned to London without saying anything more.

Melissa telephoned Jane when she got back to London.

'I think it's going to work,' she said. 'I tremble for poor Mother once the boys have settled down, but she seems to think she can cope. Father is planning to start a vegetable garden and one of the neighbours came in to offer advice, so I'm sure they'll soon make some friends. Any news at your end?'

'Quentin is talking about joining up. Martin is trying to persuade him to take his degree first, but I doubt whether he'll succeed.'

'Jane, I'm sorry.'

'It's inevitable, I'm afraid. One wouldn't want him *not* to be eager to fight, if you see what I mean.'

Melissa bit back the comment that Jane's way of thinking perpetuated wars. After all, Hitler had to be defeated. The Baumanns' experience was enough to demonstrate that.

'I've joined the WVS,' Jane went on. 'And Francesca is going back to driving an ambulance, just like she did in the last war.'

'Not in France, surely?'

'No, in London – if and when it becomes necessary.'

At first it seemed that all their forethought had been for nothing. A spurious lull had fallen, a phoney war which made some people think that they had been premature in leaving the capital. It gave Martin time to reinforce the cellars of his Piccadilly premises. Business was far from brisk, but an occasional sale brightened up his day. He became an ARP warden and learnt how to deal with casualties and fire bombs, all in that curious limbo which came to an end when the German Army began its sweep across Europe.

The news on the wireless became something for which everything stopped. The saga of Dunkirk reduced people to tears and to a curious, obstinate pride in what had been salvaged from disaster. The fall of France was received with horror, but with no thought of Britain following the same path.

Quentin joined the RAF and was trained in time to take part in the Battle of Britain. In October 1940, when he had leave, Jane and Martin took him to Cornwall to stay with his grandparents, a visit that benefited not only Quentin but also gave Jane and Martin a respite from the bombing of London.

'We ought to be on duty,' Jane fretted. 'But Martin has had no proper sleep for weeks and I'm a bit of a wreck myself.'

'It must be terrible,' Julia said. 'We're so quiet here. My dear, can you really stay only a week?'

'I'm afraid so. Tell me, how do you think Quentin is looking?'

'Strained. Much too nervous. And he's still not sleeping. I looked out of the window last night and he was walking round the lawn smoking a cigarette.'

'He smokes too much. He's only twenty. Sometimes I wonder whether it can be right to teach these children to kill and offer themselves to be killed.'

'What other way is there?'

'If we'd tried harder for peace . . .'

'You can't negotiate with a madman.'

'That's the line Stefan takes. I was talking to him and Melissa a few days ago and, of course, we came to no conclusion. I grew up in China during a war, you know. I saw how it brutalises people.'

For the first time in years Julia felt herself warming towards her younger son's wife. Jane had always been a self-contained woman. She ran Martin's house and organised his social life with the greatest efficiency. She undoubtedly loved him and she was devoted to their only child, but Julia had never felt close to her, not since she had been a child and Melissa's best friend.

At the end of the week they parted with great cordiality. Quentin, to his mother's relief, had obviously benefited from his quiet days in the country. He had spent his days by the sea, playing with Melissa's sons, to whom he was a hero, and his evenings reading, listening to the wireless or walking down to the village pub with his father and grandfather for a pint of beer and a game of darts.

'Not a very exciting leave for you, dear,' Julia said as he was leaving.

'I enjoyed it, Gran.' Quentin had to bend his head down to kiss her. He was taller than his father and he had Jane's smooth dark hair and almond-shaped eyes. He gave his grandmother a quick hug. 'It's funny, but it seems as if you and Grandad have always lived in this corner of the world.'

Julia, secure in her ability to make a home wherever she might find herself, smiled up at him serenely. 'Remember we're always here, dear,' she said. 'If you or your friends want a quiet holiday – and you know now how quiet it is – then I'll find a bed for you.'

He took advantage of that offer once or twice in the year that followed. Miraculously – or so it seemed to his mother – he remained unharmed, although he did once have to bale out of his aeroplane and parachute to safety on the Kent coast.

December 1941 brought America into the war and a fresh interest for Francesca.

'Victor has joined the Army,' she told Melissa.

'Do you think he'll come to Europe?'

'I can't help hoping he will. He's sent me the most marvellous food parcel. Would you like a tin of ham?'

'Would I! Are you sure you can spare it?'

'Of course. There was a box of chocolates, too, but I'm sending that on to Julia.'

'Good of you. I expect she'll give most of them to the boys, but fortunately she can be trusted not to let them make pigs of themselves. I have terrible qualms of conscience sometimes about foisting two such scamps on her, but she seems to thrive on it.'

'It's better than being in London. I was out on a couple of incidents last night.'

'Are you still going into the office every day?'

'I have to, even though business is almost non-existent, because we're so short of staff. Martin's obsessed by the idea that the Sale Rooms are going to be bombed.'

Within months Martin's fears had been realised.

'It's not quite as bad as it might have been,' he said, returning home to Jane covered in dust. 'The cellars have survived and everything stored in them is intact. The ground floor, too, is not too badly damaged. The roof and top floor have suffered most. We've got a tarpaulin on to cover the hole and I've put in an urgent request for repairs.'

'Are you putting up a "Business as Usual" sign?' Jane asked with a smile.

'The staff have already done that. They were wonderful today. Poor old Hope's, what have we come to? Myself and Francesca, three elderly men, a porter who's unfit for active service, a couple of young girls and a boy who can't wait to get into the Army. It's a far cry from the days when we had one of the finest teams of experts in the country.'

'In the world,' Jane said loyally. 'You'll build it up again.'

'Will I? Can you honestly see people ever again having the money to spend on a Degas to hang over the fireplace while they eat off a Chippendale table?'

'Some people are making money, as always happens in wartime. Not quite your old clientèle, perhaps, but the customers will come along once they're free to give their minds to collecting again.'

'I hope you're right. Is there any hot water? I'm dying for a bath.'

'I'm prepared to sacrifice my own bath to let you have a nice deep one. Cheer up, darling, at least no one at Hope's was hurt in the bombing.'

'That's true.' Martin hesitated in the doorway on his way to have a much-needed bath. 'Grandfather's portrait fell off the wall. Grandfather Speranza's, I mean.'

'Probably out of sheer indignation.'

'You could be right.'

It was another year before Victor arrived in London, and he took Francesca completely by surprise. She came home from her ambulance station, feeling tired and dirty and, although she hated to admit it, old. Francesca had had her fiftieth birthday recently and something seemed to have snapped on that important anniversary. She felt drained of life. It was the war, she told herself. Everyone was tired, right through to the bone, and there seemed to be no end in sight.

She was still living in the flat which she had once shared with Simeon, in a block which was as shabby as every other building in London. The staircase was lit only by a dim blue light and she was fumbling blindly for her keys when a figure leaning against the wall in the shadows unfolded itself in front of her.

Francesca gasped and a voice she would have known anywhere said, 'It's OK, Francesca, it's only me.'

'Victor!'

'Here I am. Come to fight the war and make the world safe for democracy. Can I have a cup of coffee?'

'If you've brought the coffee with you,' Francesca retorted, fighting to control the emotion that engulfed her.

'I've done just that. I know I can trust you to make a decent brew, which seems to be beyond the capabilities of anyone else in England.'

'Oh, Victor. . . !'

'Here, let me unlock the door. This blackout just drives me crazy. Let's get inside and put the light on.'

'Not until I've pulled the curtains,' Francesca said quickly.

When she turned to face him she was afraid that Victor would see her as a stranger. Instead, it was Francesca who was taken by surprise. Victor had filled out, and his olive-drab uniform made him look both older and more glamorous. There was an elusive difference between the boy who had been a duplicate of Simeon as she remembered him, and this man of thirty-two, mature and sure of himself. For a moment she saw an entirely different image from the one she had preserved in her mind, and it disconcerted her.

From the intent way he looked at her, Francesca suspected that Victor, too, was having to make an adjustment. She still had her slender, upright figure and her good bone structure, but her fine blonde hair had faded into a greyer tone, the sinews of her neck stood out in an unattractive way and when she was tired she looked gaunt. But when she held out her hands and smiled, Victor kissed her with what seemed like genuine affection and the changes in both of them no longer mattered.

'Tell me all your news,' Francesca demanded.

'Not much to tell. I joined up last year – but I wrote and told you that – did some training, got shipped over here. You're the one in the front line, not me.'

'Hope's has been bombed.'

'No! Is the damage serious?'

'Nothing that can't be repaired, when the materials are available, but the old place is in a bit of a mess. Martin's carrying on as best he can.'

There was a thoughtful silence and then Francesca asked carefully, 'Do you still think you'd like to come into the firm one day?'

'That's my post-war plan,' Victor said flippantly. 'I'd have been applying for a job before this if the war hadn't come along. As far as I'm concerned, it couldn't have been worse timed.'

'It's disrupted one or two lives besides yours,' Francesca said.

'That's a nice bit of British understatement! Tell me, have you had any news of the wicked Hugo? Did he stay in Morocco?'

'I've no idea. What on earth makes you ask about him?'

'Just before I sailed I was visiting some people who have a collection of modern art and they had one of his paintings – and thought very highly of it. I think Hugo's day may be about to dawn. It was a striking piece of work.'

'Melissa has two of his paintings. I can't say I really care for them. As to where he is, I have no idea. We've had better things to do since 1939 than look out for obscure painters who may or may not be living in North Africa.'

'Well, sure. I take it business is poor?'

'If you mean in the auction houses, yes, of course. It's not entirely at a standstill, though. People still die, their houses are closed up, the new poor have to raise money to live. If you've got the funds, this is the time when you might pick up a bargain.'

'Keep me posted. I might leave an occasional bid with you.'

'Always glad to be of service,' Francesca said with mock humility.

The war dragged on. Quentin survived a second crash and pointed out that he was just as much of a survivor as his Uncle Simeon had been in the First World War. Victor came and went and admitted to being profoundly bored with the lack of action until at last the day came for which they had all been waiting. The news of the Allied landings on the Normandy beaches filled everyone with excitement and dread. Even though the scent of victory was in the air there was an uneasy feeling that Hitler still had something up his sleeve and when, in June 1944, the first 'buzz bombs' arrived over England the civilian population braced itself for yet another Blitz.

'I hate these damned doodlebugs more than anything else we've had,' Francesca said. 'That moment of silence when the engine cuts out, before they explode, makes my heart stop.'

Both she and Martin were undertaking extra periods of duty with their Civil Defence units and with the two senior partners constantly absent, Hope's was doing little more than tick over. Jane was so heavily involved with her Women's Voluntary Service, helping newly bombed families to come to terms with the loss of homes and furniture that she and Martin sometimes did no more than exchange greetings in passing.

'Remember me?' Martin asked one day. 'I'm the man you married.'

'Darling . . . it can't be much longer. There were fewer bombs yesterday and our Army is making progress. There's a letter from Quentin.'

'Still all right?'

'Flourishing, if you can believe what he says.'

Mile by painful mile the Allied forces fought their way across Europe. By the autumn France was liberated and that liberation brought a most unexpected visitor to Hope's Piccadilly offices.

'There's a Miss Wood in Reception asking for you, Lady Francesca. A Miss Lynette Wood.'

Francesca sat up with a jerk. Lynette! Hugo's little girl – who must, of course, be quite grown-up now.

However, the girl who arrived in her office, hesitating in the doorway as if to size up her surroundings before committing herself to entering, looked very young. The dark red hair was unmistakable, pulled straight back from Lynette's high forehead and tied with a stringy ribbon from which it burst out in a riot of curls. She wore clumping, platform-soled shoes, a skimpy black dress which was too tight for her even though she was pitifully thin, a man's tweed jacket and an RAF silk survival map round her neck. Francesca was struck by her wariness, like some wild animal ready to run at the first sign of danger.

'Lynette, my dear child,' Francesca said, getting up and holding out both her hands.

'It is all right for me to come to you?' Lynette asked, stepping back as if she did not want to be touched. 'I have been liberated, and because I can prove that I am English I am allowed to leave France.'

'I'm delighted to see you. Sit down. Would you like a cup of tea?'

'Yes, please, and something to eat. I am very hungry.' She looked it. In fact, she looked famished.

'I doubt whether the office can provide anything but a plain biscuit,' Francesca apologised. 'But, of course, you must come home with me and let me give you a proper meal.'

'Thank you. Also I would like to stay with you because I have no money.'

'I'll be pleased to have you,' Francesca said, thinking regretfully of the spare bed she kept for Victor. Still, he was not likely to be on leave in England for some time to come and this child was in obvious need of a haven.

'Your father. . . ?' she ventured to ask.

'Papa is dead. Shot by the Boche.'

'My dear, I'm so sorry.'

'I spit on them, *les sales cochons*,' Lynette said.

'I understand how you feel,' Francesca said, surprised at her own hurt and anger at the news of Hugo's death. 'And your mother?' she roused herself to ask.

Lynette looked surprised. 'Did you not know? Mama left us many years since. She is in America. She is a film actress. I think perhaps not very successful since you do not know her.'

'You could write to her now,' Francesca suggested. 'She'll be able to help you. You might even be able to join her in the United States.'

'I think perhaps not,' Lynette said, wrinkling her nose. 'When she left I was very angry. I do not think I desire to see her. I can look after myself. Only, just at first, it is a little difficult and so I must ask your help.'

She pulled at a strand of her hair. 'Do you have hot water? I would very much like to wash my hair and myself and my clothes.'

'I think we can manage that. Have you any luggage?'

Lynette held up the canvas satchel hanging over her shoulder. 'My luggage.'

In spite of the lack of suitcases, Francesca called a taxi to take her and Lynette back to the flat. Lynette peered out of the window in an interested way.

'London is not as bombed as I thought it would be,' she said.

'You should see the East End,' Francesca said. 'The docks were very badly hit.'

'But you have not known what it is to be occupied,' Lynette said softly.

For a moment she sounded desolate, but it did not seem the moment to probe into her memories. As soon as they arrived at the flat she plunged into her programme of cleanliness and emerged from the bathroom with the first tinge of colour Francesca had seen in her face, her feet bare, wearing Francesca's towelling bathrobe, which trailed on the ground behind her. In the bathroom she left a cloud of scented steam, a wet floor, hairs in the basin and all her clothes dripping from an improvised washing line.

Francesca bit back an irritated exclamation, reminding herself that the child was weary and homeless.

'How old are you, Lynette?' she asked.

'I have eighteen years,' Lynette replied, looking approvingly at the bowl of soup Francesca placed in front of her.

'As much as that? When we last met you can't have been more than five.'

'It was fortunate that I remembered you, but Papa often spoke of you and of the important business called Hope's, so I thought I would go there first. I remembered, too, Tante Melissa, who gave me a doll, but I did not know where to find her.'

'You wouldn't have found her at home. Melissa is married, with a couple of children, and she's gone to fetch them home from the country.'

'She was a doctor,' Lynette remembered.

'Yes, and she married the other doctor who operated on your ear.'

'I have forgotten him, although I remember that I went to the hôpital when we were here in London.'

'And then you went to Morocco.'

'Yes, and Papa worked well there, but Mama wished to go back to Europe and so we returned to France, and then she met a film director and went to America and Papa and I stayed because he was not interested in painting in America.'

'And you were caught by the war.'

'Papa was foolish. I told him many times that we should leave, but he liked the light, you understand.'

Francesca did not feel she could understand anyone shutting their eyes to obvious danger just because of the quality of the light, but she thought it better to change the subject.

'Melissa and I saw one of his exhibitions in Frankfurt before the war,' she said. 'Melissa bought two of the paintings.'

'I was only a child then or I would have stopped him sending his pictures to that exhibition,' Lynette said, scowling horribly. 'He should not have allowed the Nazis to exhibit his paintings. He said an artist has no politics. Such stupidity!'

Francesca cleared away the soup plates and fetched the casserole which had been simmering in the oven ever since her cleaning woman had left that day. She had hoped to eke it out for two days, but when she ladled it out it looked meagre even with the additional vegetables.

Lynette seemed to see nothing wrong with it. 'You eat well here,' she commented.

'Rations are tight,' Francesca said. 'Have you been issued with a ration book, Lynette? If not, we must do something about that immediately. And get hold of your allowance of coupons for clothes.'

'But you are a rich woman. Can you not buy on the black market?'

Francesca froze. With her love of good things and her disdain for the second-rate it had been hard to resist using money to supplement her rations of food and drink and clothes, but she had held out, obstinately priding herself on doing nothing that would lengthen the war, and now here was this raggle-taggle child talking about the black market as if it were an obvious indulgence.

'I don't deal on the black market,' she said.

Lynette's eyes opened very wide. 'In France everyone does,' she said. 'But, of course, it was our way of outwitting the Germans.'

When the meal was over Lynette stretched herself out on the sofa and yawned. Francesca began clearing the dirty dishes and stacking them in the sink for washing up. Lynette did not stir.

'You're very like your father,' Francesca said, not meaning it as a compliment.

'You think that?' Lynette glowed. 'He was a very, very great man. Tiresome, of course, as all men are, but one day his work will be recognised.'

'I hope so,' Francesca said. 'Lynette, did you understand about our relationship?'

'You are his illegitimate sister.'

'Well . . . the other way round, but you've got the idea.'

'His father was a lord. Do you think he will give me money, this lord, if I go to see him?'

'I'm sure he won't. He'd just as soon forget that Hugo ever existed. But, Lynette, you must have some money. Surely not even Hugo can have squandered half a million pounds in a few years.'

'Our situation was very difficult. If the Germans had known that Papa was English then he would have been put in prison. So we bought many, many jewels and buried them in the garden of our house and changed our name to Du Bois and pretended to be peasants. But then there was trouble and Papa was shot and I had to run away. Perhaps the jewels are still there.'

There was a strange flatness about the way she spoke. Francesca suspected that it was because the memory of her father's death was still painful.

'His paintings, too,' Lynette went on. 'If they are still in the house then one day they will be worth much money.'

She gave Francesca a flickering look from under her eyelashes. So far this 'aunt' had been kind, not with any great warmth, but Lynette would have distrusted her if she had been too affectionate. Belatedly, it occurred to Lynette that if she was to impose herself on Francesca for any length of time then she should ingratiate herself.

'I will help you with the dirty plates,' she said, getting up and tying the towelling robe more securely round her.

'I think you should go to bed, you look exhausted. Time enough in the morning to think what you are going to do next. I'd better find you a nightdress.'

'I would like that,' Lynette said warmly. 'Something pretty.'

She murmured appreciatively when Francesca found her a pre-war nightdress. It was a mystery to Francesca how this under-nourished waif managed to make an old oyster satin nightdress, at least two sizes too large for her, look erotic, but Lynette slithered her body inside the garment and closed her eyes in pleasure at the feel of it, and to Francesca it seemed that she generated a sexual charge out of all proportion to her youth and skinniness.

Before she herself went to bed that night Francesca telephoned Jane, since with her WVS connections, she might be able to advise on the way to get Lynette settled in England and absorbed into the rationing system.

'I'll come round and see her in the morning,' Jane promised. 'And I can probably rake up some secondhand clothes for her, the sort of thing we dish out to people who've lost everything in the bombing. What size?'

'About a thirty-two-inch bust and no more than five foot four tall.'

'Quite a childish little thing,' Jane commented.

'I wouldn't say that,' Francesca said. 'I think Lynette is a very grown-up young woman.'

Francesca gave Lynette her one and only shell egg for breakfast the next day. She doubted whether the girl appreciated the sacrifice, but she did enjoy the egg and the toast and home-made jam which Julia had sent up from Cornwall.

'But no marmalade,' she said. 'Papa insisted that in England you always had marmalade for breakfast.'

'We can't get the oranges,' Francesca explained. 'Lynette, I don't want to harass you or make you feel that you can't stay with me as long as you like, but do you have any plans at all?'

'I suppose I must work,' Lynette said, with no great enthusiasm.

'What can you do?'

Lynette's face sparkled with sudden mischief. 'I can shoot a gun, and find my way through the forest in the dark and put sugar in motor-car engines. I am quite useful, but I do not think these are things which will earn me any money.'

'Hardly. Are you saying you've been in the French Resistance?'

'Of course. After . . . after Papa died I ran up into the mountains and Jacques found me and took me into the maquis. And then Jacques was captured – that was a terrible time – and our band broke up and I went with Bernard. Tell me, where in London do the artists live? Is it still Bloomsbury and Chelsea? Papa spoke of those places.'

'Yes, I suppose so, such artists as are able to work in present conditions.'

'Yes, that might be a difficulty. It is the thing I do best, you see.'

'Painting?'

'No, I have no talent. Posing. I am a very good life model. Papa used me many times and his friends, also. I am small, but I have a good line, good bones, and I can keep very, very still and hold the pose.'

Francesca despised herself for the shock she felt. There was nothing wrong in being an artist's model, and in the milieu in which Lynette had grown up it was obviously taken for granted. Absurd, to feel a slight repugnance at the idea of Lynette going out and taking off her clothes for money. After all, she was not proposing to join a strip club!

Before she could make any suitable reply, Jane had arrived.

'I thought I'd come round early in case you were anxious to get to the office,' she said. 'And look who's home on leave!'

Francesca got up and embraced her tall nephew. Seeing

Quentin in his RAF uniform always gave her a pang, remembering Simeon, even though the uniform had changed and Quentin in no way resembled her late husband, unlike Victor.

'So this is Lynette,' Jane said. 'My dear, how wonderful that you've survived and managed to get to England.'

Lynette was paying little attention to her. Her eyes were fixed on Quentin.

'I have met pilots from the RAF many times,' she said. 'I was a guide for them, you see, showing them the way to the frontier.'

'You mean you helped them escape?' Quentin asked.

'Yes. I was a member of the Resistance.'

'That's fantastic!'

It sounded fantastic to Francesca, too, but she did not doubt that Lynette was telling the truth. It explained her toughness, the matter-of-fact way she had spoken of her life after her father's death, and her self-reliance.

'Perhaps General de Gaulle will give you a medal,' Jane said. 'In the meantime, let's see if we can get you dressed.'

The look she cast at Lynette, with her wild red hair and her robe slipping off one shoulder, was critical.

'Lynette washed her only dress last night and, unfortunately, it shrank,' Francesca explained. 'Your underclothes are dry, Lynette, so why don't you try on what Jane has managed to find for you?'

Lynette skipped into the bedroom with every appearance of pleasure. She pulled a face when the contents of Jane's bag were spilled on to the bed, but she was in no position to be choosy and with a little adjustment these garments could be made presentable.

What Jane had brought with her was a good black barathea skirt, a white cotton blouse which had once been part of a school uniform, and a red knitted cardigan. Lynette took one look at herself in the looking glass and undid the top three buttons of her blouse. Then she rescued the belt of the shrunken dress and cinched it round her waist as tight as it would go. With her thick black stockings and clomping platform shoes the effect was oddly disturbing, like a depraved schoolgirl. To complete the outfit Lynette hung the red cardigan round her shoulders and tied the arms loosely in front.

'You have chic, if nothing else,' Francesca remarked when Lynette emerged from the bedroom.

'This belt is not good. I would like a leather one.'

Jane was obviously stunned by the transformation Lynette had wrought on the respectable garments she had provided.

'Quite Parisienne,' she murmured.

'Thank you, you pay me a compliment,' Lynette said. 'Now, what am I to do with myself for the rest of the day?'

From the glance she gave Quentin from under the long lashes it was obvious that she meant him to respond, but Francesca thought it was time to intervene.

'There must be masses of forms to fill in and formalities to go through,' she said. 'Jane is going to take care of you and see that everything is done properly.'

'As a British citizen living in this country you may be liable to be called up,' Jane warned the girl.

'Oh, I say!' Quentin protested. 'Lynette has done her bit in France.'

'At the very least you may be directed into some form of war work,' Jane said.

'I am going to be an artists' model,' Lynette announced.

'I don't think that'll count as helping the war effort,' Francesca said. 'Go along with Jane, my dear. I'm sure some suitable niche will be found for you.'

'Can we meet for lunch so that you can tell me what fate the authorities have in store for you?' Quentin asked. 'You, too, Mother, of course. And what about you, Aunt Francesca?'

'No, thank you, I have other arrangements. I'll see you tonight, Lynette.'

Francesca was amused, a little guiltily, that Jane's precious son had so obviously fallen for Lynette's gamine charm. There was no doubt about how he was hoping to spend his leave, which would at least take the girl off Francesca's hands. She had grown accustomed to living alone and having Lynette in the flat was disturbing: she was a strange child, a mixture of immaturity and sophistication. Something must be done about that fortune in jewels which might still be hidden in the garden in France . . . and about Hugo's pictures, too. Melissa valued the two she had and Victor had spoken of friends in America who thought well of his work. Lynette might yet end up a rich young woman, though Francesca doubted whether even that would make Jane see her as a suitable daughter-in-law.

Chapter Twenty-One

Lynette was drafted into a munitions factory, something she heartily disliked. She lived most of the week in a hostel, from which she escaped whenever she could, to descend on Francesca for meals and hot baths and what she described as 'a little civilisation'.

She was with Francesca on the day the war in Europe officially ended.

'VE Day,' she said. 'Victory in Europe. How strange it seems to be at peace. Sometimes I thought the war would never end.'

'We still have to finish off the Japanese,' Francesca pointed out. She felt none of the elation with which she had greeted the end of the First World War, only lethargy and regret for all the ruined lives.

'There will be bonfires and dancing in the streets and fireworks tonight,' Lynette said. 'Will you come with me to see them?'

Reluctantly, Francesca let herself be coaxed out into the streets. The exuberance of the young people who joined hands to dance was infectious, but there were plenty of people amongst the crowd who celebrated more soberly remembering, as Francesca did, that there was still an enemy in the Far East to be defeated and lives still to be lost. Lynette dragged her to Buckingham Palace, to wave to the King and Queen, but they were unable to see Winston Churchill, beaming and giving the Victory Salute, because of the denseness of the crowd. They visited Big Ben and the Houses of Parliament and Trafalgar Square, all the familiar landmarks which had managed to survive the years of bombing. Afterwards, the memory which pleased Francesca best was the little back streets where all the houses had their lights on, tables had been set up in the middle of the road and loaded with food, and there were bonfires round which the children danced, squealing with excitement as fireworks exploded.

It was after one o'clock in the morning when they finally got back to Francesca's flat.

'I am dead, quite dead,' Lynette said, collapsing on her favourite sofa and kicking off her slender black suede shoes.

'I'm not surprised, in those shoes,' Francesca said. 'And are those my nylons you're wearing, you fiendish child?'

'I could not resist when I saw them hanging up, so fine and well-fitting,' Lynette said, quite unrepentant. 'Victor will give you more.'

'You might have asked,' Francesca said weakly, but she was too tired to do more than make a token protest.

'So now the war is as good as over and there will be peace and I must start to make my life,' Lynette said, wriggling down more comfortably on the sofa. 'Shall I marry Quentin? I think I will.'

'What a time to start a discussion,' Francesca said.

She wanted to get up and go to bed, but felt too exhausted to move. As for Lynette and Quentin, she had followed that affair with cynical amusement, knowing how unwelcome it was to Jane and Martin. Francesca thought they were short-sighted in their opposition. Lynette might be unorthodox, but she had a vivid personality which would, in Francesca's opinion, put fire into a branch of the family which tended towards rigidity.

What Lynette lacked was a sense of property, all too well-developed in Jane and Martin. Helping herself to the nylon stockings Francesca had unwisely left hanging over the bath was only one of her minor depredations. Francesca had learnt to lock up her wardrobe when Lynette was expected, otherwise the child might disappear for a night on the town wearing Francesca's mink stole. To do her justice, she was generous when she had the means, squandering her money on bunches of flowers bought on impulse or tickets for a show Francesca had mentioned she would like to see.

'About Quentin,' Francesca said now. 'Are you in love with him?'

'Enough, I think. He is handsome and brave and he will be a good husband. We go well together. He loves me. One day he will be head of Hope & Company . . .'

'Will he?'

Lynette looked astonished. 'But is there any doubt? He will succeed his father, is that not so?'

'Not necessarily. However, even if he isn't Chairman, he'll have a good position and be well off.'

'One would like to be the wife of the man at the top,' Lynette commented.

The man at the top. That was the place Francesca coveted for Victor. The one bright thing on her horizon was that Victor was shortly coming to England on leave. Francesca had not set eyes on him since he had embarked for the Normandy invasion. He had come through the fighting unscathed and was now a major. He was thirty-five: no longer a young man, no longer biddable. A man who had held command and had seen hard fighting. She longed to see him, but at the same time was uneasy, fearing that they had grown apart.

'You are not listening,' Lynette complained. 'I am laying before you the plan for my life and you do not pay attention.'

'Yes, I am,' Francesca said hastily. 'You're arranging to ensnare my unfortunate nephew, not because you love him, but because you think he can give you a good position in life. You're a mercenary brat.'

'It is necessary to be practical. Now, listen. I do not think that Jane and Martin will welcome me as a wife for their precious son, but if I have lots of money then they will accept me. It is time for me to return to France to dig up the jewels Papa hid in the garden . . .'

'If they're still there,' Francesca said.

'It is not likely,' Lynette admitted. 'And to rescue Papa's paintings, which I think will be in the place where we left them, unless the house has been pulled down.'

'You'll have to wait. Peace may have broken out in Europe, but jaunts to France are not easily arranged.'

'I'll find a way,' Lynette said, and Francesca did not doubt that she would.

In the meantime, the more important matter of Victor's leave was on Francesca's mind.

'I can't put you up next weekend,' she said. 'Victor will be here.'

'Victor is a great nuisance,' Lynette pouted. 'Quentin has told me that he is the son of your husband, which I had guessed because the two photographs on your dressing-table are so like one another. If you do not wish people to know, you should not keep them together.'

'It's old history and no longer seems important.'

'That is a very great lie. To you it is the most important thing in the world. This Victor, he occupies your mind when you should be thinking of other things.'

'Like you?' Francesca asked.

'Like me,' Lynette agreed. 'So, if I cannot come to you next weekend I must ask Tante Melissa if she will be kind to me.'

It was interesting, Francesca thought idly, that while Lynette always addressed her by her Christian name and treated Jane and Martin with the same lack of formality, Melissa was always 'Tante Melissa', as if with her Lynette remembered the child she had once been. Francesca suspected that she had more feeling for Melissa than for anyone else in the family. She used Francesca and occasionally remembered to be grateful, even had flashes of affection for her, but Melissa she loved with unswerving devotion. Obviously she was not in love with Quentin. All the same, it might not be a bad marriage.

Lynette was safely out of the way when Victor arrived. Francesca tried to preserve the detachment for which she was known, but to her dismay she found herself sobbing on Victor's shoulder, clutching at him in her relief at his survival in a way she would ordinarily have despised.

Victor bore it well, holding on to her until Francesca broke loose, mopping at her streaming eyes.

'Don't look at me until I've washed my face,' she said. 'I meant to be so calm! I'm so pleased to see you, darling. Oh, what a fool I'm making of myself. Is that a bottle you've brought with you? Pour me a drink while I make myself presentable.'

In the bathroom Francesca looked at her reflection with disgust. Her eyes were inflamed, her nose was red and her face was blotched. And she had made herself up with such care! Resignedly, she removed her cosmetics, washed her face, splashing it with cold water, and then reapplied the delicate layer of foundation and rouge which had been meant to present her as a still young and attractive woman.

She was too preoccupied to hear what was happening in the living room and it came as a shock when she went back in to discover that Lynette had arrived and made herself very much at home, curled up in her usual place in the corner of the big settee. A glass was clutched in her hand, and she was looking at Victor over the rim of it from under her ridiculously long eyelashes. Francesca knew that look. Lynette was sizing Victor up, as she did every man, not so much for his attraction as in order to judge the use she could make of him.

Victor, Francesca was glad to see, might look amused, but he was also watchful. Lynette was not likely to put anything over on him. He was too old, too experienced and too well aware of his own value to allow this beguiling child to bewitch him.

'I wasn't expecting you, Lynette,' Francesca said.

Lynette opened her eyes very wide. 'I left my laundry here last week,' she said, which was true.

'So you did,' Francesca said gently. 'And I sent it round to Melissa's.'

'Really? She forgot to tell me. So, I have had a wasted journey.'

'Not wasted, since it's given you the chance to meet Victor,' Francesca said with the same deceptive gentleness.

'That is quite true and I am very glad of it. Victor is going to find out for me how I can get to Royan.'

In spite of her annoyance Francesca felt a spurt of amusement.

'She doesn't waste time, does she?' she said to Victor.

'Indeed she doesn't.' Victor pulled a diary out of his pocket. 'Lynette, meet me for lunch at the Ritz the day after tomorrow and I'll tell you then whether I can do anything to help you.'

'The Ritz? That will be *very* nice,' Lynette said with satisfaction. 'Now I must go.'

'Yes, you must. I want to spend this evening with Francesca.'

Francesca turned to Victor with a degree of exasperation after Lynette had left them.

'You shouldn't encourage her. She hasn't a chance in hell of getting to France at the present time.'

'I don't know about that. It might be wangled. I too should like to know what's happened to Hugo's paintings.'

'Mildewed and rotten, if they've survived at all.'

'You may be right. Now, let me look at you . . . Francesca, how do you do it? You've come out of this ghastly war looking younger than when it began.'

'Don't talk nonsense. I'm an old woman in her fifties, tired right down to the bone, old enough to be your mother – which I very much wish I was – and I've ruined the beautiful face I put on for you.'

'Nothing can change your lovely bones and you've still got the best legs in London. I knew those nylons wouldn't be wasted when I sent them to you.'

'I've had the devil of a job keeping them out of Lynette's clutching little hands.'

'We aren't going to talk about Lynette. Tell me about yourself. Tell me about Hope's.'

'Nothing very good to tell, as far as Hope's is concerned. Times are hard.'

'They'll improve. I'm going to be in Europe for a time. I've picked up rather an interesting job. I'm still in the Army, unfortunately, but it'll give me a fair amount of independence. Because of my background I'm to be attached to a team tracing lost works of art – items looted by the Germans or hidden away for safety and forgotten.'

'That sounds very interesting.'

'I'm pleased about it. Eventually, I'll have to go back to the States to get my discharge, but that won't be for some months.'

'And then?'

'I'll probably take up my old job, or make a pretence of it. I still mean to move into Hope's one day.'

'Of course. That's always been my intention. I'd love to have you here in London permanently.'

'Mother wouldn't be too pleased if that happened. Have you heard from her at all? The last time she wrote she sounded depressed.'

'Anna doesn't write to me.'

'I suppose not. Can I come into the office with you tomorrow, see the old place again?'

'I'd arranged not to go in this Saturday, but we can make a visit if you like. You'll be shocked by what you find. The top floor is still closed off and the windows are boarded up.'

In spite of her warning, Victor was dismayed the next day by the air of neglect which hung about the premises. It hurt to see Hope's in such a dilapidated state, but after spending the morning there he was satisfied that the firm would recover once trading started again in the art world. Martin was a shrewd operator who understood his market. Francesca was knowledgeable, but she was not a manager in the true meaning of the word. Victor sensed that she would be glad to retire. The directors from outside the family were getting on, too. There would be vacancies on the Board in the next few years. Cautiously, Victor dropped a hint that he would not be averse to joining the company, and he could see that Martin had been expecting this.

'If you ever find yourself at a loose end, get in touch,' he said, with all the casualness in the world. 'The market's more buoyant in the States than it is here, and you may find you prefer to stay at home once you get there, but if you ever think of basing yourself permanently in London then we'd like to have the first chance of taking you on.'

Lynette was late for their lunch at the Ritz. Victor had known that she would be and he had made himself comfortable with a long drink to wait for her arrival. When she appeared in the bar, looking round her with no trace of self-consciousness, Victor felt again the jolt he had experienced when she had walked into Francesca's flat. They had had less than ten minutes alone together before Francesca had interrupted what had started to become an extremely intriguing encounter, but that had been enough for Victor to know that Lynette was interested in him, just as he was interested in her.

Talking over her possible visit to France had been an excuse for another meeting. Victor had certainly made enquiries, but if Lynette went to France there were going to be conditions attached and everything depended on whether those conditions were acceptable to her.

She was wearing a plain black suit, rather a good one, Victor noted approvingly, with a double row of false pearls at the neck and no blouse. Every other woman in the Ritz was wearing a hat, one of the few items of clothing available without coupons, but Lynette had merely tied back her dark red hair with a chiffon scarf. With the nylon stockings filched from Francesca on her excellent legs and her new black suede shoes, Lynette might have been anyone, but she was recognisably a personality. Perhaps more than anything else she resembled a ballerina – small and poised and moving beautifully, taking the stage with aplomb.

'I would like a champagne cocktail,' she said, sitting down with him.

No other greeting. Lynette, as Francesca had observed to him, did not waste time.

'Have you arranged for me to go to France?' she asked.

'I think I can fix it, on certain conditions. For one thing, I have to come with you.'

Lynette considered this. 'I do not object, but why?'

'Well, babe, the authorities don't think you're old enough to be allowed out on your own. I can wangle a trip to France to search for lost art as part of my new posting, and I've said you have to come along to show me the location of your father's pictures, but it's strictly *my* show as an art authority and you have to do what I say.'

'That's very clever of you,' Lynette said approvingly. 'I expect they think I am just a child, which of course I am not. I will be very good, Uncle Victor, I promise.'

She looked at him wickedly over her glass, just as she had at Francesca's, and the sexual charge she generated made Victor slop his drink.

'The other thing is, I want to take the paintings to New York and show them there.'

'An exhibition is my dream. I had not thought of holding it in New York.'

'That's where the buying power is right now. No one in England is going to be purchasing modern art for the next year or two.'

'Do you know Papa's work? How is that possible?'

'I've seen the two paintings Melissa bought and I came across a man in America who has another. He raved about his Hugo Wood until I went along to see it. I was very impressed.'

'Yes, Papa was good. If the war had not come he would have been recognised. It was just beginning.'

'So that's agreed? We go together to France, we look for the jewellery and the pictures and, if we're successful, I take the paintings to the States.'

'Am I to have any say in pricing the pictures?'

'No, I'll take advice on that. Are you ready to eat?'

'Yes, please. I am very hungry.'

She had the unabashed greed of a child at a party.

'The Ritz isn't used to clients who lick their spoons clean,' Victor commented.

'A pity to waste this delicious food. At last I have had a good meal in England. On the whole, I have to tell you that I find the cooking very poor. I think I have had enough.'

'Just as well. You'll bankrupt me.'

'You're rich.'

'Fairly rich.'

'Are you planning to be Chairman of Hope's one day?'

'What the devil gave you that idea?'

'Hints. Francesca did not like it when I spoke of Quentin as the future head of the company. I should perhaps tell you that I am going to marry Quentin.'

'Lucky Quentin. Does he know?'

'He has asked me many, many times,' Lynette said with dignity.

'But you're not actually engaged?'

'I was intending to engage myself to him on his next leave.'

Victor smiled and Lynette looked down at the tablecloth she was pleating between her fingers. 'Why are you doing so much to help me?' she asked.

'You know damn well why.'

She looked up and their eyes met. 'It is a very great complication,' Lynette said. 'You are much too old for me.'

'And you're certainly too young for me. Except that you're as old as the hills, you piece of perfection. Shall we just go to France and see what develops?'

'Perhaps – afterwards – I will still marry Quentin.'

'Sure. Why not? I won't stand in your way.'

Two days later they were approaching the village of Saint Pierre-des-Eglises near Royan, driving in a jeep which Victor, in the most casual fashion, had borrowed from a US Army depot.

'I see it is very useful to travel with an American major,' Lynette said.

'And useful for me to travel with a girl who speaks perfect French. Is there a hotel in the village where we can stay?'

'There used to be an *auberge*, but we will not stay there, not in the village, not even if it has survived.'

As they drew close to her former home Lynette grew quieter

309

and quieter. She seemed to shrink, huddling in her seat and hugging her arms round her.

'Is it painful to come back?' Victor asked.

'Very painful, very difficult. Victor, we must stop. I can't go on, I can't!'

Victor pulled in to the side of the road, a dusty track marked by the passage of many heavy vehicles.

'How far are we from the village?'

'Perhaps a kilometre. I don't want to drive through the village. I don't want them to see me.'

'Why not?'

'They will recognise me,' Lynette said in a terrified whisper. 'My hair . . .'

'Have you got a scarf? Tie it over your head. Do we have to go through the village to get to your old house?'

'Yes. There is a track, half a kilometre after the last house, on the right. That leads to our house. There will be nothing there. You've seen how much has been bombed, hit by shells, destroyed. It is useless. I was a fool to come.'

'This area hasn't been badly hit and we're not turning back now. Keep your head down. I'll drive straight through.'

In a couple of minutes he reached the village, a huddle of houses on a straight road, comparatively undamaged in spite of what Lynette had said. The appearance of an American jeep aroused a momentary interest in the few people who were about. An old woman waved and Victor took one hand off the wheel to give her a casual salute.

'Mère Roget,' Lynette said under her breath. 'She has survived.'

Victor made no comment. He found the track which led down to the house where Lynette and her father had once lived. It was rutted and overgrown, as if few people had used it in the past year or two.

They passed a barn. On the whitewashed wall four crosses had been painted and the legend *Morts pour la Patrie*. Lynette shuddered and huddled closer to Victor.

The house was still there. It must have been a pleasant place once, a heavy stone building with a large downstairs room and perhaps two or three rooms above. The main door was intact, but the shutters hung loosely on their hinges, leaving the windows open for anyone to enter. Across the yard was another barn.

'That was Papa's studio,' Lynette said.

A straggle of flowers showed an area that had once been cultivated as a garden. A statue of a seated child had been toppled off its pedestal.

'I sat for that,' Lynette said. 'The sculptor gave it to Papa. I've forgotten his name.'

'Were the paintings left in the barn?'

'Yes.'

Victor waited for Lynette to move and eventually she clambered out of the jeep. He took her hand and found it icy cold. The door of the studio opened at a touch. To Victor it looked as if someone had been using it as a temporary home. There was a pile of straw on the floor and a dirty old blanket.

'This is where Papa . . . Papa . . .'

'Worked?' Victor asked.

'Killed the German.' Lynette spoke flatly. She looked round, her face drawn and old. When she spoke again it was in a horrified whisper. 'Victor, is that a stain on the floor?'

'Just a place where the earth's been scuffed up,' he said, smoothing it over with his foot. 'Bear up, honey. Remember, if we can show his pictures it will be the memorial your father deserves.'

'Yes. . .' Lynette drew a deep breath. 'If they are still there, the paintings are in the big *armoire*.'

'There's no cupboard here,' Victor said, looking round.

'But yes. There is a sliding door – look.'

Sure enough, now that he looked closer, Victor realised that the far wall was false and could be slid back, except that it fitted snugly against the wall at either side and there was no apparent handle or lock.

'It's a trick,' Lynette said. 'We need a ladder.'

There was no ladder, but Lynette found the answer to that.

'Can you bear my weight if I stand on your shoulders? I did it once with Papa when Monsieur Picard borrowed the ladder to pick apples without telling him. Papa was very cross because he could not get at his work.'

It was a scramble, but Lynette was agile and Victor was well able to sustain her light weight. He heard her fumbling about over his head and then there was a click.

'It still works,' Lynette said. 'Let me down, Victor.'

She had released a catch and a large iron handle now protruded from the smooth wall.

'Turn it to the left, like a key, and push the door along sideways,' Lynette instructed. 'I expect it will be stiff. Papa used to oil it.'

The mechanism was indeed stiff, but soon there was a sufficient gap for both Lynette and Victor to squeeze through. And the paintings were still there.

'In good condition, too, as far as I can judge,' Victor said exultantly. 'Well, that justifies our expedition, doesn't it?'

'That one is of me. Many of them are,' Lynette said.

Victor looked down at the nude portrait of a very young girl. She was lying on her side, propped up on one elbow, reading a book, a strip of crimson material draped over the length of her body from shoulder to knee.

'That was a scarf we brought from Morocco,' Lynette said. 'Papa loved it. He used it over and over again.'

She sounded forlorn, but without the terror that had seized her as they entered the village, and Victor felt able to ask, 'Shall we see if we have the same luck with the jewellery?'

Together with the jeep, he had had the forethought to borrow a spade. He fetched it and followed Lynette into what had been the garden.

She skirted the fallen statue, following a line of stones.

'This was the vegetable garden,' she said. 'We buried the box here because the earth was loose and easy to dig.'

The ground was very disturbed. Victor dug where Lynette indicated, and all around the area, but no iron box appeared.

'Too many people guessed what we had done,' Lynette said.

'You mean, someone in the village will have stolen the jewels?'

'They would not think of it as stealing. They would call it reparation.' She looked round, her face desolate. 'Perhaps they had the right.'

There was something here that Victor failed to comprehend, just as he did not understand Lynette's fear of being recognised, but for the time being he decided not to press her for an explanation.

312

'Let's get the pictures loaded into the jeep,' he suggested.

He began carrying the paintings out of the studio, but when he looked round Lynette had stopped helping him. She was sitting on the marble plinth, hugging the fallen statue and crying quietly.

Victor went to her and squatted down by her side. 'Tell me what happened,' he said.

'It was my fault,' Lynette whispered. 'It was all my fault. Papa, Papa . . .'

He put his arms round her and held her close. 'Tell me,' he insisted.

'I was very young. Fifteen. And, of course, after Mama left I ran wild. While she was with us we lived in Provence, but Papa decided he wanted a different light and we moved west. And then the war came. It meant little to me, or to Papa. We changed our name and went on living as before, with forged papers. The villagers grumbled because Papa did not do military service, but they did not give us away, even though they did not like us.'

'Why not?'

'We were different. They did not understand artists. In our village in the south they were used to us. Not here. They said bad things about me, about Papa. Wicked things. It was not true. When he painted me in the nude Papa saw nothing but the light on the flesh, the bones beneath the skin. To him I was not his daughter, not even a woman. But these things were believed and, of course, we did not go to church.'

'You were isolated.'

'I was lonely. At first, I did not know I was lonely, but then there came another one who was lonely and I understood that we were the same.'

'Tell me.'

'The Germans occupied this area. Two soldiers often came to the village. One was young, just a boy. He was good-looking. Very blond, with blue eyes and a nice smile and a fine body. I noticed these things, you understand, because I looked at people as artists looked at them.'

'He was the other lonely one?'

'Yes. Poor Hans. He had not asked to go into the Army. He would have liked to be at home for the harvest. He was quite simple, you understand, just a country boy. I liked him. We were friends. It was not important to me that he was a German.'

Victor was silent. He thought her attitude naive, but he recognised that his reaction was coloured by having fought his way through a bitter campaign. And, as she had said, she was very young.

'The other German was different,' Lynette went on. 'Fat, gross, not a nice person at all. He was angry because I was Hans's friend. He was jealous.'

There was a long pause and then Lynette said, 'I played a trick on him. Papa had a picture, a copy of a Titian . . .'

'Dear God, not the *Young Man with a Feathered Hat*?'

'But yes! You knew it? It was very good.'

'So I remember,' Victor said grimly.

'I let this fool, this pig think that it was an original painting. He had already heard a rumour that we were richer than we seemed to be and he thought Papa had put his money into this fine painting. He was so ignorant! He stole it. I knew he would. I thought it was a big joke. I told Hans about it, but to him it was not funny.'

'And the other soldier found out?'

'He showed it to an officer who knew something of pictures. He was made to look stupid – which he was. He came back and he was very angry. He caught me alone. In the studio. He attacked me . . . he got me down on the floor . . .'

'He raped you?'

'Yes.' Long shudders were running through her body. She was rigid with the remembered horror. 'Papa came back. His knife was there, the sharp one he used for making the mounts for his pictures. He stuck it in the pig. He killed him.'

'My dear, my dear. That was why your father was shot?'

'Yes, and it was Hans who betrayed us. Hans, who had been my friend.'

'But the other soldier was his comrade, his fellow countryman . . .' Victor fell silent, knowing he would never get her to understand that point of view.

Lynette sat up. 'It was not only Papa,' she said in a flat voice. 'They took four of the villagers as well, two young boys, two old men, and shot them too. That is why I am afraid to be seen here.'

'You were blamed?'

'Of course. The women said I had flirted with Hans, that I had teased the other man, that I was bad – bad right through. I had to run away. I went to the mountains and Jacques found me and I joined his band. We were Resistance fighters.'

'You were only a child.'

'No, I was Jacques's woman and he protected me. Then he was captured and the band split up. I escaped and went with Bernard. I stayed with him until the end of the war. I helped RAF pilots who were shot down to escape into Spain. It was a hard life and I did not really like Bernard, but he looked after me.'

'He was your lover?'

'Of course. He was not kind, like Jacques. I was very, very sad when Jacques was taken. He was good to me.'

The bald little recital was at an end. Victor was more disturbed than he had ever been in his life before. He had suspected something, but not this. Tragedy piled on tragedy.

'You were eighteen when you first came to England, weren't you?' he asked, almost disbelievingly. 'And you'd been on the run for three years.'

'It seemed much longer. A lifetime. I had forgotten what it was like to be at peace. Until I came here today I thought I had put it behind me – the pointing fingers, the whispers . . . the blood. The beast's blood spurting all over me and my own blood running down my legs. He hurt me, oh Victor, he hurt me.'

Once again Victor rocked her in his arms. 'My little girl,' he said. 'My poor little girl.'

Lynette made a futile attempt to clean up her face with the wisp of handkerchief which was already wet through.

'I want to forget,' she said fiercely. 'When I went to Francesca, it was a gamble. I expected her to throw me out. Instead, she helped me to make a new life. Now you have made me tell you the past and I am angry because I didn't want anyone to know.'

'Not even Quentin?' Victor asked.

'Of course not! Least of all Quentin. He is the most important part of my new life.'

'Is he? Lynette, you can't marry a man and keep secrets like this from him.'

'I can! I will!' She sprang to her feet. 'Don't follow me,' she said.

315

'There's something I am going to do while you finish putting Papa's paintings in the jeep.'

She ran back into the studio and a few moments later came out again carrying a tube of oil paint and a brush. She disappeared back down the track towards the village. Victor went on carrying the canvases from their hiding place to the jeep, thinking hard as he did so. What a story. He was full of compassion towards Lynette and, at the same time, excited by the possibilities for publicising the Hugo Wood Exhibition.

When Lynette returned she looked calmer; there was a splash of vivid blue on her skirt. She got into the jeep and waited until he had loaded and secured the last painting. When Victor turned the jeep towards the village she put the scarf over her head again.

As they passed the barn near the village Victor saw that a fresh cross had been painted on the wall in vivid blue.

'Five people were shot,' Lynette said in a fierce whisper. 'Five! They shan't forget Papa, they shan't!'

They found a small hotel a few miles away, where Lynette was sure she would not be known. Equally important, the hotel had an empty garage in which the jeep and the paintings could be locked for the night.

'You'd like me to take two rooms?' Victor asked gently.

Lynette looked at him with haunted eyes. 'I don't want to be alone.'

All night she lay in his arms, shaking and crying, and sometimes dropping into an uneasy doze, until at last near dawn she fell into a heavy sleep. Victor slept himself and woke to find Lynette bending over him, her strange, dark red hair brushing his cheek.

'This is not the way you thought to spend your nights when you planned to bring me to France,' she said.

'True.'

'I meant to make love with you.'

'That was in my mind, too,' Victor said gravely.

'Now?'

Victor laughed and pulled her down hard against him.

She was small and smooth and supple as a snake. As Victor explored her body she moved against him, urging him towards the satisfaction he was denying her, teasing her with touches of his hands and lips, until Lynette sank her sharp little teeth into his shoulder. Victor laughed again, a laugh that turned into a groan of pleasure as he entered the pulsating tunnel of her body. There was no holding back, no moment of adjustment; from the first they moved in unison, joined in perfect harmony. Wave after wave of exquisite sensation swept over them until at last a hoarse sound came croaking from Victor's dry throat and he heard Lynette cry out, 'Ah, *chéri, chéri* . . . ah!'

He lay on top of her, too spent to move until, raising his head and looking down at Lynette's face, he saw that although she was faintly smiling, tears were seeping from behind her closed eyelids. He licked them away with his tongue, tasting their saltness, and Lynette sighed and opened her eyes, looking up at him with a deep, unfathomable gaze. Victor moved to lie on his back, his arm under her shoulders and their heads together. He was profoundly astonished, not by their mutual passion, but by the tenderness he felt towards her. Love, he thought ruefully; a damned disabling emotion. I've gone in deeper than I expected, over my head and drowning.

Somewhere cups were rattling. Victor was not hungry, but he was intensely thirsty.

'We'll have to get up,' he said.

'Yes.'

Lynette sat up, cautiously, as if she was not quite sure whether she had control of her body. She slipped out of bed and stood for a moment with her hand on the bedpost.

'I'll go and see if there's enough water for a bath.'

Half an hour later they were sitting outside on a dusty little terrace with one struggling bay tree in a tub. There was good bread, butter and honey to eat, but the so-called coffee made Victor screw up his face in disgust.

'I think it's made of acorns,' Lynette said. She licked her fingers and then laughed and flushed as she caught Victor watching her. Her eyes had a heavy, sleepy look, not surprising after her disturbed night and the intensity of their lovemaking, but she looked peaceful, in spite of her fatigue.

'I feel strange,' she said. She frowned, puzzled by the change she sensed within herself. 'Smoothed out.'

'Is that the way you usually feel after making love?'

'No, this is different.' She looked up and caught his eye again. 'It was good, our love. For you, too?'

'Unbelievable.'

'Yes. At first, I only meant to say thank you, but . . .'

'You were carried away. And so was I.'

'Would it be like that if we did it again, do you think?'

'We'll take an early opportunity of finding out,' Victor said, and he was amused and pleased by the way the colour rose in Lynette's face. It made her look very young and again he felt that unwelcome lurch of the heart, the desire to cherish and keep her. Love, damn it.

'I suggest that the reason you feel different is that at last you've shared the story of what happened to you at Saint Pierre,' he said deliberately. 'It's like going to Confession if you're a good Catholic – you feel purged of your sin, although in my eyes you committed no sin. You've never talked about it to anyone else, have you?'

'Only to Jacques. He knew. But after he died, no, not to anyone else.'

'There's nothing you can't tell me,' Victor said quietly.

'And you?' Lynette said. 'Will you also confide in me?'

'I will. I'll tell you all my sneaking ambitions and I'll tell you what I've got on my mind right now, although you're not going to like it and at this particular moment I'd do anything in the world to please you.'

He took a deep breath and then said abruptly, 'This story of yours is going to have to come out. No, don't interrupt, listen to what I have to say. Now that the war's over, people like your villagers are going to be looking for vengeance. They'll tell their story: four men – five men – shot because one of them tried to defend his daughter from rape. They'll want the head of the man who ordered the execution.'

'That's true,' Lynette admitted reluctantly. 'But now that I am living in England there's no need for me to be involved.'

'Your father's paintings,' Victor said. 'I want to show them. That's what you want, too, isn't it?'

'Of course, otherwise I would not have forced myself to come back for them.'

'Inevitably, that'll lead to your identification. The story will be

318

told, possibly with the wrong slant. You've got to get your version into the Press first: you were wronged – God knows that's true – your father murdered; four other males, totally innocent, suffered the same fate. The thing you've got to get into your head, Lynette, is that it was *not your fault*.'

'I flirted with Hans and I made a fool of Heinrich. The villagers said it, and it was true.'

'Forget that. Were you and Hans actually lovers?'

Lynette shook her head, mute with the remembered horror of those days. 'When that pig took me I was a virgin.'

'My poor darling. Well, then, you've nothing to reproach yourself with. Reasonable men don't rape young girls because they're annoyed and jealous. He was what you keep calling him – a pig. Now, let's get on to the rest of your story. You joined the maquis, you helped in the Resistance, you led Allied airmen to safety. You were a heroine. You deserve a medal and I'm going to see that you get it.'

'It was just a thing I did, it was a game,' Lynette said helplessly. 'Jacques and Bernard – especially Bernard – scolded me because I did not take it seriously enough. I was lucky not to be caught.'

'But you weren't caught. You were successful. I'm afraid you're going to have to get used to being treated like a heroine. It'll go over like a bomb in the States. The other thing I'm going to have to say that you won't like is that because of your story your father's paintings will sell like hot cakes.'

Lynette absorbed this in scowling silence. All her former relaxation had disappeared.

'Must I do this?' she pleaded with him.

'I can see no help for it. There's something else, too. I've stepped out of line in bringing you to France to search for Hugo Wood's paintings. I'm supposed to be looking for Old Masters stolen from great collections, not rescuing the work of an unknown modern artist. If we can arrange a successful show then I'll be justified and maybe keep my head off the block.'

'Papa's paintings should succeed on their own merit.'

'They will, but the publicity will ensure that they get the attention they deserve. Let me talk this over with our Public Relations Unit, Lynette.'

Lynette shrugged. 'I suppose it must be as you say. You talk

319

sensibly and perhaps it is true that if I am not blamed I may be able to feel less guilty.'

'That's my girl.' Victor paused and then repeated softly, 'My girl.'

Something of the look of strain began to disappear from Lynette's face.

'I'll be there to help you,' Victor said.

'Will you?'

'I'll apply for permission to marry you as soon as we get back to England.'

'Marry?' A mischievous smile showed for a moment on Lynette's lips. 'You haven't asked me,' she pointed out. 'And I'm seriously thinking of marrying Quentin.'

'Over my dead body! I haven't asked you because I've seen what you do to men who propose: you just keep them dangling. I'm telling you – you're going to be my wife.'

Chapter Twenty-Two

The diamond necklace lay on the black velvet pad between the two men, the light artfully trained on it to bring out the play of colour in every faceted stone.

'If you want to give your wife a truly memorable present, you can hardly do better than this,' the dealer said persuasively.

'It's not quite . . . appropriate,' Martin said. 'I had in mind something quieter and not necessarily jewellery.'

'The reason I brought this out is that there is a family connection. Those five central stones were purchased from your father many years ago and made into this magnificent necklace. The owner died recently and I bought the necklace back from her heirs.'

'And you remembered where five individual diamonds had come from?'

'Indeed yes. You used the right word – individual. Stones of this quality are recognisable. In any case, it was one of the first transactions my own father entrusted to me, and I designed the necklace myself. I couldn't forget it.'

The man swung the necklace between his fingers and it sparkled with reflected light.

'I'm tempted,' Martin said. 'But no, this isn't the occasion for a diamond necklace. What about jade? My wife was brought up in Shanghai and is almost Chinese in her devotion to jade.'

'I have one or two pieces. Another necklace, of incised plaques – very old and rare – threaded on silk cord; a delightful collection of small beasts . . .'

'N-no, I think not.'

'Wait one moment.' The dealer got up and went into an inner room. When he came back he was carrying a small white bowl on a wooden stand which he set down in front of Martin. The bowl was quite shallow, carved out of pure white jade in the form of a lotus flower.

Martin picked it up and cradled it in his two hands, feasting his eyes on its perfect form and delicate decoration.

'Yes,' he said. 'This is what I want.'

'It'll cost you nearly as much as the diamond necklace,' the dealer said with a smile.

'That's not important. It's the rightness of it that matters.'

He was too much of a dealer himself not to haggle a little about the price, but he was anxious to secure the bowl for Jane and so he did not try to drive too hard a bargain. When he left the dealer's premises he took the bowl with him. He walked slowly back to Piccadilly, through the Burlington Arcade. He felt tired and sad and strangely surprised at what was going to happen to him. Not long, the specialist had said . . . and he still had to tell Jane.

He waited until after dinner that night before he gave Jane her present although it was not easy to hold back the news he had to give her. Fortunately, they were on their own.

The package was heavy because the bowl and its stand were housed in a wooden box, plain and highly polished. Jane opened it with pleased exclamations at the unexpected present and then fell silent as she took in the perfection of the jade bowl.

'You like it,' Martin said, watching her face.

'Like isn't an adequate word.' Just as Martin had done, Jane took the bowl and held it in both hands. 'It looks as if the jade had been waiting for the artist to discover the lotus inside it,' she said. 'That exquisite line . . . and it has such a feeling of tranquillity.'

'I hope you'll look at it in years to come and feel the same tranquillity,' Martin said.

Jane looked up quickly from her entranced regard of the bowl.

'It's not just a surprise present,' she said. 'You have a special reason . . . Martin?'

'I went back to Harley Street this afternoon.'

'Martin, you promised I should go with you.'

'In the end I found it easier to hear the verdict on my own. It's as we feared, my dear: cancer of the pancreas.'

'An operation?' Jane said automatically.

'No, dear, no operation. No treatment, really, until . . . unless I happen to need painkillers.'

'A second opinion. You must see another doctor. Martin, you can't just accept it.'

'I've had every examination and test that can be devised.

There's no doubt about the diagnosis.' After a brief pause he added, 'Nor about the outcome.'

Very carefully, Jane replaced the jade bowl in its box.

'How long?' she asked.

'Perhaps six months, possibly less. Oh, my dear, don't look like that! The thing I mind most is leaving you . . .'

In a flash Jane was at his side, with both her arms wrapped round him.

'And you've given me a jade bowl,' she whispered. 'Darling, do you imagine that's going to help?'

'I wanted to give you one last good present, something to remind you of how much I have loved you, still love you.'

For a moment they clung to one another, dry-eyed and despairing.

'I don't know how I'm going to bear it,' Jane said.

'By remembering the good times. That's what I've been telling myself. We've been happy, let's hang on to that.'

To Jane, furiously rebellious, looking at past happiness did not seem like a recipe for curing present desolation, but she heard Martin's voice waver and in that moment something in the quality of her love for him changed; she became not only his wife, but his mother and his nurse. His strength was failing and she must uphold him.

'I'm not a courageous person,' she said, 'but I'll try to be brave. I'd like us to spend as much time as we can together.'

'I'll tell the Board at the next meeting and give them my resignation.'

'Your mother and father?'

'I dread telling them.'

'Would you like me to do it?'

'No, dear, I must do it myself. And Quentin, too.' Martin leaned his head against hers for a moment and sighed. 'I'm so tired.'

'Let's go to bed. You must keep up your strength as much as you can.'

They moved towards the door and then Jane turned back and picked up the jade bowl, to stand in their bedroom in a place where they could both see it.

*

323

Martin was too obviously a sick man for his colleagues on the Board not to have wondered what was wrong with him. For all that, they were unprepared for the starkness of the verdict he passed on to them.

Martin looked round the long table at the colleagues he had reduced to stunned silence. At Francesca, thin as a rake and immensely distinguished with her smooth white hair and her upright carriage; at the three directors who had come on to the Board since the end of the war five years earlier; at the Company Secretary, who had known him since he was a boy; at Quentin, just thirty and an authority on books and manuscripts; and at Victor who, after his discharge from the Army and his marriage to Lynette, had returned to the United States for three years, but had come back to London to join the Board of Hope & Company two years ago. He had made his mark from the day he arrived. A clever man, Victor, an innovator, a natural leader – Simeon's son, though one mustn't say so – and at forty just about the right age to take over from Martin. Except that that was not what Martin wanted.

'I had hoped to remain as Chairman for at least another six years,' Martin said. 'I won't disguise from you that my idea was that if I retired at sixty-five then Quentin would be seen to be my natural successor. That would still be my preference, but it's possible that he may be thought to lack the necessary experience, especially considering the six years he spent away from the company during the war.'

'I was gaining experience then,' Quentin said quickly. 'I'd like to point out that I was a squadron leader by the time I was twenty-five.'

Martin was glad that his son had spoken up, but it had thrown him off-course. He had planned what he was going to say very carefully and so he only smiled and nodded to acknowledge Quentin's intervention.

'There are two – no, three – courses open to the Board,' he said. 'One is to appoint an interim Chairman with the clear understanding that Quentin is to succeed in, say, five years' time. In that case, my candidate would be you, Francesca.'

He had taken her by surprise and she was not at all sure how to react. Chairman of the Board of Hope's? A woman? That'd raise some eyebrows. Flattering, but she had no intention of keeping a seat warm for Quentin. Better not to say so, not for the time being, so she merely smiled and inclined her head.

'The second possibility is to appoint a permanent Chairman, other than Quentin.'

'From inside or outside the company?' Victor asked.

'With the talent we have on the Board I hardly think it would be necessary to look outside,' Martin replied.

It was not the moment to say that none of the three directors from outside the family would be his choice for Chairman. He considered them – Gerald Westley, formerly a merchant banker and now their Marketing Director; Bridget MacWilliams, who had come from the Victoria and Albert Museum to be the expert on British and Continental furniture and brought with her not only knowledge but useful connections; and Douglas Fairman, with his deceptively lackadaisical manner, his acute financial mind and flair for modern paintings.

'And the third possibility is to appoint Quentin immediately, in spite of his comparative youth. As he himself has pointed out, he had command of men at an even earlier age, he's been responsible for much of the recent restoration of Hope's to its pre-war position in the market, he has the Hope name – and there's a lot to be said for continuity – and I believe he has the strength of character to lead the company into the era of expansion we have already started to plan.'

It was the end of his prepared speech. Martin leaned back in his chair.

'We're not expected to arrive at a decision today?' Francesca asked.

'Certainly not. The reason I've tossed the subject in at the end of today's meeting is to allow time for private discussion. And, of course, it mustn't be forgotten that the other family shareholders will have to be consulted.'

Not that there were many of them. Anna was known to have acquired her sister's shares many years earlier. No doubt she would opt for Victor, just as Francesca would, that went without saying. Melissa, he remembered, had sold out, fortunately to their mother, and Nicholas had retained only a minor holding.

He counted up, as he had already done many times in the

sleepless nights that plagued him: himself, his mother and father for Quentin, Anna and Francesca for Victor; then how many of the three 'outside' directors could he count on? Douglas Fairman had the biggest shareholding and he was a shrewd fellow. Could he be swung behind Quentin? Gerald Westley would almost certainly go for Victor. They were cronies and Gerald would distrust Quentin's inexperience. Bridget MacWilliams? A solid woman in her mid-forties who seemed to be related to every upper-class family in Britain, including Francesca's. The idea of the succession of the next son ought to be ingrained in her, but with Bridget one could never be sure. She had a decidedly Bolshie streak in her and might prefer the older man with, one had to be fair, all the exciting enthusiasm of the New World in his veins.

The meeting broke up and because he knew that his announcement had embarrassed as well as upset his colleagues, Martin made a quick exit, leaving them to talk amongst themselves.

Francesca, too, left quickly, expecting Victor to follow her, but Victor lingered, his face a picture of concern, to say to Quentin: 'We all realised that Martin was ill, but this has been a shock.'

'To us, too,' Quentin said. 'Mother . . . she's taken it quietly, but underneath she's desperately unhappy. Obviously, they want to get away and have some time to themselves.'

'Of course. Please give her my love and sympathy.'

It was very nicely done, just the right degree of compassion, and spoken just loud enough for his fellow directors to hear. Quentin went on looking grateful until he felt his face going rigid. His gaze followed Victor as he stopped for a quiet word with Gerald and Bridget. Douglas Fairman saw the look and concealed a smile. No love lost there, even though Quentin was acute enough to hide it. He moved from the other side of the table to speak to him.

'Victor started his lobbying?' he said.

Since this was exactly the thought in Quentin's mind it made him start.

'If he is then perhaps I should follow suit,' he said. 'Do I get your vote, Douglas?'

'My dear boy, don't be tactless! I might have come across to ask you to support *my* candidature.'

'I'm sorry. Well, if it came to a choice between you and Victor then I'd prefer you.'

326

'And if it were a choice between me and Gerald?' Douglas asked softly.

'I'd have to opt for Gerald.'

'Such honesty! You'd never make a politician, Quentin.' He paused and then added, 'I'm *bloody* sorry, old chap.'

'It's been a blow.'

Douglas nodded and made towards the door. It was only then that Quentin realised that he had avoided answering the question – Quentin or Victor for Chairman?

'Tante Melissa, I am not happy.'

Melissa laid down her pen and suppressed a sigh as Lynette whirled into the room. That was the end of her letter-writing session and the boys would complain, yet again, that her letters always arrived late.

As usual, Lynette was formidably chic. Her summer dress was simply cut, but it was of cinnamon-coloured silk, cinched in at the waist by a broad suede belt, with shoes and handbag to match.

'You look very nice,' Melissa said.

'I've been to a private viewing which Victor wished me to see. I'm very cross with Victor.'

'You'd better tell me about it,' Melissa said, resigning herself.

'You know about Martin's illness?'

'Yes – dear old chap. I'm very grieved about it.'

'Of course; we all are,' Lynette said. 'And you know that a new Chairman is to be appointed?'

'I gather that it boils down to a straight choice between Quentin and Victor.'

'Victor is trying to persuade everyone to choose him.'

'I suppose that's natural since Victor is an ambitious man.'

'Why can't he be ambitious in America? When I married him, yes, I thought it would be agreeable to be the wife of the Chairman of Hope's, but that was before we had spent three years in New York. I was very, very happy living in New York. Victor *knows* that. Now, since two years we have been in London and I don't like it. London is dull. England is dull. For five years the war has been over and still there is misery and greyness and shortages and gaps in the buildings.'

'It takes time to recover from a six-year war,' Melissa said mildly. 'So, you want to live in America . . .'

'In New York. New York is exciting.'

'And Victor is determined to become Chairman of Hope's, which will mean living in London. One of you is going to have to make a sacrifice.'

'Not me! I must tell you that I am expecting a baby.'

'Lynette! My dear, I'm so pleased.'

Lynette grimaced. 'It is not always very pleasant, but I do not complain. All I ask is that my baby should be born in America.'

'Surely that could be arranged . . .'

'And brought up in America. I have been an expatriate all my life and then, when I went to the United States, I thought yes, this is where I want to be, and I thought it would be for ever because I had married an American husband. That foolishness about Hope's, I thought he would forget it when he saw how much better it was to live in America. Coming back to England – such dullness! – I thought that would cure him, but it has not done so at all and I am very annoyed.'

'You've discovered that Victor's a secret European,' Melissa suggested.

'Yes, and that's why I need your advice. You're one of the family, you understand how the company works. What must I do to stop Victor becoming the next Chairman?'

'Dear me . . . that's a facer. You could buy up the shares – if you could persuade anyone to sell and if you could afford it.'

'Not possible. I have some money since Papa's paintings became fashionable and began to sell, but not enough to buy my way into Hope's.'

'You could lobby the other shareholders, but it would be an odd thing to do, working against your own husband's interest.'

'Victor would never forgive me if he found out.' Lynette gave an exaggerated sigh, her shoulders slumped and she looked a picture of despair. 'I am helpless.'

'Are you sure Victor understands how you feel?'

'He just laughs. I thought I could rely on him to give me anything I wanted, but now I see that he loves Hope's more than he loves me.'

'A man's work is a very important part of his life.'

'It's not the work, it's the power that Victor wants. To be head of the company as his father would have been if he had lived – his real father, your brother Simeon, I mean. He resents the secret of his birth.'

'He shouldn't. Bradley Coppett did a generous thing when he married Anna, and Victor should remember that his style of living comes from Coppett money, not Hope's.'

'He never speaks of this man, Bradley. I think he tries to forget him.'

'How did you get on with Anna when you met her?' Melissa asked.

'Much, much better than I expected. A mother-in-law, you know, one's hopes were not high, but she received me kindly. She wept over my story. She said her father would have acted in the same way as Papa did.'

Melissa had a vision of Lynette and Anna, both with a flair for the dramatic, weeping on one another's shoulders and liking one another the better for it, whereas she would have shuddered away from such a scene. It would have counted with Anna, too, that Francesca disapproved of Victor's marriage, but it was better not to mention that.

Uncannily, Lynette echoed her thought. 'I believed she would resent Victor's marriage, as Francesca did. I thought it very strange, that old woman trying to hang on to a man who was, after all, no longer young himself. It was time for Victor to be married and he loved me very much.'

'And still does?'

'Oh, yes! Only sometimes we disagree, as we do now.'

'A pity, especially with the baby coming along. Well, Lynette, I don't know what I can do, but I'll think about it.'

'I'll go to New York and stay there and not come back,' Lynette threatened.

'That'll show him,' Melissa agreed. 'On the other hand, will you be happy?'

'No, I will be miserable without Victor and Victor will be miserable without me, but I shall have the baby so perhaps he will be more miserable than I am.'

'It seems an unnecessary amount of suffering, and speaking as a children's doctor I can't approve of the effect on your unfortunate child. I've said I'll try to help and I will. In the meantime, do look after yourself. Stop fretting. A placid frame of mind, that's what you should be cultivating.'

'I am not of a placid nature,' Lynette said with dignity.

Melissa gave her tea and a lecture about pre-natal care, to which Lynette reacted with horror, and sent her away calmer, if not reconciled to Victor's plans. On her own, Melissa sat for a long time over the cold tea cups.

At last she pushed the trolley away, took a sheet of paper and began to write, not to her neglected sons, but to America.

'*My dear Anna* . . .'

Anna's reply to Melissa's letter came promptly and Melissa took it round to Martin straight away.

'You see what she says – "*How can I support the appointment of a young man I've never met?*" Could you find an excuse to send Quentin to America?'

'It would have to be done quickly. Very quickly – because the Board Meeting is only three weeks away.'

'He could fly.'

'True, he could do that. Victor will be furious, though, if he hears of an attempt to influence his mother in Quentin's favour.'

'So can you find some other excuse?'

'There's one possibility,' Martin said thoughtfully. 'Otto Romano's dying, the old rogue.'

'And the ghouls are gathering, trying to snatch the chance of handling the sale of his collection?'

'Don't put it like that. It'll be a wonderful sale when it happens. Victor would be the obvious person to send because he already has the necessary connections.'

'Lynette is pregnant.'

'Really? Oh well, one wouldn't want to drag him away from her side. Quentin must go.' He leaned back in his chair and smiled at his sister with affection. 'It's a pity you went into medicine,' he said. 'You would have done well in this business.'

Melissa stowed Anna's letter away in her battered old handbag, preparing to go. The door opened and Quentin came in.

'Hello, Aunt Melissa. Sorry to interrupt, but I thought you'd like to know this straight away, Dad. Otto Romano died at five o'clock this morning.'

He looked at his father and aunt in bewilderment as they burst out laughing.

'Fate has intervened,' Martin said. 'Quentin, start pulling the strings to get yourself a quick visa. You're off to New York on the first available flight.'

'For a man who's supposed to be sick you're doing a remarkable amount of work,' Victor said, but although he spoke lightly his face was concerned as he looked at Martin, grey with fatigue and obviously at the end of his tether.

'Word's got out that I'm going,' Martin said. 'Inevitable, of course. The result is something wholly unwelcome – at least to me. I've had an approach from Sotheby's suggesting an amalgamation.'

'That'd be the end of Hope's.'

'They say not, but of course we'd be subordinate to them. They're by far the bigger company. I've staved them off for the time being, but if the offer is made more officially then I'll have to put it to the Board.'

For a moment Victor toyed with the idea of entering into a larger field, of playing the auction game at a slightly higher level. Would there be a place for him in the enlarged company? Surely. Getting hold of him would be one of the attractions of the merger.

All the same, he agreed with Martin. Hope's was Hope's – a very special identity. To say 'I'm a Director of Sotheby's' would be highly prestigious; but to say 'I'm Chairman of Hope's' was even more special.

'We have a unique position,' he said out loud.

'I'd like to hang on to it,' Martin said. 'And of course, we have our own expansion plans.'

'If we can finance them.'

'Ah, there's the problem. Between us, we and Sotheby's – or we and Christies, because I suspect they may also nibble if they hear the opposition have been after us – we could dominate the auction world. Alone, even an enlarged Hope's will be just one fish in the pool.'

'A very fine fish.'

'Oh, gold-plated! Well, we'll see. I hope I can swing the Board against it if the offer is repeated.'

Victor fidgeted round the room and then asked, 'Have you had any news from Quentin?'

'Not yet.'

Victor topped playing with the tassel on Martin's window-blind and turned to face him.

'Why did you send Quentin and not me?'

'I heard that Lynette was in the family way and thought you'd rather stay with her.'

'She could have spared me for a week or two; the infant's not due for another seven months. Don't fob me off like that, Martin.'

'Very well. For several reasons, but at the back of all of them is the same thing – I want Quentin to be the next Chairman of Hope's. If you'd gone over and secured the Romano sale you would have come back in triumph and made it even more difficult to resist appointing you.'

'Just what have you got against me? Apart from the fact that I'm not your son, of course.'

Martin eased his position in his chair, wishing he felt less tired and better able to deal with this confrontation.

'I don't like the way you've spent the better part of your life exploiting Francesca,' he said. 'She's my brother's widow and I'm fond of her. For years she's yearned over you, seeing you as the son she should have had, and you've milked the situation for all it's worth.'

'I've never taken money from her, if that's what you're hinting.'

'You didn't need to, did you? Your father left you extremely well off. Yes, I said your "father" and I meant it. Bradley accepted you, gave you a name, brought you up, provided you with every luxury. Simeon never set eyes on you. In my opinion you should have had the decency to stay loyal to the man whose name you bore. Half our acquaintances seem to know you're Simeon's son – and our side of the family certainly didn't tell them. Francesca doesn't seem to mind, but I doubt whether Simeon would have liked it and I'm damned sure Bradley would have hated it.'

'Is any of that at all relevant to my fitness to be Chairman of Hope's?' Victor asked.

'I think it is,' Martin said slowly. 'Loyalty, Victor. When I told you about Sotheby's approach, the first thing you thought of was whether it could be turned to your advantage. Quentin would have thought first of Hope's – the employees, the directors, the family. In moneymaking terms you'd probably be the best Chairman, but when it comes to holding the company together – which is what I've worked for all my life – then I have to back Quentin.'

From Victor's baffled look Martin was not sure whether he had really got through to him, and the suspicion was confirmed by Victor's next words.

'Have you thought about what I may do if I'm not appointed?'

Go elsewhere, Martin thought grimly, and take your expert knowledge and as many clients as you can secure to our opposition.

'That's the second part of my brief to Quentin,' he said equably. 'You know we've been putting out feelers for an opening in the United States.'

'You're going to ship me back to America.'

'I can't force a man of your age to do anything he doesn't want to do. Let's wait and see what report Quentin brings back.'

'Is he seeing my mother?'

'I hope so. Anna wrote to Melissa recently and mentioned that she'd never met Quentin. I expect he'll try to spare time to repair that omission.'

'Oh, I'm sure he will! He's wasting his time. Mother will support my desire to be Chairman.'

Victor spoke with confidence, but at the back of his mind was the uneasy knowledge that his mother would very much prefer him to be on the other side of the Atlantic. And then there was Lynette, exceedingly outspoken in her wish to return to the States. The women might gang up against him, Victor thought, and he still had sufficient sense of humour to smile wryly at the idea.

The Board Meeting was attended not only by all the executive directors of Hope's, but also by Nicholas and Julia.

Nicholas was very frail and had to use a stick, with an unobtrusive hand from Quentin under his arm. Julia still walked unaided, but she seemed to have shrunk and the clothes she was too thrifty to throw away hung on her with distressing looseness. They both seemed a little bewildered at being brought to the Board Meeting, but Quentin sensed that Nicholas straightened his shoulders and looked about him with renewed alertness as he entered the oak-panelled room with the portraits of Charles DuFrayne and Vittorio Speranza and himself on the walls.

They took their seats and dealt briskly with the Minutes of the last meeting and one or two minor items of business. Then Martin looked round, using his long experience at the rostrum to gather together the wandering threads of attention and to hold it with a sure hand.

'As you know, Quentin returned from New York only yesterday evening. He has some good news for us. Quentin?'

'I've secured the Romano sale for us,' Quentin said.

There was a buzz of comment and Victor forced himself to say, 'Congratulations.'

'Thank you. There are one or two strings attached. To begin with, it will be at least a year before the sale can take place. I've spoken to the executors, the lawyers and Otto Romano's widow and they all agree that the complexity of his estate makes it impossible to start disposing of his assets any earlier.'

'We are certain they want to sell?' Douglas Fairman asked.

'Under the terms of the Will they have no option. The second condition is that they want guarantees.'

'A guaranteed sale price? That's risky, expecially looking a year ahead,' Gerald Westley, the former banker, remarked.

'They want to be sure of eight million . . .'

'Not eight million pounds?'

'No, dollars. The reason is that five million is committed to found a College of Art in Romano's home town. The remaining three million – at least – is to be split between the rest of the family.'

'They're a large family, aren't they?' Francesca asked.

'Otto had eight children, seven of whom have survived him, and there are fifteen grandchildren.'

'And the widow.'

'And the widow. Mrs Romano lives in New York with the only child – a daughter – of the son who died in the war; the girl is coming to Europe shortly and she'd like a job at Hope's. I said I

334

was sure we could find a niche for her. In the circumstances, I could hardly do anything else.'

'That's a minor point,' Martin said. 'You've seen the collection, Quentin. Most of us are aware of individual items in it, but you've seen it in its entirety?'

'Yes.'

'And you're confident it'll fetch eight million dollars?'

'I'm prepared to stake my future on it,' Quentin said deliberately.

'I didn't have you down as a gambler,' Victor said.

'Sometimes you have to take a risk. The other contenders hesitated and I jumped in and agreed while they were sending back home for instructions.'

'Rather exceeding your authority, weren't you?'

Quentin looked round the long oval table. 'I expect the Board to back me,' he said. 'I haven't finished my report. The executors are adamant that the sale should be held in America. I suggest that we push ahead with our plans to open in New York and make the Romano Collection our first sale. The prestige will be enormous.'

'What about premises?' Victor asked.

'I've taken an option on a suite of rooms in a building which will be completed in two months' time. It's extremely modern, in an excellent location and with ample space for offices and sale rooms. It's expensive, but worth it, I think. I've brought back the figures, of course, for examination and, I hope, approval.'

'You have been busy,' Victor said.

'I've hardly drawn breath.'

'And we're expected to rubberstamp these deals?'

Victor was nettled. A mistake to let it show, Martin thought.

'Not today,' Quentin said equably. 'I'm preparing a written report and I suggest we get together again when everyone's had time to digest it.'

'And who is going to take charge of this project in New York?'

Quentin leaned back in his chair. This was the nub of the question, as Victor very well knew.

'That depends who is appointed Chairman,' he said.

'Which brings us neatly to the real point of our meeting today,' Martin intervened quickly. 'I've sounded out the other executive directors and what it comes down to is a straight decision between

Quentin and Victor. As you know, I support the appointment of Quentin and his report to us today has reinforced my belief that he is qualified to lead Hope's into the second half of the century. I suggest I go round the table asking for opinions.' He turned to his left and asked, 'Gerald?'

'I have to say I see Victor as the only man for the job. He is more mature, has wider experience – I have to give him my vote.'

'I see. Bridget?'

'I'm afraid I agree with Gerald. Quentin in ten years' time – yes; at the moment I think he has something to learn and the way he's rushed ahead with these American plans confirms my opinion.'

'Douglas?'

'Quentin's American adventures have influenced me in exactly the opposite way. I admire him for seizing the moment. I came here today still ready to be swayed either way, but now I'll settle for Quentin.'

Quentin relaxed slightly. At least one of the working directors was prepared to back him.

Francesca was jabbing absentmindedly at the blotting pad in front of her with a pen she seemed intent on ruining.

'Victor,' she said, looking up with a start. 'It was always my hope that he would take over one day. I can't go back on that.'

'That leaves myself and Father and Mother. I take it we all three wish to see Quentin appointed?'

He collected nods of agreement and Victor said, 'It seems that if my own mother supports me then we have four straight votes each. A difficult situation. Are we going to have to start counting up voting shares?'

'Have you heard from Anna?' Francesca said.

'No, I haven't,' Victor said. He was frowning. 'We may have to send her a cable or get her on the telephone.'

'Anna has written to me,' Julia said.

It was so unexpected that they almost missed her quiet intervention. Julia gathered herself together. She had no intention of quoting Anna's letter, that was far too personal.

'. . . Victor has married a girl I can like and is going to give me a grandchild, and still Francesca is doing her best to entice him away permanently to live in England. All my life I have paid for the wrong I did when I forced Simeon to love me. Bradley* *was a sick man with all the jealousy of a husband who desires a wife who will not satisfy him. His touch was not pleasant to me and I went back on the bargain I made when he married me, except on rare occasions. My little daughter died. If only she had lived I might have been happier. As it was, Victor was the only person left to me to love. Am I to lose him to the ambition Francesca has fostered all these years? I am impressed by Quentin and I think Papa would have liked him, but I cannot bring myself to vote directly against Victor . . .'*

At that point in the letter Julia believed that Anna was going to give her vote to her son, but the next page contained a surprise, one which Julia now produced for the Board.

'Anna has appointed me her proxy,' she said, 'with the right to use her vote as I think fit. Yes, Victor, it is a proper proxy, drawn up by a lawyer.'

'And you, of course, are going to use it to support Quentin,' Victor said bitterly. 'Really, you know, this is a farce. The wish of a mother to have her son by her side is not a valid reason to refuse to appoint him to be the Chairman of a company of international standing.'

'This is a family company still,' Nicholas said unexpectedly.

'Those of us who are outside the family can see Victor's point of view,' Gerald remarked.

'Victor has already agreed with me in private conversation that the American venture is going to need strong management,' Martin said. 'If Mother casts her proxy vote in favour of Quentin's appointment then I would like to offer the American office to Victor.'

'On that basis, I give Anna's vote for Quentin,' Julia said.

Francesca finally succeeded in breaking the nib of her pen.

'I'm sixty,' she said. 'I think the time has come for me to retire. I'd like to offer you my resignation, Martin.'

'I'm sorry, but if that's how you feel I'll reluctantly accept it. Is there anyone else who feels they'd like to go?'

'I'll stick,' Gerald said. 'Sorry, Victor. You were my man as long as there was any hope, but that's not to say I can't work under Quentin.'

'I'd like to offer myself as an assistant to Victor in New York,' Bridget said. 'I've lived there in the past, I can be useful.'

'If I accept the post,' Victor said.

'You'll be a fool not to,' Bridget said bluntly. 'In my opinion, it'll be more exciting there than it will be here. Go where the money is, that's the secret of successful trading – and there's not a lot of it about in Europe at the moment.'

'You may be right.' Victor looked round the oak-panelled room with regret and a recognition that he was saying goodbye to a long ambition.

'My wife is desperate to get back to the States and I suppose that ought to count for something. The details will have to be worked out, Martin, but in principle I think you can take it that I'll be running the new subsidiary.'

'Then it only remains to congratulate Quentin and to repeat what I have said before, that I have every confidence in him.'

Martin took Quentin and his mother and father back home with him after the meeting so that they could have a quiet celebration.

'Just the five of us,' he said to Jane over the telephone. 'I wouldn't want Victor to think we were gloating, but I can't help being pleased that it's my son who will succeed me.'

She had the champagne chilled and waiting when they arrived.

'Quentin, congratulations; you'll be a wonderful Chairman,' she said, kissing him. 'I'm so proud of you, dear.'

They kept off the subject of Martin's health, but when Jane fetched her jade bowl to be admired Julia, for one, understood its significance.

'That reminds me,' Martin said. 'Father, do you remember selling some fine diamonds to Jacobi's many years ago? They were made into a necklace which has come back on the market and I was offered it when I was looking for this present for Jane.'

'I remember the diamonds well,' Nicholas said. For a moment he toyed with the idea of telling the whole story, but then he decided against it. It was an old tale now and better forgotten. And so he contented himself with saying, 'Your grandfather used them as collateral for a loan which helped him to buy his way into the original company. He redeemed the stones and gave them to me just before he died. I sold them to buy out Serafina. You could say they were a part of our company history.'

'I'm almost sorry I let the necklace go,' Martin said.

338

'I'd much rather have my jade bowl,' Jane told him.

When his grandparents left, Quentin helped his grandfather out to the car. His grandmother, that surprising woman whose quiet intervention at the Board Meeting had counted for so much, followed behind.

'Everything seems to be turning out most satisfactorily,' she said. 'Victor will do well in New York. How clever of you to secure that enormous sale, Quentin. I could see he was absolutely itching to get control of it. Tell me, what was the granddaughter like?'

'Susanna Romano?' Quentin asked, following her train of thought with surprising ease. 'She was extremely helpful. A clever girl, I thought.'

'Yes, dear. And when did the idea of her coming to Hope's crop up?'

'Only just before I had to leave. We'd had dinner together . . .'

'How nice. And she said she'd like to come to London?'

'We'd been talking about Hope's – naturally. She said she'd majored in art and had always taken an interest because of the Romano Collection and she'd love the chance to work for us, if only for a short time.'

'How old is she?'

'Twenty-two. Grandmother, are you matchmaking?'

'As if I would!'

'As if you wouldn't!'

'Just tell me what she looked like.'

'She's a squat, ugly little girl with a pug nose.'

'Oh . . . but a nice nature and intelligent?' Julia's eyes were twinkling as Quentin helped her into the car.

'Both those things and, as a matter of fact, quite beautiful.'

'Yes, dear, I know the men of my family; you wouldn't have taken her out to dinner if she hadn't attracted you. So, tell me what she really looks like.'

'She's got jet-black hair, a skin like that magnolia in your garden, a nose that wrinkles up when she laughs and legs that go on for ever – and I think she's coming to London because she wants to see me again. Are you satisfied?'

'Delighted, dear. As Chairman of Hope's you'll need a wife. Isn't that so, Nicholas?'

'I'd never have managed without you,' Nicholas said. And to

Quentin he added, 'I have to say that or she'll give me hell when we get home.'

Quentin stood on the pavement and waved as their car moved away.

'I suppose it'll be all right,' Nicholas said. 'He's very young.'

'Not as young as you were, dear, when you persuaded me to marry you and broke away from your father. We managed, didn't we?'

'I started in a small way, not as Chairman of a great company.'

Nicholas eased himself into the corner of the car seat so that he could turn to look at his wife.

'Funny thing, those diamonds surfacing again. I was thinking . . . I could well afford to buy that necklace – would you like it?'

'Bless you, dear, I'm past the age of wanting diamond necklaces. But I can understand that you'd like to have it in the family. Why not ask for it to be reserved for you as a possible wedding present?'

'You're thinking of Quentin and this girl in New York? He hardly knows her.'

'He's very attracted and it's the right time for him to get married. Something will come of it, you wait and see.'

'I'll do just that, but it's a good thought about the necklace. I wonder how Quentin would react if he knew the whole story?'

'He's very quiet, but Quentin is a bit of a pirate – like you. I think he'd laugh and take the diamonds for his wife without a qualm.'

'You may be right. Will he be a good Chairman, I wonder?'

'Very good. He'll follow in your footsteps and what could be better than that?'

'I'd be happier if it wasn't for Martin . . .'

Julia took his hand and held it. 'We must be very strong and brave. Martin will need us and poor Jane, too.'

'It's a hard thing for an old man like me to see both his sons die before him.'

'We've still got each other,' Julia said gently.

'So many years . . . and you've always been my prop and stay. Do you remember the joke we used to have when we lived over the shop?'

'The thing our old charwoman used to say, "I live in hopes, mum"?'

340

'And we picked it up and made it our motto – "We live in Hope's".'

'And Hope's lives in us,' Julia said. 'Pull the rug over your lap, dear. It's chillier than it seems at first.'

Epilogue

The chattering crowd was silent. The tension could be felt, stretched almost to breaking point. Quentin Hope – Sir Quentin Hope – had the gavel in his hand and was raising it. He glanced towards his son, manning the telephone line to Tokyo. Richard caught his eye and held up his hand, palm outward, signalling that his father was to wait a moment. He was sweating; Quentin could see the perspiration on his forehead, and guessed that Mr Yakamoto had become excited and Richard was having to use his Japanese. Quentin saw him give a vigorous nod and then he looked towards the rostrum again and moved his thumb upwards.

'Two million four hundred thousand pounds,' Quentin said, as if he were talking about fourpence. 'On the telephone, two million four hundred thousand pounds.'

He looked towards the end of the third row. 'It's against you, sir. Two million four hundred thousand . . .'

The dealer nodded. Who was he buying for? Quentin let the question drift through his head as he proceeded, again looking towards Richard.

'Two million five hundred thousand . . .'

An affirmation from Richard.

'Two million six hundred thousand . . .'

The dealer shook his head. He was out. Quentin looked round to make sure no one had decided to come in late to the bidding. No one stirred. No hand was lifted, no catalogue was raised, no eyebrows twitched.

'Two million six hundred thousand pounds on the telephone. For the last time . . . two million six hundred thousand pounds.'

The gavel crashed down, the tension sagged, everyone began to talk. Mr Yakamoto had got his Matisse.

The sale went on. Quentin was getting tired, but no hint of his fatigue showed in his face or his voice. He seemed indefatigable, looking round the room, alert for every signal, reciting the details of the paintings on offer. At least there was no need tonight to boost the bidding by force of personality. This was a high-quality sale and the bidders were eager.

Richard allowed his attention to wander, searching the room for a delectable red-head. As one of the two Hugo Woods went under the hammer he saw a determined movement of a catalogue. The girl was bidding and apparently she was in the market for a picture of a red-haired child which had once been owned by his own great-aunt. That would be something he could talk to the girl about when the sale was over. In fact, a very good way of approaching her.

She got the painting, too, paying four hundred thousand pounds for it without apparently turning a hair of her well-groomed head. Was she a dealer? A bit young for that.

He caught up with her when she went to discuss payment for the picture and its collection.

'. . . at Claridge's . . .' he heard her say, which was another step in the right direction; now he knew where she was staying. Claridge's – and four hundred thousand pounds for a painting! Was he falling for the daughter of a multi-millionaire? And did it matter?

Richard put his hand firmly under the arm of the red-headed girl and led her away.

'Let me get you out of this crowd,' he said. 'And do have a glass of champagne. I feel I deserve one myself after my efforts in Japanese.'

He cornered two glasses very neatly and handed one to her.

'It was stretching things a bit to put the Hugo Woods into an "Impressionist and Post-Impressionist" sale,' he said. 'But they both did very well. They used to be owned by my Great-Aunt Melissa and, in fact, the child in the picture you bought was also a family connection. I thought you'd like to know that as you're interested in Hope's family history.'

She was smiling now as if at some secret joke. 'What you tell me isn't news,' she said. 'The child in the picture is my mother. I bought the painting on her behalf. She wanted it both as a memento of her father, Hugo Wood, and of your great-aunt.'

'Then you are . . .'

'Veronica Coppett.'

'Of course! How could I have been so stupid. I say, we're sort of cousins, aren't we?'

343

'The ramifications of our family relationships are far beyond my poor brain to work out. Look, I think Sir Quentin is trying to attract your attention.'

Richard took hold of her wrist and pulled her behind him. He was not going to let go of her now.

'Father, this is Veronica Coppett, from New York,' he said.

'Let's see, you're Victor and Lynette's youngest daughter, aren't you?' Quentin said. 'We heard you were in London and Susanna means to get in touch with you. Claridge's, isn't it? And you bought the Hugo Wood? I'm glad about that. The market scene is going to the Tate, but the painting of Lynette ought to stay in the family. I shall look forward to seeing more of you, my dear.'

'I'll take you home. How about dinner?' Richard said.

'I have another engagement. Perhaps . . . another evening? Call me, why don't you?'

'I'll certainly do that.'

Richard watched her go with regret, his father with amusement.

'Taken with her?' he asked.

'Who wouldn't be? I'm going to marry her.'

'My dear Richard! On the strength of five minutes' acquaintance?'

'Look who's talking! Who went to New York and hijacked the girl he fancied to come and work in London? How long had you known Mother before you decided?'

'A couple of days,' Quentin admitted. 'I can only wish you luck. Veronica's a lovely girl and a match between the two branches of the company would be interesting.'

'Don't talk as if we're founding a dynasty. She wasn't wearing a ring, was she? How could a girl like that not be engaged or spoken for or something?'

'You can ask her tomorrow. In the meantime, I suggest you do what my dear old grandmother always recommended.'

'I know,' Richard said with a grin. 'I live in hopes.'